CONTENTS

EXPLANATORY NOTES

The heading for each letter gives the location of the letter and cites any previous publication of it. Not cited is the recent biography of Kelvin, *Lord Kelvin: The Dynamic Victorian* (University Park and London: The Pennsylvania State University Press, 1979), by Harold Issadore Sharlin in collaboration with Tiby Sharlin, which cites or quotes from nearly seventy Stokes–Kelvin letters. Also not cited is Crosbie Smith, 'Engineering the universe: William Thomson and Fleeming Jenkin on the nature of matter', *Annals of Science*, **37** (1980), 387–412, which quotes from letters 161–2 and 164–5.

Somewhat more than the first half of the correspondence is almost entirely in the hands of Kelvin and Stokes themselves. In 1878, much to the relief of his correspondents, Stokes began using the first of three typewriters. It had all capital letters and he used it from 1878 to 1885. In 1886 he began using the second, which also had all capital letters, though larger than those of the first typewriter. The third typewriter, with both capital and small letters, was used from 1890 to the end of the correspondence. Only fifteen letters from 1878 to 1901 are in his own hand. Most of Kelvin's later letters are in his own hand, but some are in Lady Kelvin's hand, in the hand of one of his assistants, or typed. I have noted the form of the letter when relevant to the reading of the letter. I have also noted when letters appear to be copies or drafts of letters, rather than the letters themselves.

The order of the letters in this book is sometimes different from that in my *Catalogue* of their collections in the Cambridge University Library. This is because I have now been able to give at least approximate dates to all the undated letters and have discovered that a few letters were misdated by Kelvin or Stokes. Also, letters S559 and S560 in the Kelvin Collection are not included here because I now think that neither is a letter to Kelvin. Each is an undated fragment of a letter consisting of one sheet signed by Stokes. Written in Stokes's hand, S559 appears to be a letter to W. J. M. Rankine from 1857. Typed on the second of Stokes's three typewriters, S560 dates from the late 1880s and is possibly to William Abney.

Notes to the letters include ones by me, ones by Kelvin and Stokes to their own letters, and a few by Larmor, which he wrote on the letters themselves. The notes explain which are by whom.

I have referred to Kelvin as Kelvin throughout, even though he was not raised to the peerage until 1892. I have referred to his first wife as Lady Thomson, even though she enjoyed that title only from 1866 until her death in

vii

1870. I have referred to Kelvin's second wife as Lady Kelvin, even though she was Lady Thomson from 1874 to 1892 and Lady Kelvin only from 1892.

I have silently modified punctuation in very few cases, adding full stops and an occasional apostrophe. On the other hand, until 1852 Kelvin usually wrote 'your's' (especially when signing letters), and I have left that uncorrected and not followed it with *sic*.

Unless otherwise noted, square brackets [ ] enclose material added by me. Pointed brackets ⟨ ⟩ enclose material written by Kelvin or Stokes and then deleted.

Stokes's and Kelvin's articles are cited in the notes by numbers, the number of each corresponding to its number in the Index of their publications. The numbering of the articles in the Index is based on that in the *Catalogue of Scientific Papers*, compiled by the Royal Society of London, 19 vols., vols. I–XII (London, 1867–1902), vols. XIII–XIX (Cambridge, 1914–25).

Abbreviations used by me in the notes are:

Kelvin

Baltimore Lectures (1884)	*Notes of Lectures on Molecular Dynamics and the Wave Theory of Light* (Baltimore, 1884)
Baltimore Lectures (1904)	*Baltimore Lectures on Molecular Dynamics and the Wave Theory of Light* (London, 1904)
MPP	*Mathematical and Physical Papers*, 6 vols. vols. IV–VI edited by Joseph Larmor (Cambridge, 1882–1911)
PEM	*Reprint of Papers on Electrostatics and Magnetism*, 2nd edn (London, 1884)
PLA	*Popular Lectures and Addresses*, 3 vols. (London, 1889, 1894, 1891)
TNP	W. Thomson and P. G. Tait, *Treatise on Natural Philosophy* (Oxford, 1867)
Thompson	Silvanus P. Thompson, *The Life of William Thomson, Baron Kelvin of Largs*, 2 vols. (London, 1910)

Stokes

Burnett Lectures	*Burnett Lectures. On Light*, 3 vols. (London, 1884–87)
Memoir	*Memoir and Scientific Correspondence of the Late Sir George Gabriel Stokes*, ed. Joseph Larmor, 2 vols. (Cambridge, 1907)

viii

MPP	*Mathematical and Physical Papers*, 5 vols., vols. IV and V edited by Joseph Larmor (Cambridge, 1880–1905)

Journals

Brit. Assoc. Rep.	*Report of the British Association for the Advancement of Science*
Camb. Dub. Math. J.	*Cambridge and Dublin Mathematical Journal*
Camb. Math. J.	*Cambridge Mathematical Journal*
Comptes Rendus	*Comptes rendus hebdomadaires des séances de l'Académie des Sciences*
Phil. Mag.	*The London, Edinburgh, and Dublin Philosophical Magazine and Journal of Science*
Phil. Trans.	*Philosophical Transactions of the Royal Society of London*
Proc. Camb. Phil. Soc.	*Proceedings of the Cambridge Philosophical Society*
Proc. Roy. Inst.	*Proceedings of the Royal Institution of Great Britain*
Proc. Roy. Soc. Edinb.	*Proceedings of the Royal Society of Edinburgh*
Proc. Roy. Soc.	*Proceedings of the Royal Society of London*
Trans. Camb. Phil. Soc.	*Transactions of the Cambridge Philosophical Society*
Trans. Roy. Soc. Edinb.	*Transactions of the Royal Society of Edinburgh*

THE CORRESPONDENCE
(1870–1901)

265 KELVIN to STOKES, 14 February 1870
Stokes Collection, K170

Glasgow College
February 14th 1870.

MY DEAR STOKES,

I quite agree with you that Hel⟨l⟩igoland would be a very unsuitable station for comparing levels on the continent of Europe with the average sea level; but for the investigation of the tides of the North Sea, which is a very important and useful scientific problem, I believe that observations at Hel⟨l⟩igoland, by a self-registering tide gauge, kept up permanently from year to year, would be very valuable. I have not, however, hitherto learned enough about the tides in the North Sea to be able to judge whether ⟨for⟩ merely for the sake of tidal observations, it would be advisable to choose Hel⟨l⟩igoland as a Station. For the geodetic purpose I believe that an accurate self-registering tide-gauge, kept up from year to year at some convenient station on the German or Dutch coast would be more valuable than anything that could be done at Hel⟨l⟩igoland.

I am going to London tonight and hope I may be able to see you at the Royal Society tomorrow evening, but my plans are necessarily somewhat uncertain.

I remain
Yours Very truly
WILLIAM THOMSON

Professor Stokes

266 KELVIN to STOKES, 7 March 1870
Royal Society of London, RR.7.51

The College
Glasgow 7th March 1870

MY DEAR STOKES,

I have read Rankine's paper[1] with great interest. The simple elementary method by which he investigates the condition for sustained uniformity of type is in my opinion very valuable. It ought as soon as it is published to be introduced into every elementary book henceforth written on the subject. I consider also that the thermo-dynamic question raised; namely, can the condition for uniformity of type become fulfilled in virtue of conduction of heat, due to the changes of temperature produced by the changes of density is a very important one; and even its suggestion is in my opinion ⟨of publis⟩ well worthy of publication in the tran[s]actions of the Royal Society. But I do not feel satisfied with the answer in §7 in which it is stated that 'when the

343

disturbance is not sudden' it is probable that 'the assumption as to transference of heat is fulfilled in an approximate manner only, and if such is the case it follows that *the only longitudinal disturbance* which can be propogated [*sic*] with absolute permanence of type is a sudden disturbance'. It seems to me on the contrary ⟨probable⟩ certain that the sudden disturbance constituting a condensing ⟨place would spread itself out by the conduction of heat, or that the length through the disturbance⟩ pulse, if existing at any instant, would spread itself out forwards to an infinite distance ⟨forwards⟩ by the conduction of heat. Practically the distance forwards from the place of greatest disturbance to ⟨the⟩ places where the disturbance would be so small as to be insensible, would be very small because of the great velocity of sound.

Unless, therefore, there is something (which I cannot see at present) against permanence in the region which has been passed over by the condensation pulse, the condition of permanence of type is in reality realizable through the thermo-dynamic changes of temperature ⟨of⟩ due to the conduction of heat.

In Rankine's paper it seems to be assumed that a pulse consisting of a sudden rarefaction as well as a pulse of sudden condensation ⟨as a⟩ is of permanent type ⟨with⟩ when thermal conduction is neglected. Mathematically speaking this of course is true, in as much as a reversal of the motion constituting a pulse of sudden condensation would give a pulse of sudden rarefaction superimposed upon a certain uniform motion of the whole matter concerned. But the slightest deviation from suddeness in the case of a pulse of rarefaction would give rise to a⟨n⟩ ⟨very⟩ constantly increasing[2] diminution of suddeness, and therefore the permanence of a pulse of sudden rarefaction is of the same character as the permanence (if we choose to call it permanence) of unstable equilibrium. The statements regarding waves of oscillation (§10 and appendix) are not satisfactory. They imply that a series of sudden compressions followed by gradual dilatations would constitute ⟨would constitute⟩ a type of permanence, which is not the case: and the difficulty pointed out in your own paper of Nov. 1848[3] is not overcome in Rankine's paper. The conduction of heat must in reality ⟨constitute⟩ give rise to a gradual diminution of Amplitude the farther from the source of waves of alternate condensation and rarefaction; the consideration of which will probably show how to get over the whole difficulty for oscillatory waves. The suggestion in the last clause of the last sentence preceding the appendix, cannot be accepted, as it would imply a loss of energy in the reflection and refraction of light greater in all probability than any which really takes place.

With some modifications I think Rankine's paper ought to be published in the transactions. If you desire it I shall be glad to confer with him on the subject but before doing so I would be glad to have your own views if you have already looked into the paper. In the mean time I return it by book post along with this.

Yours very truly
WILLIAM THOMSON[4]

1 W. J. M. Rankine, 'On the thermodynamic theory of waves of finite longitudinal disturbance', *Phil. Trans.* (1870), 277–88.
2 This appears initially to have read *a very increasing* and then to have been changed by Kelvin first to *an increasing*, next to *a constantly increasing*.
3 Stokes (19).
4 Stokes has written at the bottom of the letter, '1870 Rankine (Thermodynamics) by Thomson'.

267 KELVIN to STOKES, 9 May 1870
Royal Society of London, RR.7.52

Largs Ayrshire
May 9, 1870

DEAR STOKES

On account of the very severe illness of Lady Thomson[1] I have been unable to go to Glasgow since my last lecture a fortnight ago, and indeed if the session had not come to an end I should have been unable to continue. I shall therefore not be able to see Rankine. I return my report[2] to you, which if you think proper you can send to him. I hope you will be able to enter on the subject yourself soon (as I presume your lecturing will soon be over.) You will readily resolve any doubt that may [be] left.

The solution

$$v = C\epsilon^{-m(x-\alpha t)}; \quad \left(\text{where } m = \alpha\frac{c}{k}\right)$$

for $x > \alpha t$, & $v = C$ for $x < \alpha t$

of $\quad \dfrac{d^2 v}{dx^2} = \dfrac{c}{k}\dfrac{dv}{dt}$

expresses the effect of moving a source of heat along a bar at veloc. α. From this solution it seems to me most probable that what I said in my report as to the possibility of a permanent form of wave not infinitely steep being propagated in a frictionless elastic fluid or solid is true.

If you think proper you might send this along with my report to Rankine. I am not able for more at present.

Yours very truly
WILLIAM THOMSON

1 Lady Thomson died on 17 June 1870.

2 This letter and the previous one are the only reports in the Royal Society by Kelvin on Rankine's paper. For Rankine's paper, see the previous letter, note 1.

268 KELVIN to STOKES, 1 June 1870
Royal Society of London, RR.7.28

Largs Ayrshire
June 1, 1870

MY DEAR STOKES

I am sorry I have not been able to send you back 'Researches on Solar Physics No II' sooner.[1] I return it by book post, of the same despatch with this.

I am of opinion that it ought to be printed in the Transactions. The observations and reductions which it contains are most valuable and interesting.

The only part of which I feel any doubt as to advisability of publication without ⟨m⟩ some qualification or more prominent *caution* than that contained in the sentences No^s 2 & 4 from end (marked in pencil X_____X X_____X) is that ⟨with⟩ given at the end of the paper, & relating to planetary influence. The whole amounts of ⟨effects⟩ the variations indicated in the four several summations are so very small in comparison with the irregular and the 10½ yearly variations that I think the publication of that part of the paper as it stands might tend to mislead. ⟨In fact⟩ Most probably it would be taken up as proving the planetary influence referred to by the great majority of readers and all the popular scientific journals, not withstanding the warning given by the authors that the planetary influence is scarcely rendered probable by the numbers they give. I write all this however under reserve as I have not been able to go into the question carefully enough to make sure of any opinion as to the weight of the numbers given in these summations. But I think that very clearly the sentence No 3 from end, marked * is stronger than the facts warrant. Instead of there being the close agreement between the form of variation in the four periods, the facts seem to be as follows:– The time of minimum in the anomalistic period of Mercury is when the angle from perihelion is 85°, & the maximum when the angle is 290°. Mercury & Jupiter give

min. at 100°
max [at] 320[°]

These cases are given in a Postscribe and are ⟨in the⟩ held as somewhat confirming the conclusion stated at the end of paper preceding the P.S. to the effect that the min^m for Jupiter & Venus is 180° & max o[°] and the same for Venus & Mercury.

But the figures for Venus & Mercury give the minimum about 100° instead of 0°; & thus there remain only the other three points out of four as it were in favour of the supposed conclusion. I think it would be satisfactory to the authors to try similar summations for several arbitrary periods (as for example a period equal to ¾ of each of the periods they have chosen) and look at the results, in comparison with those they give in the M.S.S., before they throw out any suggestion of planetary influence having been discovered in the observations.

I do not quite understand ⟨the⟩ two points connected with the curves, & description in p 5. The 'slight repetition of the same process' does not to me explain what is done, but rather puzzled me. The black curve has points, giving zig zags, as if there were points marked at intervals corresponding to a small fraction of the smallest horizontal division (2 months): that is to say it ⟨they⟩ looks like a direct graphic representation of weekly or fortnightly observations: but it is stated to be a representative of the 3 monthly means. It ought therefore either to have ⟨an⟩ *angles* ⟨corresponding to⟩ one for every three months: or if smoothed into a curve to have no angles at all.

There are also angles and roughnesses (apparently not accidental in the drawing) in the red curves which seem to be inconsistent with the mode of drawing described.[2]

Excuse haste as I have made an effort to get this & the paper despatched by today's post considering that there will probably be a meeting of Council tomorrow.

I hope to return Mr Barlow's paper[3] almost immediately.

Yours truly
WILLIAM THOMSON

1 W. De la Rue, B. Stewart, and B. Loewy, 'Researches on solar physics. – No. 2. The positions and areas of the spots observed at Kew during the years 1864, 1865, 1866; also the spotted area of the sun's visible disk from the commencement of 1832 up to May 1868', *Phil. Trans.* (1870), 389–496.

2 Stokes has written near here, '1870 De la Rue &c by Thomson'.

3 W. H. Barlow, 'On the cause and theoretic value of the resistance of flexure in beams', *Proc. Roy. Soc.*, **18** (1870), 345–7. William Henry Barlow (1812–1902), who became a fellow of the Royal Society in 1850, was an engineer who worked with several English railways and designed the new Tay Bridge in 1882.

Largs
Ayrshire
June 8, 1870

MY DEAR STOKES

Mr Barlow's paper on Flexure[1] is not suitable for publication in the Transactions. It is wrong from beginning to end, and shows the author to be altogether ignorant of the terms, grammar, and principles of the mathematical theory of elasticity, (and even of the explanation of the flexibility of a rope. See p. 3.) The question, or difficulty, presented by the ordinary theory, in respect to stresses of mutual action between longitudinal filaments[2] and the strains produced by them, which constitutes Mr Barlow's present subject, was completely solved by St Venant in a paper of the same date (1855)[3] as the first to which he refers back. If, after St Venant's investigation, experiment were wanting, it is furnished amply in experiments ⟨on flexu⟩ (as for instance those of Everett's in the Transactions)[4] showing quite the same values for the Young's modulus calculated from observations of flexure, according to the ordinary theory, as those which direct measurements have given for the same substances. St Venant's theory is given in Thomson & Tait's Natural Philosophy §§711 ... 718.[5]

The discrepance [*sic*] from the ordinary theory in respect to the *strength* of beams, pointed out by Mr Barlow in his papers of 1855, 1857[6] is in no degree explained in his present paper, which if it were correct would prove the same discrepance in the flexural rigidity within the limits of elasticity, from that calculated ⟨by⟩ from the Young's modulus according to the ordinary theory. ⟨from the Young's modulus⟩ The ⟨observation⟩ discovery of that discrepance which it seems ⟨was dis⟩ is due to Mr Barlow is of great importance practically, and of much theoretical interest in respect to properties of matter. It may be considered whether the Appendix to the present paper, farther illustrating that discrepance might not be proper for separate publication, whether in the Transactions or Proceedings.

The discrepance is not itself to be wondered at, as the *breaking* of a rod or wire by direct pull, and of a bar by flexure, is ⟨determined⟩ dependent on various complex circumstances connected [with] change of temper produced by stress, and flaws in the free surface. The ⟨very different⟩ circumstances of a filament in a bent bar, and an equal portion of the same substance detached and pulled lengthwise, are so very different that we cannot expect ⟨both⟩ the resistance of the beam to permanent flexure, or to rupture, to be the same as that calculated from the longitudinal strength of the outer filament: and Mr Barlow's result that the beam is ⟨nearly⟩ about twice as strong as ⟨would⟩ the calculation would make it is very much what might be expected, although of course ⟨not wha⟩ it could not have[7] been anticipated without more knowledge than we have of the subtle properties of matter concerned.

M[r] Barlow's photographs of effects of direct pull on ⟨certain⟩ round bars of steel or wrought iron with an 'outer skin' as described in p 18, are curious and interesting.

Yours truly
WILLIAM THOMSON

I return the paper by book post with this.

1 See the previous letter, note 3.
2 Kelvin has added a footnote here reading, 'That is mere geometrical imaginary divisions: not fibres. The whole idea of *fibre* so much pressed on by Mr Barlow, is foreign to the theory of elasticity of homogeneous solids'.
3 Saint-Venant, 'Divers résultats relatifs à la torsion d'un prisme à base de triangle équilatéral, à celle de deux prismes ou cylindres parallèles rendus solidaires, etc.', *L'Institut; Journal des Académies et Sociétés Scientifiques de la France et de l'Étranger*, **23** (1855), 248–50, and 'Sur l'élasticité des corps, sur les actions entre leurs molécules, sur leurs mouvements vibratoires atomiques, et sur leur dilatation par la chaleur', *ibid.*, **23** (1855), 440–2. Adhémar Jean Claude Barré de Saint-Venant (1797–1886), a graduate of the École Polytechnique, began in 1823 twenty years with the Service des Ponts et Chaussées and spent the rest of his life teaching and doing research.
4 J. D. Everett, 'Account of experiments on the flexural and torsional rigidity of a glass rod, leading to the determination of the rigidity of glass', *Phil. Trans.* (1866), 185–92, and 'Account of experiments on torsion and flexure for the determination of rigidities', *ibid.* (1868), 363–70.
5 Kelvin and Tait *TNP*.
6 W. H. Barlow, 'On the existence of an element of strength in beams subjected to transverse strain, arising from the lateral action of the fibres or particles on each other, and named by the author the "resistance of flexure"', *Phil. Trans.* (1855), 225–42; (1857), 463–88.
7 Stokes has written here, '1870 Barlow by Thomson'.

270 KELVIN to STOKES, 5 January 1871
    Royal Society of London, RR.7.141

Glasgow College
Jan 5, 1871

DEAR STOKES

My delay in returning Varley's paper[1] to you was owing to a visit I expected from him, which would give me an opportunity of talking over the subject with him.[2] The point you noticed about assuming it either as proved or rendered probable that the evolution of hydrogen in the exp[t] described in the paper was in any sense electrolytic was clearly an error as it stood. I thought with you that it was altogether wrong, and recommended to him to cancel a few lines which he did accordingly. But he described to me another very curious experiment which he had made, and had in his mind when he was writing the paper, leading him to the electrolytic idea most naturally. I recommended him to write an ⟨short⟩ addition to the paper describing this experiment which he has accordingly done. It shows clearly a very curious electrolytic action, in which hydrogen escapes from mercury via liquid to a platinum surface & thence out as gas.

Altogether I think the paper a valuable one. It describes very new and very important phenomena, and contains measurements which measure something quite measurable & yet never before measured or made a subject for investigation. I think it ought clearly to go into the Transactions, whether the hypothesis as to electrostatic condenser with gas dielectric between metal & electrolyte be thought probable or not. I view the thing rather as way of *putting* the thing, when the subject dealt with is molecular and solids fluids and gases blend into one another, than as a proposition that can be unqualifiedly asserted or denied. But substantially there is a result of a definite character which is the same as would be produced by a badly insulating condenser of capacity augmenting with the electric force (as for instance ⟨would⟩ a condenser of elastic metal sheets, attracting one another nearer & nearer the higher the charge) this condenser being rendered badly insulating by a moist thread let us suppose, connecting ⟨a⟩ two platinum wires one of which is coated with an infinitesimal layer of zinc.

However there are facts enough for a Transactions paper, and enough to let the[3] author have a little range for hypothesis. Much cruder hypotheses have had place in many of the best papers in the Transactions.

If you please the paper may be communicated by me.

Yours truly
W THOMSON

P.S. I return it, with addition, by book post, same address as this.

I think Varley's paper would interest Clerk Maxwell much. Dalbeattie Glenlair is his present address.

1 C. F. Varley, 'Polarization of metallic surfaces in aqueous solutions. On a new method of obtaining electricity from mechanical force, and certain relations between electrostatic induction and the decomposition of water', *Phil. Trans.* (1871), 129–36. Cromwell Fleetwood Varley (1828–83), who became a fellow of the Royal Society in 1871, was an electrical engineer employed by the International Telegraph Co. from 1846 to 1868.
2 Kelvin has written near here, 'He came, and left me only yesterday, with the addition to his paper'.
3 Stokes has written near here, '1871 Varley by Thomson'.

271 KELVIN to STOKES, 7 January 1871
Stokes Collection, K171

Glasgow College
Jan 7, 1871

DEAR STOKES

I am to be in London this day week on account of the fault in the French cable, and on Wed^y the 18th to attend the first meeting of the Commission on the Captain.[1] Will you be at home and would it be perfectly convenient to you, for me to stay with you at Lensfield Cottage from *Sat* (the 7th) till Monday the 9th. I have just received a short paper from one of the Persian Gulf telegraphists (Mance) which I recommended him to write for the Proceedings of the Royal Society.[2] Will there be room for it on the programme for Thursday week? If so I could read it if you please, and might also read a short paper (which I would write out complete before hand) on a closely related subject.[3]

Your truly
W THOMSON

1 The Admiralty Committee upon the Designs of Ships of War was appointed in January 1871 in response to the catastrophic sinking of H.M.S. *Captain* the previous September. W. J. M. Rankine and W. Froude were also members of the committee, which made its final report in July 1871. (Thompson, II, 731–3.)
2 H. Mance, 'Method of measuring the resistance of a conductor or of a battery, or of a telegraph-line influenced by unknown earth-currents, from a single deflection of a galvanometer of unknown resistance', *Proc. Roy. Soc.*, 19 (1871), 248–52, and 'Measurement of the internal resistance of a multiple battery by adjusting the galvanometer to zero', *ibid.*, 252. Henry Mance was superintendent of the Mekran Coast and Persian Gulf Telegraph Department, Kurrachee.
3 Kelvin (182), which mentions Mance's work.

272 KELVIN to STOKES, 5 February 1871
Stokes Collection, K172

Edinburgh
Feb 5/71

DEAR STOKES

I hope you have before now received the memorial. I gave it to Blackburn who was to sign it and send it to Tait who was to sign it & send it to Mr Justice Blackburn,[1] who was to sign it & send it to you. I am with Tait at present and he tells me that the programme had been correctly carried out so far as the despatch from Edinburgh.

Yours very truly
WILLIAM THOMSON

273 KELVIN to STOKES, 3 March 1871
Stokes Collection, K173

Glasgow College[1]
March 3/71

DEAR STOKES

On the part of the Committee on designs for Ships of War[2] I am to put the following questions to you.

1. Did you observe waves at Portrush (Ans. yes)

2. State particulars including date (I have some of them, which I wrote in my pocket book: but in confirmation & extension of them I w^d be much obliged by your giving all the particulars you think proper) These would be all published in our report, as evidence from you. Would you not give them to the R.S. so that they might appear in the Proceedings before our report comes out?[3]

3. (?) ⟨What are t⟩ The longest waves that have been observed? – by whom? – their length from crest to crest? – & height from hollow to crest? This also we would like to publish.

4. Do you think longer waves than those longest are likely to be ever met with?

I have been working out the oscillations of a ship and find I

can get a very good result thus.

$$\theta = \text{inc}^n \text{ of wave to hor[izo]n}$$

$$\phi[= \text{inclination of] ship [to horizon]}$$

$$\frac{d^2\phi}{dt^2} + f(\phi\langle + nI \sin nt\rangle + \theta) = 0,$$

⟨where I is maxim. inc. of wave & $\frac{2\pi}{n}$ its period.⟩
Put $\theta + \phi = x$

Then $\dfrac{d^2\phi}{dt^2} = \dfrac{d^2x}{dt^2} + n^2 I \sin nt$

if $I \sin nt$ be the inc^n of the water to the horizon, at time t.

Hence $\dfrac{d^2x}{dt^2} + fx + n^2 I \sin nt = 0$

& put $fx = y$

Let
$$x = \alpha \sin nt + \beta \sin 3nt + \gamma \sin 5nt \qquad (1)$$

$$\therefore \quad n^{-2}y = \alpha' \sin nt + 9\beta \sin 3nt + 9\gamma \sin 5nt, \qquad (2)$$

where $\alpha' = \alpha - I$

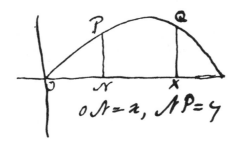

$O\mathcal{N} = x, \ \mathcal{N}P = y$

This is what the (Admiralty) ship-wrights now call the curve of stability

Let OX, the extreme inc of ship to water, (at the end of its range in an oscillation) be given. Call it X. Take XQ from the curve of stability. Call it Y.

Hence, putting $nt = \dfrac{\pi}{2}$ in above equ^{ns}

$$\alpha - \beta + \gamma = X$$
$$\alpha' - 9\beta + 25\gamma = Yn^{-2}$$

Again let $\dfrac{y}{x} = q$ when $t = 0$. Find q from the curve of stability (the tang. of inc^n of its tangent, at o)

We have, by putting $t = 0$, in the above [(1) & (2)]^4

$$\langle n^2(\alpha' - \alpha). \rangle$$
$$n^2\alpha' - \alpha + (27n^2 - 1)\beta + (125n^2 - 1)\gamma = 0$$

These three equ^{ns} give α, α', β in terms of X, Y, n, and γ. The remaining unknown quantity (γ) is determined by choosing some value of t, say such as to make $nt = \dfrac{\pi}{\langle 2 \rangle 4}$. $\langle$Eliminate$\rangle$ Two equations, cases of (1) & (2),

$$x = P + P'\gamma, \quad y = Q + Q'\gamma$$

are thus found, in which Q, Q' P, P' are all known, and x and y (unknown) are so related that y is the ordinate of the curve of stability for abscissa x. Hence the point (x, y) is that in which the straight line

$$\frac{x}{P'} - \frac{y}{Q'} = \frac{P}{P'} - \frac{Q}{Q'}$$

cuts the curve of stability. From this it is easy to find γ, and then α, α', & β are known. $\alpha - \alpha'$ the ⟨greatest wave⟩ inclination of the wave at its place of greatest slope is thus found, so that we know what magnitude of wave is required to produce any stated degree X of rolling.

Have you compared Rankine's solution for noninfinitesimal waves with yours?[5] Yours is truly 'irrotational'; Rankine's is not. In yours I think each particle has average translatory motion, in Rankine's not. If the surface were brought to rest in your motion the whole water w^d come to rest: in Rankine's it would be found moving horizontally with a velocity decreasing from the surface downwards.

The wave surface appears to agree very closely in the two cases.

I am very glad Maxwell is standing for the Professorship.[6]

Yours always truly

WT

1 Kelvin has written at the top of the letter, 'Excuse this scroll. I wrote against time to finish it on Saturday, unsuccessfully'.
2 See letter 271, note 1.
3 Stokes did not.
4 Kelvin's brackets.
5 See letter 227, note 1. Stokes (29).
6 Maxwell became the Cavendish professor at Cambridge in 1871.

274 STOKES to KELVIN, 10 April 1871[1]
Stokes Collection, NB21.36

Cambridge 10th April 1871

MY DEAR THOMSON,

I have had a letter from Airy[2] in which he expressed considerable alarm lest the method you have published[3] of finding another [?] place at sea should lead to disasters in consequence of people forgetting that the place so determined is liable to a shift east or west depending on the unknown error of the chronometer, which practically forms the grand [?] source of uncertainty in the determination of places at sea. For this reason a ship's place in latitude is much more accurately known than her place in longitude unless the chronometer has been just [?] recently compared with a time signal [?]. Moriarty's[4] position was quite perilous [?], as he got to Greece [an illegible word] time every day through the week.

It would be well you should put [?] in a caution in the introduction to your tables lest from relying [?] on charts Cap^s should forget that the whole figure was liable to a shift east or west depending on the error of 'error' for Chro[no]meter.

Yours truly

G. G. STOKES

1 This is Stokes's press copy of the original letter.
2 G. B. Airy to Stokes, 5 April 1871, Stokes Collection, A381, published as, 'Remarks on the determination of a ship's place at sea', *Proc. Roy. Soc.*, **19** (1871), 448–50.
3 Kelvin (184).
4 Henry Augustus Moriarty (1815–1906) became a captain in the Navy in 1874. In his (184), Kelvin said he learned the method he was describing from Moriarty during the Atlantic Cable expedition of 1858 when Moriarty navigated H.M.S. *Agamemnon*.

275 KELVIN to STOKES, 1 July 1871
Stokes Collection, K174

Yacht Lalla Rookh Southampton [to] Cowes
July 1, 1871

DEAR STOKES

Can you tell me approximately the dates[1] of (1) Miller's accurate comparison of positions between the bright line of the sodium-spirit flame and the Fraunhofer solar D.

(2) Foucault's statement that a spirit flame (? did he allude to sodium?) augments the darkness of the solar D (? produces dark line D in spectrum of electric arc? did he find this?)

(3) your teaching to me or others ⟨that the cooler vapour of sodium⟩ of the dynamical theory of the generation of bright lines and of ⟨the⟩ dark lines, by the same vapour, and of the essentialness of ⟨di⟩ [?] sodium in the wick or otherwise to the generation of the bright line D in artificial flames. The date of (3) is certainly prior to the summer of 1852. My impression is that it was in 1850 or 1851. It was certainly when we were walking about in Cambridge (? in St John's Coll grounds or the backs).

I taught the whole dynamical theory as I had it from you in my class certainly as early as session 1852–3. I also pointed out solar & stellar chemistry as to be investigated by trying various metals in artificial flames, and comparing the⟨y⟩ bright lines they give, rigourously with the positions of dark lines in the spectra of sun and stars. I treated not as a conjecture but as a thing absolutely proved and discovered by you that the dark line D in the spectr⟨um⟩a of the sun and of certain stars in which it had been observed is due to vapour of sodium in their atmospheres absorbing precisely the kind of light shown in the sodium flame. I used constantly to show the spectrum of light from white clouds (and from the sun when I could get him in my old lecture room) with a spirit lamp flame with salt on the wick, behind the slit, producing a bright prolongation of the Fraunhofer D.

I was sorry to miss the opportunity of seeing you in London on Thursday. I should be much obliged by a line in answer addressed Post Office, Cowes, Isle of Wight, if posted on Monday next, or Athenaeum Club London if later.

Yours truly
W. THOMSON

1 Kelvin obviously asked these questions in preparation for his presidential address to the British Association at Edinburgh in 1871. (Kelvin (173). The discussion of these issues, featuring Stokes's idea, is in Kelvin's *Popular Lectures*, ii, 169–73.)

276 KELVIN to STOKES, 4 July [1871][1]
Stokes Collection, K175

Yacht L. R. Portsmouth
July 4 [1871]
address
Athenaeum Club
Pall Mall
London

DEAR STOKES

Sir E. Sabine told me that Dr Robinson is preparing a memoir of Sir John Herschel. Can you give me either from your own knowledge, or from Dr Robinson, such information or suggestions as would help me to refer appropriately to Sir John Herschel in my address? He was I believe an early promoter of the Assoc^n, but it would, in the case of such a man, be his own work for the Advancement of Science, rather than official or ⟨p⟩ [?] active connection with the Assoc^n that should be noticed.

I should be greatly obliged by your telling me what strikes you as the best, or the most noteworthy, things which he has done.

If anything else occurs to you that you think could be of use to me in my present straits I need not say it will be thankfully received.

Yours always truly
WILLIAM THOMSON

1 John Herschel died on 11 May 1871, and Kelvin discussed his work in his 1871 presidential address to the British Association. (Kelvin (173), in *Popular Lectures*, ii, 135–40.) See also the postscript to letter 279.

277 STOKES to KELVIN, 5 July 1871[1]
Stokes Collection, NB21.42

Lensfield Cottage Cambridge, 5 July 1871

MY DEAR THOMSON,

1. You are doubtless aware of Fraunhofer's original observation of the coincidence in position between the double bright and double dark D. Gilbert's Annalen Vol 74 or 14 (1823) p. 374.[2]

2. Miller tells me the apparatus with which he worked was got in 1836 and the observation was made, perhaps that year, but more probably early in 1837.

3. A pamphlet[3] by book post will answer your question about Foucault. I don't recollect that Foucault observed D-absorption by the flame of a *spirit lamp*. It was the voltaic arc he used.

4. I first became acquainted with Foucault's remarkable discovery of the simultaneous emission and absorption of D-light from a conversation I had with him at the house of Dr Neil⟨l⟩ Arnott,[4] who asked me to dinner to meet him when he came to receive the Copley Medal which was awarded to him in 1855. I was greatly struck by it. On his return to Paris he sent me a copy of the number of l'Institut containing his paper. This I was thinking of translating for the Phil. Mag. and putting in an illustration borrowed from sound, but neglected to do so and so the matter rested till after the labours of Kirchhoff and Bunsen.[5]

5. As to the chemical application of bright lines, I think more was known in England tha⟨t⟩n Kirchhoff gives us credit for, but I don't know that I had any special knowledge on the subject. Read what Herschel says in art. 524 of 'Light' Encyclopaedia Metropolitana.[6] Remember that Fox Talbot[7] long ago discovered the bright line due to lithium, and showed how by the prism you could instantly distinguish between salts of lithium and salts of strontium, though both impart a red colour to the flame of a spirit lamp. The excessively minute quantities which produce the effect were ⟨exa⟩ expressly noticed both by Herschel and Fox Talbot. Now being that salts of sodium give a copious and purely homogeneous yellow, and being that such minute quantities of a salt suffice to produce the effect, the conjecture lay close at hand that the prevalence of the bright D in artificial flames was due to traces of soda. I think I always felt that it belonged to him to assert this who went through the great chemical labour of removing all traces of sodium in suspected cases. My only contributions to this (and those were never published) were to show that bright D was absent in a candle flame when the wick was snuffed close so as not to project into the luminous envelope, and from an alcohol flame when the spirit was burnt in a watch-glass. These I looked on as too meagre a portion of the laborious enquiry I contemplated as being undertaken by some one to justify me in publishing them.

When Foucault told me of his observations about the bright D in the voltaic arc, I suspected a trace or more of sodium, and I asked him whether anything had been put on the poles – I forget whether I asked especially whether a salt of soda had been put on the poles. He told me that various salts had been on the poles. [dipping into the reports of the British Assoc^n I find in the report of the 1842 Meeting Sections p. 16 l.7 that Brewster[8] supposed the D line of a tallow candle to be due to 'muriate of soda' [properly chlorine of sodium as in tallow it would not probably be in aqueous solution] existing in the tallow.)[9]

6. I supposed the dark D to be due to sodi*um* not chloride of sodium or a

salt of soda because I knew no instance of a body which absorbed in the state of gas but was non-absorbent in the state of liquid or solution. In the latter case it is true we know not the *very rapid* transitions from comparatively transparent to comparatively opaque that we have in the former, but the general absorption answers in the two cases. I supposed therefore that on the sun and in the voltaic arc such intense actions were present as to set free sodi*um* notwithstanding its powerful affinities. And as I took for granted there were no such powerful actions present in a mere spirit lamp flame, and no free sodi*um* present in such a flame from a salted wick, I never thought of looking for D-absorption in such a flame. I perceived that the connexion between D-emission and D-absorption was *explicable* on dynamical principles, but I did not perceive that it was *necessary*. I may remark that judging by the present state of science on the matter I believe that I was optically right and chemically wrong; that I was wrong in assuming that there was no free sodi*um* present in the flame of a spirit lamp with salted wick. And my chemical error would have been exposed had I perceived, which I did not, the *necessary* connexion between absorption and emission; had I in fact anticipated Balfour Stewart's discovery of the extension of Prevost's Law of exchanges.[10]

Accordingly when Stewart's paper[11] came before the Royal ⟨discov⟩ [?] Society it struck me with all the force and freshness of an original and important discovery. I refer to his papers on light: I was not at the time, though I might have been, acquainted with his previous on radiant heat,[12] from which to light the transition is easy. I now look on his papers on heat as virtually containing the whole discovery.

7. I don't know the date of my conversation with you about bright and dark D. It must have been later than Nov. 30, 1855 if, as I am almost sure, it was on the occasion of his visit to London to receive the Copley Medal that I met Foucault at Dr Arnott's. Notwiths[t]anding the proved coincidence of bright and dark lines in the case of sodium, and a similar coincidence asserted by Sir David Brewster [but since proved to be not quite exact][13] in the case of 'deflagrating nitre' as compared with certain dark solar lines,[14] I did not at the time think that all, or even I think most, of the dark solar lines were to be connected with bright lines produced suppose by electrical discharges. I thought that many if not most of the dark lines were due to absorption by compound gases formed in the cooler parts of the Sun's atmosphere and exercising selective absorption as we have examples in peroxide of nitrogen and other known gases. When *you* jumped to the conclusion (since borne out) that to find what elements were in the sun and stars we must examine the bright lines in artificial flames *I* thought you were going too fast ahead. That some other elements besides sodium might be identified seemed likely

enough, but *I* thought that a good part of the dark lines were due to absorption by compound gases.

The coincidence of bright and dark D, made known to the world by Fraunhofer in 1823, was long known to me. I cannot say when I first thought of my piano illustration. That a medium was simultaneously D-emissive and D-absorptive struck me with all the freshness of originality when Foucault told me it in 1855.

Yours sincerely
G. G. Stokes

1 This is Stokes's press copy of the original letter.
2 J. Fraunhofer, 'Kurzer Bericht von den Resultaten neuerer Versuche über die Gesetze des Lichtes, und die Theorie derselben', L. W. Gilbert's *Annalen der Physik*, **74** (1823), 337–78.
3 Perhaps a reprint of Stokes (69).
4 Neil Arnott (1788–1874), who became a fellow of the Royal Society in 1838, took his M.A. and M.D. degrees at Aberdeen and practised medicine in London from 1811 to 1855, when he retired to pursue his own researches.
5 Robert Wilhelm Eberhard Bunsen (1811–99) took his Ph.D. at Göttingen in 1830 and, after several years as professor of chemistry at Marburg, was at the University of Heidelberg from 1852 to 1889. In addition to his collaboration with Kirchhoff, he is known for developing laboratory instruments such as the Bunsen burner. See Stokes (69).
6 See letter 99, note 12.
7 William Henry Fox Talbot (1800–77) was twelfth wrangler in 1821, became a fellow of the Royal Society in 1831, and is known for his researches which were involved in the development of photography. In his 'Some experiments on coloured flames', *The Edinburgh Journal of Science*, **5** (1826), 77–81, he discussed the correspondence between various colours of light and various substances (though not lithium), suggesting 'that whenever the prism shows a *homogeneous* ray of any colour to exist in a flame, this ray indicates the formation or the presence of a *definite chemical compound*' (p. 81).
8 D. Brewster, 'On the luminous bands in the spectra of various flames', *Brit. Assoc. Rep.* (1842), part 2, 15–16.
9 The preceding three brackets and one parenthesis are Stokes's.
10 Pierre Prévost (1751–1839), professor at Geneva, presented his theory of exchanges in 1791, stating 'that all bodies regardless of temperature are constantly radiating heat and that an equilibrium of heat between two bodies consisted in an equality of exchange'. (*Dictionary of Scientific Biography*.)
11 B. Stewart, 'On the light radiated by heated bodies', *Proc. Roy. Soc.*, **10** (1859–60), 385–93, and 'On the nature of the light emitted by heated tourmaline', *ibid.*, 503–5. The latter reports on an experiment suggested by Stokes to Stewart.
12 See, for example, B. Stewart, 'An account of some experiments on radiant heat, involving an extension of Prévost's theory of exchanges', *Brit. Assoc. Rep.* (1858), part 2, 23–4, and *Trans. Roy. Soc. Edinb.*, **22** (1861), 1–20.
13 Stokes's brackets.
14 D. Brewster, 'On luminous lines in certain flames corresponding to the defective lines in the sun's light', *Brit. Assoc. Rep.* (1842), part 2, p. 15.

Lensfield Cottage Cambridge
6th July 1871

My dear Thomson,

On referring to your letter I see you are positive as to the date of our conversation, and *I* am satisfied that it was when I met Foucault at dinner that I first heard of a medium being simultaneously emissive and absorptive for light of definite refrangibility. I thought Foucault's experiment formed part of our conversation, but I may be mistaken in this, and it is quite possible I may have talked with you before that of the coincidence of position of bright and dark lines, and of the illustration of ⟨such⟩ the possibility of such coincidence borrowed from sound.

I mention all this merely to give you as accurate information as I am able in answer to your question, not wishing to claim any priority for myself. Indeed all I did in the matter beyond indulging in conjectures open to anyone lay in the two simple experiments I mentioned in my last.

It is difficult to place the merits of Herschel in a clear light before a popular audience for the reason that his name is not, so far as I recollect, associated with any one discovery of a peculiarly brilliant nature. His fame arises in great measure from his extensive and at the same time profound acquaintance with so many branches of physical science ⟨and to⟩ as he was of mathematics, and to ⟨a⟩ his singular clearness of exposition, and graphic power. In the first place he and Peacock[2] were the joint introducers of the Continental mathematics into Cambridge, an important furtherance of science if no direct discovery. Among his discoveries I may mention the discovery of hyposulphurous acid and investigation of the properties of its salts which just came in the nick of time to be available for the fixation of the photographic image. It was he who discovered the connection between the hemihedral faces of quartz and the direction of its rotation of the plane of polarization of polarized light. It was he again who found that in borax the plane containing the optic axis varied from colour to colour. These are not very striking taken individually but his papers nearly all bearing the stamp of originality are very numerous [I cannot say I have read all or nearly all, but that is the general character].[3] In Astronomy I suppose he will be best known by his Cape observations and his various catalogues of double stars and the very complete catalogue of nebulae and clusters which forms Part I of the Phil. Trans. for 1864.[4] I am sorry I am not able to help you better but perhaps other of your friends will make further contributions on the subject. I feel personally indebted to Herschel for leading me to fluorescence, which I was led to by considering what he had done about epipolic dispersion.[5]

Yours sincerely
G. G. Stokes

1 This is Stokes's press copy of the original letter.
2 George Peacock (1791–1858) was second wrangler in 1813, was Lowndean professor from 1837 to 1858, and was Dean of Ely from 1839 to 1858. See J. M. Dubbey, 'The introduction of the differential notation to Great Britain', *Annals of Science*, **19** (1963), 37–48.
3 Stokes's brackets.
4 J. F. W. Herschel, 'Catalogue of nebulae and clusters of stars', *Phil. Trans.* (1864), 1–138.
5 Stokes discussed this aspect of Herschel's research at the beginning of his (42).

279 KELVIN to STOKES, 7 July 1871
Stokes Collection, K176[1]
Printed in Stokes's *MPP*, IV, 374–5.

Admiralty
London July 7/71

DEAR STOKES

Many thanks for your letters[2] & printed paper which are most valuable to me.

It was certainly prior to the summer of 185⟨3⟩2 that you taught me solar and stellar chemistry. I never was at Cambridge from the summer of 1852 until we came there in 1866, and the conversation was certainly in Cambridge. I had begun teaching it to my class in session 1852–3, (as an old student's note book which I have shows)[3] and ⟨possibly⟩ probably earlier although of this I have not evidence. I used always to show a spirit lamp flame with salt on it, behind a slit prolonging the dark line D by bright continuation. I always gave your dynamical explanation, always asserted that certainly there was sodium ⟨in⟩ vapour in the sun's atmosphere and in the atmospheres of stars which show Fraunhofer's D;[4] and always pointed out that the way to find other substances besides sodium in the sun and stars was to compare bright lines produced by them in artificial flames with dark lines of the spectra ⟨observed⟩ of the lights of the distant bodies.

You very probably learned more from Foucault of what he had done when you met him in 1855, but you certainly told me of a French man (I don't recollect the name you then gave me, or even that you mentioned the name, though it is most probable you you [*sic*] did) having obtained the dark line by absorption.

Yours truly
W THOMSON

P.S. I think of using almost all you say of Herschel, in my address,[5] as from you.

1 K177 in the Stokes Collection is a copy of K176 in neither Stokes's nor Kelvin's hand. Probably, Larmor had the copy made for the printer to use. See note 4 below, for example.
2 Larmor's printed version reads *letter*.

3 Kelvin has added a note here reading, 'I speak from memory. I believe it was of session 1852–3. I have it in Glasgow'.

4 Both K177 and the printed version read *show presence of the D's*, instead of *show Fraunhofer's D;*.

5 Kelvin (173).

280   KELVIN to STOKES, 23 July [1871][1]
Stokes Collection, K362

L.R.
Spithead
July 23

DEAR STOKES

I should be much obliged by a line from you addressed Athenaeum to say if *Foucault*, or Fizeau and Foucault, should be referred to for laboratory correction of velocity of light. Also who of astronomers found the correction ⟨did the same m⟩ and did they find it independently or after Foucault and in verific^n of him.

Yours
W T

1 Like the previous letters, this one was in preparation for Kelvin's presidential address. Kelvin mentioned Foucault's work on the velocity of light in his (173) in *Popular Lectures*, II, 160.

281   KELVIN to STOKES, 7 October 1871[1]
Stokes Collection, K178

DEAR STOKES

I ought long ago to have sent back Siemens' paper[2] with report. It is sent by today's post (if not yesterday's) from Glasgow direct to the Royal Society (addressed to Mr White). I have been reading it within the last few days on board the L.R. and brought it up with me to Glasgow yesterday morning where I left it to be posted.

My report is that it is deserving of publication. There is a good deal that is interesting and valuable in point of science in each of the three parts. The practical applications are both important and interesting. I do not think the author has chosen quite the best plans, in several particulars, for carrying out his method of thermometry, but the subject has been referred to a Committee of the British Association,[3] and no doubt members of the Com^{ee} (of whom I am one) will have opportunities of conferring with Mr Siemens.

I may add that rather more than 11 years ago (in the summer of 1860 to the best of my recollection) I had a letter from Fleeming Jenkin suggesting the same method of thermometry.[4] Jenkin's suggestion to me was certainly prior to the date of Siemens' publication of the method. Siemens' is however altogether independent.

Yours truly

W THOMSON

L.R. Largs   Oct 7/71

1 Kelvin's letter is *preceded* by one from Kelvin's assistant, John Tatlock, written on behalf of Kelvin. Tatlock's letter ends in the middle of one page, and Kelvin's letter on Siemens fills the bottom half of the page plus an additional page. At the top of the page containing portions of both letters, Stokes has written '1871 Siemens by Thomson'. Presumably to keep Kelvin's report on Siemens separate from Tatlock's letter, Stokes has copied the entire last page of Tatlock's letter on to the reverse side of another page of his letter. See letter 285 in which Kelvin requested the return of his report on Siemens. Tatlock's letter is as follows:

Loch Fyne[a]

Yacht 'Lalla Rookh'

6th October 1871.

SIR

I am directed by Sir William to say to you that he is sorry at having been so long in answering your letter with regard to M[r] McFarlane's paper.[b] Having been cruising about in the West highlands and elsewhere he had taken his work with him and has been engaged, he desires me to say, in working at vortex motion and the theory of waves under joint influence of gravity & cohesion.[c] Having been becalmed while sailing with Professor Helmholtz and Professor James Thomson in the west highlands, an excellent opportunity offered itself for determining the minimum wave-velocity. A fishing line was hung at a distance of two or three feet from the vessel's side. (Previous to this some some [sic] curious phenomena had been observed in the neighbourhood of the point where a fishing line cuts the surface of the water. An extremely fine and numerous set of short waves preceded the 'solid'; (the vessel meantime moving at a speed of about a quarter to three quarters of a mile per hour) much longer waves following it right in the rear, and oblique waves streaming off at a definite angle, on each side, into which the waves in front and the waves in rear merged so as to form a beautiful and symmetrical pattern). The fishing line was ⟨sunk⟩ kept nearly vertical by a weight.[d] The speed was determined by throwing pieces of wetted paper into the sea and observing their times of transit across parallel planes at a distance of 912 centimetres asunder, fixed relatively to the vessel by marks on the deck and Gunwale. By watching the pattern of ripples ⟨of⟩ and[e] waves connecting the waves in front with the ripples in rear, it was seen that it included a set of parallel waves, slanting off obliquely on each side, and presenting appearances which proved them to be waves of critical length giving the minimum speed of propogation [sic]; so that the component velocity of the fishing line perpendicular to the front of these waves, was the true minimum velocity. The angle between the two sets of parallel waves ⟨and⟩ of ridges and hollows was measured, and at the sane [sic] time the velocity with which the ⟨ship⟩ fishing line was dragged through water. The angle was measured by holding a jointed two foot rule with its branches parallel to the sets of lines of wate[r] ridges. The angle to which the ruler had to be opened in this adjustment, was the angle sought. By laying it down on paper and drawing two straight lines by its two edges, and completing a simple geometrical construction with a length introduced to represent the measured velocity of the moving solid, the required minimum wave velocity was readily obtained. The following are four of the results:–

Velocity of Moving Solid	Deduced Min[m] Wave Velocity
51 centm[s] per sec.	23.0 cent[s] per sec.
38 „ „ „	23.8 „ „ „
26 „ „ „	23.2 „ „ „
24 „ „ „	22.9 „ „ „

The theoretical formulae will be given in a paper communicated to the Royal Society of Edinburgh.[f] ⟨It is proposed to call ripples all⟩ The theoretical result calculated from .073 of a gramme weight per cent[e], as the cohesive surface tension for pure water was [illegible deletion of two very short words] ⟨If⟩ 23 centimetres per second. ⟨be taken.⟩

This gives 1.7 centimetres as the wave length corresponding wave length. as [sic] the minimum speed, they [sic] 1.7 centimetres as the corresponding wave length.[g]

The levelling force to which the motions of ripples are chiefly due, is cohesion, that for waves chiefly gravity. The introduction of cohesion into the theory of undulations, explains a difficulty, in considering the phenomenon of standing ripples seen on the surface of water in a finger glass made to sound by rubbing a moist finger on its lip. If no other levelling force than gravity were concerned, the length from crest to crest corresponding to 256 vibrations per second would be 1/400 of a centimetre. When cohesion is taken into account the wave length is .19 of centimetre.

When gravity is neglected, the formula for the wave length (l) and the cohesive tension of the surface (T) and ζ the density of the fluid is,

$$P = \sqrt{\frac{l^3 \zeta}{2\pi T}},$$

where T must be measured in Kinetic units. For water we have $\zeta = 1$, and, according to an estimate from experiments by Gay Lussac, contained in Poisson, $T = 982 \times .074 = 73$, 982 being the weight of one gramme in Kinetic units of force reckoned as centimetres per second. Hence for water

$$P = \frac{l^{3/2}}{\sqrt{2\pi \times 73}} = \frac{l^{3/2}}{21 \cdot 4}$$

when l is anything less than a quarter of a centimetre the error from neglecting gravity is a small per centage of the period.

With regard to M[r] McFarlane's paper: his own original title, Sir William thinks may perhaps be better than the one he (Sir W) proposed, as the original title agrees strictly with the subject. It seems that bodies of considerably different shapes and dimensions agree with more closeness than could be expected, in their rates of cooling by radiation and convection, but hitherto we have had no absolute value of the rate of cooling in any one case. The chief value of the experiments described in M[r] McFarlane's paper consists in their giving a very accurate, absolute determination of the rate of loss per unit of surface in the cases actually experimented upon. The further experiments proposed by coating a Copper ball with a polished silver surface, will help to determine according to Lesliee's[h] [sic] original principle, what proportion of the cooling depended on convection, and so will give us absolute values for the cooling by radiation, which of course will apply to any surface prepared in the same way as the Copper ball, whether blackened, or any other of the conditions experimented upon.

(Should have been signed J. Tatlock)[i]

a Kelvin has written at the top of the letter, 'The College, Glasgow is my proper address. I oscillate between the Laboratory & the LR in ⟨per⟩ [?] weekly period, passing longest in latter end of range, (? because?) better adapted for work'. Also, *Loch Fyne* is in Kelvin's hand. Unless otherwise noted, the letter is in Tatlock's hand.

b D. McFarlane, 'Experiments made to determine surface-conductivity for heat in absolute measure', *Proc. Roy. Soc.*, **20** (1872), 90–3.

c Kelvin has interlined the phrase, *under joint influence of gravity & cohesion.*

d Kelvin has deleted *sunk* and added *kept nearly vertical.*

e Kelvin has deleted *of* and added *and.*

f See Kelvin (177A), (178), (179), and (180).

g This much-altered portion of the letter was left somewhat garbled. At one stage it appears to have read:

The theoretical formulae will be given in a paper communicated to the Royal Society of Edinburgh. ⟨It is proposed to call ripples all⟩

If 23 centimetres per second be taken as the minimum speed, they [sic] 1.7 centimetres as the corresponding wave length.

No doubt the phrase *as the minimum speed . . . corresponding wave length* was intended to be deleted but was overlooked because it is at the top of a new page.

h John Leslie (1766–1832) was professor of mathematics at the University of Edinburgh from 1805 until 1819 when he became professor of natural philosophy. See Richard G. Olson, 'A note on Leslie's cube in the study of radiant heat', *Annals of Science*, **25** (1969), 203–8.

i The statement (*Should have been signed J. Tatlock*) is in Kelvin's hand.

2 C. W. Siemens, 'On the increase of electrical resistance in conductors with rise of temperature, and its application to the measure of ordinary and furnace temperatures', *Proc. Roy. Soc.*, **19** (1871), 443–5. Carl William Siemens (1823–83), born and educated in Germany, became a naturalized British subject in 1859. His technical innovations in electricity and metallurgy brought him wealth and prominence. He served, for example, as president of the Institution of Mechanical Engineers, the Society of Telegraph Engineers, and the British Association for the Advancement of Science.

3 See the 'Preliminary report of the committee on Siemens's electrical-resistance pyrometer', *Brit. Assoc. Rep.* (1872), 134–5.

4 Jenkins's letters to Kelvin for 1860 are in the Kelvin Papers in Glasgow University Library. However, none of the six written during the summer (J37 to J42) discuss thermometry.

282 KELVIN to STOKES, 31 October 1871
Stokes Collection, K179

Glasgow College
Oct 31/71

MY DEAR STOKES

I feel quite sure that you will agree with me in considering Helmholtz as much the most deserving of the candidates named for the Copley medal.[1] I do hope you and others who feel this way will convince the council and secure the award to Helmholtz. The more I see of Helmholtz's work the more I value it, and I am very anxious that what I believe is the right award should be made in this case. I hear that Foster[2] is anxious to be well supported and that is why I write to you now. I wrote to Foster himself last June or about that time, but I am afraid too briefly to have weight in respect to Helmholtz's actual work. You (and Foster too,) however know it well enough to be able to tell the Council something of its value.

Believe me

Yours always truly
W. THOMSON

P.S. I have been reading Cauchy & Poisson of the great 'Concours de 1815'[3] and for the first time know about a 'solitary wave' (or rather that it cannot be) in deep water. Their function

$$\int_0^\infty \cos mx \cos(c\sqrt{m})\,dm$$

365

must be tabulated by the function-calculating committee.[4]

1 Helmholtz did not receive the Royal Society's Copley medal until 1873. Julius Robert von Mayer won in 1871, and Friedrich Wöhler in 1872.
2 Probably George Carey, not Michael, Foster, since he became a fellow of the Royal Society in 1869 while Michael did not do so until 1872, the year after the date of this letter. George Carey Foster (1835–1919) was professor of physics at University College, London, from 1865 to 1898 and principal from 1900 to 1904. Michael Foster (1836–1907) received his M.D. from University College, London, in 1859 and was professor of physiology at Cambridge from 1883 to 1903. He was secretary of the Royal Society from 1881 to 1903.
3 See Cauchy, 'Mémoire sur la théorie de la propagation des ondes à la surface d'un fluide pesant d'une profondeur indéfinie', *Mémoires présentés par divers Savans à l'Académie des Sciences de l'Institut de France; ou Collection des Mémoires des Savans Étrangers*, 1 (1827), 3–312, and Poisson, 'Mémoire sur la théorie des ondes', *Mémoires de l'Académie des Sciences*, 1 (1816), 71–186. Both papers were presented in 1815.
4 See the 'Report of the committee . . . on mathematical tables', *Brit. Assoc. Rep.* (1873), 1–175. Both Stokes and Kelvin were members of the committee.

283 KELVIN to STOKES, 20 November [1871][1]
Stokes Collection, K368

Nov 20
Glasgow College

DEAR STOKES

The approximate formulae, given by Cauchy and Poisson, particularly Poisson, show the general character of the function

$$\int_0^\infty \cos x\sqrt{n} \cos n\, dn$$

very well. But I think it most desirable that it should be tabulated, and curves drawn illustrating its character. The want both of a table of numerical values and of graphic representations is greatly felt in reading either Cauchy or Poisson. A great part of what they have to say would be much shortened even by the addition of graphic representations, and it would be much easier for any one (the authors I believe included) to understand the whole character of the phenomena investigated, with illustrations like this of the chief function on which the⟨ir⟩ expression of them depends. If you agree with me, I think the thing might be put into hands at once, for the B.A. committee.[2] I am writing to Cayley and asking him to speak to you about it.

Yours truly
WILLIAM THOMSON

P.S. I had almost forgotten to answer your question about what I had done in respect to elastic solid.

There is nothing much worth publishing that I have not published, of what I have thought of as to the 21 coefficients. In 'T and T'' (i.e. Thomson and Tait) §§684 and thereabouts,[3] and App. C, you will find nearly all I have to say. When we come to 'Properties of matter' I may show how out of a ⟨piece⟩ solid fulfilling Poisson's limitation, one may be built up which shall have 21 independent coefficients. If you look at an india rubber sponge (I presume you know what that is) you will see the effect of cellular structure curiously illustrated, giving high rigidity and low resistance to compression like cork. I do not however feel sure that this was the subject (or generally the independence of the 21 coeff^s) on which you thought it possible I might have something useful not yet published. I do not see how the independence of the 21 coeff^s could settle the difficu[l]ty of determining whether the vibrations are in perpendicular to the plane of polarization. Do you not think that kinetic considerations, (even without going so far as the nature of the ultimate molecules) may help?

Second P.S. I think it is worthwhile, and very desirable to calculate

$$1 + \frac{x^2}{2^2} + \frac{x^4}{2^2 \cdot 4^2} + \&c$$

though it was not the very first thing I wanted. For the solution of the columnar vortex problem when the mass of fluid does not extend to infinity but is enclosed in a cylindrical case, that function is necessary. It is however because of the failing convergence or certainty of the semiconvergent expression, it will be difficult to calculate for large values of x. Cayley seems satisfied with the semiconverging series in respect to practical calculation.

1 The date is determined by the similarity of the letter to the postscript of the previous letter.
2 See the previous letter, note 4.
3 Kelvin and Tait *TNP*.

284 KELVIN to STOKES, 29 November 1871
Stokes Collection, K180

Glasgow College
Nov 29, 1871

DEAR STOKES

I shall ask Macfarlane to make an abstract of his paper,[1] so that if you think proper it may go into the Transactions. If you think however that it would be better placed in the Proceedings we should be of course quite as well pleased.

The cooling effect effect [*sic*] of currents of air is far from insignificant. Roughly speaking, it is about half of the whole effect experienced. The merit of the investigation consists in its being a really accurate determination of the rate of cooling of the body tested, in *absolute measure*⟨s⟩. The elaborate investigation of Dulong & Petit described in a long paper[2] published in the 'Mémoires' of the French Institute gives no result in absolute measure; only *comparisons* of the rates of cooling in the various circumstances of their experiments.

Our investigation will be continued ('if we are spared') so as to show the absolute rate of loss of heat of the same copper globe in the best vacuum we can get. Then we shall be able to tell with some accuracy what proportion of the cooling in the experiments already completed was due to radiation. The residue will show what part was due to convection.

I am sorry not to have been able to write sooner as to strain in a medium. You will have seen already that I have nothing useful to say as to the ideas you are now working out. Many thanks for your letters. I hope you are getting out something satisfactory.

Yours always truly
WILLIAM THOMSON

P.S. When a table of successive values of a ⟨function⟩ transcendent is to be formed, an indefinite integral is particularly convenient, as the 'quadratures' give the successive values required by simple additions; and with great care when the function to be integrated is so simple as $\sin(x^2)$. If the one in question has not been done already, it will be ⟨a⟩ very moderate labour to ⟨tab⟩ calculate it in a form convenient for waves.

1 See footnote b to the letter included in footnote 1 to letter 281.
2 Dulong and Petit, 'Recherches sur la mesure des températures, et sur les lois de la communication de la chaleur', *Annales de Chimie et de Physique*, 7 (1817), 113–54, 225–64, and 337–67. (See the *Dictionary of Scientific Biography* article on Dulong.)

285   KELVIN to STOKES, 9 December 1871
     Stokes Collection, K181

Glasgow College
Dec 9, 1871

DEAR STOKES

I shall be obliged by your sending me my letter[1] in which I reported on Siemens' paper.[2] I shall consider carefully whether or not I should retract any part of it, after what I learn as to what others have done in the subject, &c, by the report of the other referee.[3]

Yours truly
WILLIAM THOMSON

P.S. I shall observe what you say as to writing reports on separate paper in future if I am again so unfortunate as to have a paper referred to me.

1 Letter 281.
2 See letter 281, note 2.
3 The Royal Society archive of referee's reports contains none for Siemens's paper.

286 KELVIN to STOKES, 8 February 1872
Stokes Collection, K183

Glasgow College
8th Feby 1872.

DEAR STOKES,

At least a year's observations would be necessary to get a somewhat accurate determination of the mean sea level for any place; and the observation ought to be either by an accurate self-registering tide gauge with a constant zero or datum line, or accurate personal observations made at least every hour. I have written to Roberts for information as to his last results respecting long period tides. I cannot recollect whether this question formed part of your letter which I received a few days ago and which I have unfortunately mislaid, although no doubt I shall find it again. I shall write to you again when I hear from Roberts, but I do not wish to delay answering your letter so far as I can. The long period tides have hitherto baffled us. We have got no ⟨constant⟩ consistent lunar fortnightly or monthly tides depending on declination and ellipticity. We have solar semi-annual and annual tides, greater in am⟨m⟩ount than the calculations have given, for lunar fortnightly and monthly, and inconsistent with the supposition that they are due to astronomical causes. They are no doubt genuine tides depending upon meteorological circumstances. Roberts has, however, latterly been engaged on the subject, for places in low latitudes, and I hope we may get trustworthy lunar fortnightly and monthly Astronomical tides. I am ordered by the council and a committee[1] of the British Association to apply to the British & Indian governments for assistance to defray the expense of calculations and to promote the establishment of tide gauges at certain specified localities, and I shall be obliged therefore if you will inform me, so far as you ⟨may think proper⟩ feel at liberty to do so, what the state of the case is, as regards the communication from Government to which you refer in your letter.

I remain
Yours Very truly
W. THOMSON

Professor Stokes

1 The Committee for the Purpose of Promoting the Extension, Improvement, and Harmonic Analysis of Tidal Observations.

Glasgow University
24th April 1872.

MY DEAR STOKES.

I have carefully read M[r] Siemens' letter[1] and I now return it along with the accompanying documents. I am sorry that I have not been able to do so sooner. With reference to his remark, that the referees seemingly passed over his 'more exhaustive investigations of Platinum', I had not his paper[2] in my hands when I wrote my supplementary report on the 8th of January 1872,[3] or else no doubt I should have mentioned it also as valuable. I did not in either report enter upon the question of empirical formulae for representing resistance; and on this subject I can only say, that without theoretical knowledge, which we do not yet possess, no empirical formulae can, in my opinion, be trusted to for expressing electric resistance, except within the range of actual observation, and through a comparatively short difference of temperature on each side of it. In the present state of science regarding this subject, it appears to me that the use of empirical formulae is merely to facilitate the construction of curves, or the calculation of tables, or the calculation for temperatures not shewn in the tables.

In his letter M[r] Siemens alludes to a suggestion 'to do away with the metallic tube protecting the delicate measuring coil against the chemical or local action of the flame or hot substance'. In making the suggestion to which no doubt M[r] Siemens here refers, I did not mean that the delicate coil should be left unprotected but that its protecting material if metallic, should not ⟨be⟩ form a continuous metallic communication between the envelope ⟨and⟩ of the coil and the cool exterior of the furnace. It would in my opinion be necessary to prove by actual experiment that the temperature of the coil is not considerably reduced below that of the furnace, or other hot material immediately round it, before M[r] Siemens' method, with the details described in his paper, could be considered as scientifically satisfactory. At a meeting of the Committee[4] on M[r] Siemens' method, held in University College last Nov[r] I suggested a method for testing this question, but I have not yet heard whether it has been carried out. In due time I have no doubt but that M[r] Siemens will either have experimental evidence to give, that the conduction of heat along the iron tube which he uses does not interfere with the accuracy of his result, or will make the requisite modification in the details of his apparatus, to do away with the error. I must also add that even although M[r] Siemens has proved that his electrolytic method of measuring resistance which he employs is capable of giving definite results. I cannot but think that a suitable galvanometer (with resistance coils for occasional comparison) would be both more accurate and more easily worked, whether on shore or at sea.

I still think the best ⟨suggestion⟩ conclusion in the circumstances would be to accept for the transactions the portion or portions of Mr Siemens' paper containing new scientific results, unless Mr Siemens himself would prefer to write afresh a short paper embodying them. I would also think a detailed description of his method for furnaces, thoroughly suitable for the transactions, if the question of the conducting away of heat through the iron tube was disposed of satisfactory. The fact of its being an industrial instrument of proved practical value, which I believe it to be, is in my opinion strongly in favour of the el⟨l⟩igibility for the transactions of a paper describing i⟨n⟩t in detail.

I cannot for a moment think that any 'insinuation' such as that to which Mr Siemens refers towards the conclusion of his letter can in any way have been intended.

WILLIAM THOMSON

1 C. W. Siemens to Stokes, 9 March 1872, Stokes Collection, RS841, in which he wrote, 'Regarding Part I of my Paper the Referees concede that I have extended the range of observations on Electrical Resistance from 1 or 200 to 3 or 400 °Cent. but they seemingly pass over my more exhaustive investigations of Platinum to which I attach the greater importance'.
2 See letter 281, note 2.
3 This report is not in the Royal Society.
4 See the 'Preliminary report of the committee on Siemens's electrical-resistance pyrometer', Brit. Assoc. Rep. (1872), 134–5, and a fuller report in ibid. (1874), 242–9.

288 KELVIN to STOKES, 25 May [1872][1]
Stokes Collection, K184A

Yacht L. R. Torquay Sat May 25

DEAR STOKES

I have an excellent paper by Latimer Clark 'on a Voltaic Standard of Electromotive Force' for communication to the R. S.[2] I hope to be present on Thursday. Can it be brought on then, supposing (as I do doubtfully) there is a meeting on that day. I might relieve you of the trouble of reading it, by reading extracts from it and giving a very short acc^t of the remainder. I am writing to Clark to send an abstract forthwith, addressed to you at the R. S., which would be enough to read if by accident I am not present with the paper which mean time I keep by me.

I want also to communicate a paper of my own (which has been written out in full for twelve years) on 'Contact Electricity'.[3] I kept it till I should be able again to work on the subject which is now the case. I have materials for a continuation which will very soon follow the first paper, but mean time I wish not to delay it longer. Would next Thursday evening do?

I should be glad to find a line at the Athenaeum answering the two questions, when I arrive there, Tuesday, Wednesday, or Thursday (according to the strength and direction of the wind in the interval).

I have just had a forenoon⟨s⟩ at Froude's[4] seeing his experiments and work (which are quite splendid, and will give exceedingly valuable results) and am on the point of sailing for Land's End to visit the 'siphon' there.

Yours
W T

1 The date is determined by the date of the paper in the next note.
2 L. Clark, 'On a voltaic standard of electromotive force', *Proc. Roy. Soc.*, 20 (1872), 444–8. The paper was read on 20 June 1872.
3 Kelvin did not communicate the paper to the Royal Society.
4 William Froude (1810–79), the naval architect who became a fellow of the Royal Society in 1870, built a tank 250 feet long at Torquay in the early 1870s for testing scale models of ships.

289 KELVIN to STOKES, 14 October 1872
      Stokes Collection, K185

14th October 1872.

MY DEAR STOKES

Thanks for your letter of the 8th. I was on the point of answering your previous letter on the subject, but I might have allowed the 'point' to extend over next Thursday, through the difficulty of finding time to do today what may possibly be done tomorrow.

I gave information to Admiral Richards[1] immediately about my sounding with steel wire, and have seen him several times on the subject. He was disposed to give it a trial in the circumnavigation expedition, and thought it might be useful as a ready means of making soundings, whether from boats or from the ship when a mere sounding, with a small specimen of the bottom, is required. The heavy apparatus for dredging which the expedition requires cannot of course be superseded by anything such as I have used, the chief value of which must be to allow deep sea soundings to be made at small expense, and by ships not specially fitted for the purpose. I am glad, however, to find that Admiral Richards considers my plan may be even of some practical value in the circumnavigation expedition. A new wheel, with appliances which I found wanting, on my first trial, and the wheel I actually used, illustrating the want of such appliances, are at present at the Admiralty. I intend to be in London sometime in November, and if my plan is to be tried in the expedition, I would be glad to meet with any officer or officers, who may have charge of the soundings and point out as far as possible all that seems to me needing attention, to carry it out suc[c]essfully and easily; meantime something should be done about securing the requisite quality and quantity of wire. For this purpose I enclose to you a letter I have today received on the subject. The wire referred to is a coil which had been sent to me by Mess[rs] Johnson,[2] and which at their request, I returned to them to be galvanized. What is to be done now is to test its strength, and to find how it behaves when coiled on the wheel. As the wheel is at the Admiralty I think the best plan would be to send the wire there to have it tried immediately with a view to deciding as to the wire to be ordered for the expedition, and whether it should be galvanized. If, however, no one there can take charge of testing and examining it, I would have it returned to me here, and I would at least have its strength tested in my laboratory. But I think if the plan is to be tried at all in the expedition the wire should immediately be sent to the Admiralty [?] and taken in hand there. I am writing to Johnson today to keep the wire until they receive instructions from you or the Admiralty, but in the mean time to make their own test of strength on a few pieces cut from it. If it is decided to have it sent to the Admiralty, will you let instructions be sent direct from London, as I shall not be much at home until November?

As to the question of rusting, we do not know enough at present to be able to reckon with certainty on the same wire being used many times for soundings, with considerable intervals of time between. But I fully anticipate that when we have experience on the subject the same piece of sounding wire may be used for years if properly protected from rust, whether by keeping the wheel with the wire on it under oil, when out of use or by applying the Phosphoric Acid preservative of which, hitherto, I have made no trial. I have a small piece of very fine wire on board my Yacht at present which was prepared that way last April. I shall endeavour to give it a thorough trial before November.

The only other suggestion that occurs to me for the expedition is that no opportunity should be lost for making tidal observations. Careful observations made by aid of a properly placed tide pole in any part of the world will be valuable. Accurate measurements of the sea-level once every hour for a fortnight (the time of course being kept) would be very valuable information.

It will be of great importance for telegraphic enterprise that a line of soundings from the Azores to Bermuda, and soundings in the neighbourhood of Bermuda, and between Bermuda and St Thomas should be taken as early as possible. I understand that such soundings can conveniently be taken in the commencement of the work, and would properly belong to the programme of the expedition. For the sake of the Great Western Telegraph Company, of which Professor Jenkin and I are engineers, I hope this may be done; and I understand that favourable replies have been given official[l]y to an application to that effect made to the Admiralty by the Directors of the Company.

I remain,
Yours Very truly
WILLIAM THOMSON

Professor Stokes

1 George Henry Richards (1820–96), Rear-Admiral in the Royal Navy, became a fellow of the Royal Society in 1866 and was a member with Kelvin of the British Association's committee on tides. As Hydrographer to the Admiralty, he was instrumental in planning the *Challenger* Expedition carried out with H.M.S. *Challenger* from 7 December 1872 to 26 May 1876.
2 See letter 208, note 6.

290   KELVIN to STOKES, 17 October 1872
Stokes Collection, K186

L.R.
Oct 1⟨6⟩7/72

DEAR STOKES

I fear the phosphoric acid preservative for steel is not going to answer for sounding wire. I enclose a specimen of the fine wire to which I applied it last April. It has been kept on board since then, but nothing done with it, only once uncoiled and coiled up again. Yesterday I found it all looking rusty (something as the specimen) and I dipped the coil in sea water and hung it up in the open air on deck, to see how it keeps during the next fortnight. I have not much expectation of anything satisfactory. I believe however that keeping the whole wheel with wire coiled on it will answer well; and probably also the galvanizing which may very probably save the trouble of keeping the wire under oil. I find the galvanized iron wire rigging (now in general use on board ship) shows very little appearance of rust though constantly exposed to air and salt spray.

The sounding wire which I used is considerably thicker than the specimen enclosed.

I hope the four papers are to appear, now without delay. Is the Wave surface of Iceland Spar in type?[1]

Yours truly
W THOMSON

1 Stokes (87). Stokes (86) is the only other paper he published in 1872, while (87A) and (88) are the only ones published in 1873.

291 KELVIN to STOKES, 17 October 1872
Royal Society of London, RR.7.166

Yacht 'Lalla Rookh'
Clyde
Oct 17, 1872

DEAR STOKES

I return to M[r] White, by same post with this, 'Researches on Solar Physics III' by De la Rue, Balfour Stewart, and Loewy.[1]

The tables, of which a specimen is given, will no doubt form a very valuable contribution to knowledge of the subject. I believe that the publication of the whole series of tables will be useful in the present stage of the investigation, and I therefore am of opinion that they should be published, with the paper, in the Transactions of the Royal Society.

I remain
Yours truly
WILLIAM THOMSON

1 W. De la Rue, B. Stewart, and B. Loewy, 'Researches on Solar Physics – III', *Proc. Roy. Soc.*, 20 (1871–2), 289.

292 KELVIN to STOKES, 19 December 1872[1]
Stokes Collection, K187

Glasgow University
19 Dec[r] 1872.

MY DEAR STOKES

Your letter about the cylindrical vortex followed me to Lizard I believe, and certainly to London where I received it last Monday. I tried for an hour in the Athenaeum to answer it, but only succeeded in wasting some of the Club paper. My difficulty consisted in seeing precisely the *modus operandi* of the head and tail when the former overtakes the latter. Steady[2] stable motion, with some such configuration of the rotationally moving part as is indicated by figs. 1 and 2, is undoubtedly possible; and the stability of the motion in such a case, for instance, as when the vortex is approximately circular and central prevents me from admitting the configurations which you represent by red in your diagrams, as possible consequences from an initially symmetrical circular motion. I believe I am right and correctly represented by you in the first diagram of your former letter, which you may remember, resembles my figs. 1 and 2. In the steady motion represented by these ⟨motions⟩ diagrams the head and tail must be symmetrical. In fig. 1 I have purposely represented them as unsymmetrical to show a resolvable doubt which I have not yet resolved,[3] as to the place of sharpest curvature. Taking such a case as either of these,

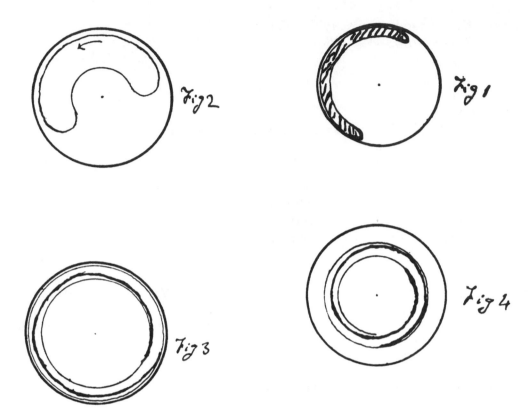

suppose energy to be lost through inperfect [*sic*] rigidity and inperfect [*sic*] elasticity of the containing vessel; the vortically[4] moving portion of liquid will spread itself to a greater length round the circumferance, [*sic*] and if this degradation be extremely gradual and the envelope become again rigid, I believe the altered motion would be found to be again stable and very approximately steady. Of all this I was sure when I tried to write to you, but since the thing occurred to me a year and a half ago, I have been puzzled to see how the transition represented in fig. 3 can take place. I always felt certain that somehow or other, the head would get outside of the tail, and after that the state represented in fig. 3 would be ⟨rigid⟩ reached, through further subtraction of kinetic energy. Since trying to write to you I have become almost convinced that the amount of kinetic energy with which there can be stable steady motion, as in figs 1 and 2 has in inferior[5] limit, and that when the head approaches within a certain distance of the tail[6] through the gradual subtraction of energy the[7] configuration of steady motion becomes unstable. The subtraction of an infinitesimal amount of kinetic energy would I believe then leave the motion such that even without the subtraction of more energy the head would shoot round into the space next the containing vessel, and the vortically moving portion of liquid would get drawn out into a spiral as shown in fig 3, where the thick coarse spiral represents irrotationally moving liquid; the outer thick circle the containing vessel; the space between it and the fine circle irrotationally moving liquid; and the space within the inner circle fluid nearly at rest, but with no rotational motion. Thus the rough spiral fig 3, is what you call the irrotational canal. Fig. 3, with the irrotational canal continually drawn out finer and finer, and ⟨re⟩aquiring [*sic*] more and more turns represents what I formerly thought and still think to be, the case when more and more energy is gradually taken away;[8] but there must be what I cannot show in the diagram, – a continual diminution of the space between the containing vessel and the outer boundary of the rotational vortex. In the liquid approaching more and more nearly, rigid, but not ⟨rigid⟩ reached in any finite time, the space of irrotationally moving liquid outside the vortex becomes infinitely narrow. I now see what I did not see before, that if we commence with a central circular vortex, draw off energy with extreme slowness till, through the head too nearly overtaking the tail, the motion becomes unstable, and then give perfect rigidity to the containing vessel, so that there shall be no more loss of energy, such a state of things as that represented in fig 3. will supervene; the irrotational canal become longer and thinner and ⟨re⟩aquiring [*sic*] more and more turns, *ad infinitum*.

Suppose now, as would be the case after an infinite time, the irrotational canal to be absolutely extirpated, or to make a more ⟨a more⟩ practical supposition, suppose we start with a hollow cylindrical vortex, that is to say a configuration of motion in which the liquid is qui[e]scent throughout the space within a certain circle, and another larger concentric one; and possesses irrotational vortex motion in the space outside this outer circle, as far as the boundary of the containing vessel. Suppose the containing vessel to be not perfectly rigid and to be imperfectly elastic. There would be a continual loss of energy until the condition of absolute minimum of[9] energy is reached at the end of an infinite time. As the interior qui[e]scent liquid is separated by an impassible vortex barrier from external irrotationally moving liquid, it is necessary that in time the ⟨former⟩ latter must drag a film of rotationally moving liquid into the interior, and thus convolutions of the continually elongated film or streak of the vortically moving liquid, through the approximately quiescent irrotationally moving liquid will be formed. As time advances, the labyrinthi⟨an⟩ne film of the vortically moving liquid will become thinner and thinner. After the end of an infinite time there will be infinitely little of the vortically moving liquid inside a certain circle, and infinitely little of the irrotationally moving liquid outside that circle; and thus we have the condition of absolute minimum of energy. I have always hitherto supposed that when we start with circular vortex from the centre outwards, ⟨we⟩ to a certain circle, and irrotational revolution outside that circle, the progress towards the minimum of energy is through spiral configurations like fig. 3; and that the irrotationally moving liquid next the outside gets ⟨thrown⟩ drawn[10] through the irrotational canal into the interior space: but now today for the first time I see that if, after a certain amount of energy is gradually drawn off, no more is drawn off for a long time, one stage ⟨w⟩could be infinitely nearly a shell vortex: and that if after waiting till that stage is sensibly reached, we begin ⟨again⟩ to draw off energy more rapidly, there would be complex convolutions, and the irrotationally moving liquid would get into the centre, ⟨and⟩ not through the irrotational canal, but by pushing through and drawing into a film the intervening vortex barrier. Thus seeing that my old supposition of the irrotationally moving liquid getting into the centre, altogether through the irrotational canal, is not generally true, it may be generally false. I began to think that it is possible with no arrangement as to drawing off energy does the rotationally moving liquid come in entirely by the rotational canal. I see that possible streaks of irrotationally and rotationally moving liquid mixed up and drawn out, may be in every case produced. One thing remains absolutely certain, that if the containing vessel be imperfectly rigid and imperfectly elastic, the state approached infinitely near to in an infinite time is that ⟨of⟩ in which all the vortically moving liquid circulating next the containing vessel, and all the liquid which had either no motion or irrotational motion only, in the end infinitely nearly quiescent in the form of a circular cylinder inside the vortex shell.

This is an extremely difficult subject to write upon as you perceive and probably have felt yourself. I hope what I have written now will be intelligible to you. I should be exceedingly glad to hear again from you on the subject. If you write tomorrow or Saturday address, Care of Prof. Tait, 17 Drummond Place, Edinburgh: if you write on Monday or Tuesday, Knowsley, Prescott. I am to be there till Thursday.

Yours Very truly
[WILLIAM THOMSON]

Prof. Stokes

P.S. An imperfectly elastic solid is slow but sure poison to a vortex. The minutest portion of such matter would destroy all the atoms of any finite universe. I therefore do not admit that this [convolution][11] of structure, indefinitely increasing with the time does not seem very promising for the explanation of atoms. Any number of all true three-dimensional vortices in a finite frictionless liquid contained in a rigid vessel, however great the space, and however closely packed the vortices, can never become more than finitely interstreaked. I think indeed on the contrary that the more or less of labyrinthian which must supervene from a too crowded initial configuration of vortices is the true explanation of the condensation of a liquid on the sides of the containing vessel. I of course must ignomineously [*sic*] use a rigid body or containing vessel for temporary illustrations, but the ladder is to be kicked away from under our feet when it has us where we wished. Of course all rigid bodies ⟨re⟩present a deceitful simpleness of rigidity; and real elastic solids must when we understand them properly, be recognized as properly packed crowds of vortices, prevented from dissipating into space by vortices moving about more freely outside, and sometimes getting entangl[e]d in the group; sometimes swerving off, and giving on the average as much accession to as there is loss from the crowd.

1 The letter is in John Tatlock's hand, though there are corrections in Kelvin's hand. At the top of letter 296 are a series of corrections and comments regarding this letter. These are mentioned in notes 3, 4, 5, 7, 9, and 10, below. Although one would expect Stokes to have made the corrections in response to Kelvin's directions, most of them appear to be in Kelvin's hand, not Stokes's.

2 Tatlock has added a footnote here for Kelvin reading, 'I am using a somewhat altered definition of the word "steady," and am here applying it on the understanding that it means that suc[c]essive states of motion are precisely similar to one another'.

3 See letter 296, note 2. This is page 2, line 10, of letter 292.

4 See letter 296, note 2. The letters *ly* have been added to *vortical*.

5 See letter 296, note 2. The words *in inferior* have been inserted, apparently by Kelvin, in the space left by Tatlock between *has* and *limit*. Hence, letter 296 apparently was asking for *in* to be changed to *an*, a correction that Larmor has made in pencil on the letter.

6 See letter 296, note 6.

7 See letter 296, note 2. Kelvin has added a footnote here reading, 'I believe that for any given amount of energy there is one and only one stated configuration of steady motion; it being understood of course that the quantity of liquid which possesses irrotational motion is given. I am supposing for simplicity, the molecular rotation to be uniform through that portion of the liquid which has rotational motion'. Contrary to the directions of note 2 in letter 296, *steady* has not been substituted for *stated* but has been inserted (by Kelvin or Stokes) before *motion*. Except for the word *steady*, the footnote is in Tatlock's hand.

8 In his own hand, Kelvin has added a footnote here reading, 'For modification of this opinion see p 6'. Page 6 of the letter begins with the passage, *the irrotational canal, but by pushing through and drawing into a film*, and includes the rest of the letter except the postscript.

9 See letter 296, note 2. The words *minimum of* have been inserted, apparently by Kelvin.

10 See letter 296, note 2. The word *drawn* has been substituted for *thrown*, apparently by Kelvin.

11 Tatlock left a blank space here, and Larmor has inserted *convolution*.

293 KELVIN to STOKES, 1 January 1873
Stokes Collection, K189

Train to Manchester
Jan 1/73

DEAR STOKES

Is the enclosed an irreversible decree? I cannot think that the reporters can have taken into consideration the great scientific importance of absolute measurement, and its great rarity, hitherto, or they would have unhesitatingly advised the publication of Latimer Clark's paper[1] in the Transactions. If I had thought there was a shadow of a doubt as to its being accepted I should not have 'communicated' it, but got it communicated by some one else, in order that there might have been a chance of its being referred to me as one of the reporters. It contains two distinct measurements of the electromotive force of the cell, in absolute electromagnetic units. So far as I know, no such measurement has hitherto been made (at all events, with any approach to the same accuracy) in any scientific laboratory in the world. I doubt if 1 percent of the professors of natural philosophy or physics in Europe or America could do it at all without learning a good deal that they do not yet know and constructing or procuring apparatus which they do not possess. The new form of cell is I believe a very valuable addition to the means of obtaining with ease, an accurate standard of electromotive force, and I believe Clark's paper contains thoroughly scientific evidence that it is so.

It would I think be a great discouragement to practical men and an injury to science if when they do anything so exceedingly good as this in the way of raising the scientific character of their profession, the Royal Society should throw cold water on their efforts.

I am very curious to hear from you again regarding the labyrinthine degradation of a vortex. If you write address Glasgow as I shall be there by Friday evening. Wishing you all a happy new year.

I am yours truly
W THOMSON

1 See letter 288, note 2.

294 KELVIN to STOKES, 1 and 2 January 1873
Stokes Collection, K188

Train Manchester to Selkirk
Jan 1, 1873

DEAR STOKES

Here is a case (of a more general solution) which I worked out more than a year ago in the Lalla Rookh & which I think will interest you

$\phi = A\epsilon^{-my} \cos m(x - \alpha t)$

$\langle u = \rangle$ for $\langle$negative$\rangle$ positive values of y

$\phi = -A\epsilon^{my} \cos(mx - \alpha t)$ for $\langle$positive$\rangle$ negative [values of y]

$u = \dfrac{d\phi}{dx}, \quad v = \dfrac{d\phi}{dy}$ for positive [values of y]

$u = \dfrac{d\phi}{dx} \langle + \rangle - \langle \frac{1}{2} \rangle \, 2\omega y, \quad v = \dfrac{d\phi}{dy}$ [for] negative [values of y]

Instead of 'positive' and 'negative' substitute greater than or less than

the ordinate of the stream line whose mean ordinate is zero, this stream line being infinitely nearly straight and therefore infinitely nearer a curve of $\langle$signs$\rangle$ sines.

Then, if $\alpha = \dfrac{\omega}{\langle u \rangle m}$ you have no slip at this transitional stream line irrotational motion on the positive side of it and rotational motion with molecular angular veloc^y ω on the negative side.

This is the case of waves in a bottomless vortex ocean. Imagine first all space on the positive side of OX to be occupied by motionless liquid, and all on the negative, by liquid with vortex motion (red)[1] parallel to OX. Let now there be a bounding plane, parallel to XOZ, at a distance from XOZ a great multiple of $\dfrac{2\pi}{m}$, and let this plane be suddenly corrugated and left at rest in its corrugated form: the ridges of the corrugations being parallel to OY and the length from crest to crest equal to $\dfrac{2\pi}{m}$. The preceding equations express the consequent

state of the liquid. The velocity of propagation of the waves is ⟨inversely⟩ directly as ⟨its⟩ their length, not as the square root of the length as in deep sea gravity-waves.

Th⟨is⟩e preceding is a particular case of vortex motion infinitely nearly circular, with infinitely nearly quiescent liquid inside; then an infinitely nearly circular cylindrical shell of vortex and outside, irrotational motion. Introducing a fixed circular core inside, and a finite fixed circular boundary, we have a case amenable to analytical investigation. I have worked it out for any possible infinitesimal disturbance from the circular motion: the disturbance not confined to planes perpendicular to the axis but then 'columnar harmonics' are necessary. When the disturbance is confined to planes perpendicular to the axis, circular functions, and exponentials, of course suffice. Broadmeadows Selkirk Jan 2. I have worked out the details with columnar harmonics for the case in which the core and the space of approximately quiescent liquid vanish and the outer boundary is infinitely distant, and have got exceedingly interesting results which I hope to get written out & published soon,[2] with numerical results to be calculated from Glaisher's tables of columnar harmonics.[3]

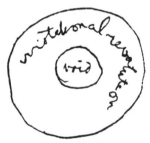

Another very interesting case is an irrotational vortex with hollow core. This I have worked out in detail for the case w[h] is of course exceedingly simple when there is a circular rigid cylinder as containing vessel and the ⟨vortex⟩ motion is infinitely little disturbed from being in circles. When the thickness of the shell of liquid is small in comparison with the radius of the containing cylinder, the waves at the surface separating liquid from void follow simply the law of gravity-waves (deep or shallow water) with ⟨me⟩ ⟨mean ang vel⟩ with [sic] radius x (mean ang vel)^2 for g, when the direction of propagation is parallel to axis of cylinder. Waves travelling round the cylinder also follow a very simple law relative to the rotation (I suppose it is that veloc of propagation relatively to the liquid, whether forwards or backwards, is the same as the simple veloc of propagation in the other case, but have not time to make sure, before post).

Yours
WT

P.S. I showed my letter to you about Latimer Clark's paper[4] to Joule yesterday & he approves & hoped the decree might not be held to be irreversible.

Void-cored ring vortices, with varieties of knots, serve well for atoms, *being expansible* yet rigourously permanent & stable. The analysis of them is also simpler in some respects than of the ordinary cored vortex.

1 None of the figures in this letter contain colours. Kelvin may have been referring to a previous letter by Stokes which has not survived. See the next letter, note 2.
2 Possibly Kelvin (196A), read 3 March 1873.
3 James Whitbread Lee Glaisher (1848–1928) was second wrangler in 1871, was lecturer in mathematics at Cambridge from 1871 to 1901, became a fellow of the Royal Society in 1875, and edited *The Messenger of Mathematics* and the *Quarterly Journal of Mathematics*. He had done a great deal of work on mathematical tables in the early 1870s and was the author of the British Association committee's report on mathematical tables in 1873 (see letter 282, note 4).
4 See letter 288, note 2.

295 STOKES to KELVIN, 6 January 1873[1]
Stokes Collection, NB21.56

Cambridge 6th Jany 1873

MY DEAR THOMSON,

As I saw that your letter of Decr 19 would demand consideration, and as there were other matters pressing at the time I laid it aside for a time; and perhaps you may have found how apt a thing when once laid aside is to remain lying about; at least I find it so with me. I was not however *altogether* idle in the matter, but made one or two small investigations on points connected with the subject.

You don't define what you mean by steady motion in the extended sense, ⟨but⟩ [?] at least don't fully define it, but confining myself for simplicity to motion in two dimensions within a circular cylinder, I suppose you mean motion which would become steady if kinematically compounded with a uniform motion of rotation of the whole about the axis. I shall assume this to be your meaning.

As a matter of curiosity, though not required for our problem, I worked out the condition that the compound motion should be dynamically as well as kinematically possible, and find it to be that the molecular angular vely should be a function of the radius vector (drawn of course from the centre of the ⟨cylr⟩ circle which is a section of the cylr. From this it is easy to show (the velocity being finite and continuous) that the motion will be in concentric circles and will be steady.

In the case you supposed of a cylindrical mass revolving like a solid, and surrounded without slip by irrotationally moving fluid, if the motion be

383

disturbed, suppose by a temporary deformation of the vessel, such that it is ultimately restored to its primitive shape and kept so, I see no reason whatsoever for supposing that the motion will be steady even in the extended sense. This could only, I should say, be possible under very peculiar conditions.

My figures in red[2] were not drawn subject to the condition of the motion being approximately alike all round the centre. I described in words the modification that that condition would introduce.

I thought at first that if the disturbance were symmetrical with respect to a certain plane passing through the axis (in an extended sense of the word symmetrical) it would continue to be symmetrical with respect to a plane passing through the axis and revolving uniformly. I scratched out what I had written about this because I did not see my way clearly. You however appear also to assume it true as I did at first. In what immediately follows I shall at first suppose, with you, that it is true.

You seem to accept my first figure. I had it in view if you did to take a crackshot [?] at it, as here it goes.

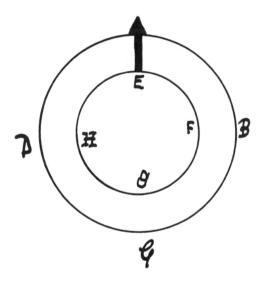

After an infinite time the state of things would be this. We should have a central cylinder $EFGH$ of fluid at rest and a divided annulus $ABCDAEHG$-FEA. The division AE is an infinitely thin irrotational canal and there is a similar inf[y] thin canal along $ABCD$. As to the motion of the annulus, AE may be treated as a mere surface of discontinuity. AE is supposed to remain radial, but may be at rest or revolve. Infinitely near the mouth E of the canal the fluid of the inner cyl[r] may be in motion. I use of course this mode of expression for shortness' sake in lieu of what would be expressed at length in the language of limits. The molecular angular vel^y in the annulus is the original angular vel^y say ω.

The exact motion in the annulus may be expressed by a Fourier series, but I shall not have occasion to write it down.

First attribute to the annulus a rotation ω like a solid or in other words give it everywhere a tangential vel^y ωr. This will satisfy the molecular angular vel^y so that the actual motion is got by superposing a certain irrotational motion on this. It will err by giving the circle *EFGH* a velocity ωa instead of zero, *a* being the radius.

To rectify this, superpose irrotational motion of a complete annulus such as to give a velocity $-\omega a$ to the inner boundary. This will give a total tangential vel^y (p) i.e. vel^y perpendicular to the radius vector

$$p = \omega\left(r - \frac{a^2}{r}\right)$$

The remaining fault is that *AE* tends to pass into the position $A'E$ whereas it ought to remain straight and pointing towards the centre. To complete the ⟨motion⟩ determination of the motion within the annulus we must regard the fluid of the annulus as initially at rest and confined within concentric circular boundaries and treat *AE* as a partition moving with a normal velocity

$$\omega'r - \omega\left(r - \frac{a^2}{r}\right)$$

where ω' is a disposable constant. The motion in the split annulus can be expressed by a Fourier series, but without expressing it we can see that there *must* be tangential motion along *EH* and *EF* which there ought not to be. Hence the supposition we started with is altogether impossible.

The way in which the rotational fluid gets to the outside, at least if the energy is gradually withdrawn, is I am satisfied utterly different. In consequence of the disturbance certain parts have too great or too small a transverse velocity to correspond to their radial distance, and so they shoot ahead or are left behind. It is not easy to draw but I will try

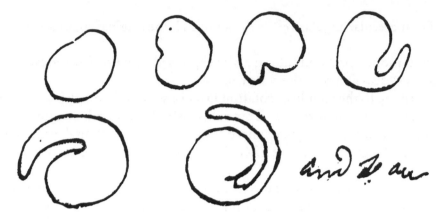

As time goes on, the number of spines increases indefinitely. The breadth of the irrotational canal decreases indefinitely but so does that of the intervening, separating rotational canals, and I see no reason to believe that the ratio of the sum of the breadths of the former to that of the breadths of the latter decreases indefinitely, or that irrotational fluid is squeezed through the indefinitely lengthening irrotational canal from the outside to the inside. That is not the way in which irrotational fluid gets to the outside, but by the formation of a fresh corkle-nose composed of rotational fluid streaked or not streaked with irrotational canals, and forming a fresh spiral.

When I wrote about labyrinthine structure I did not mean in the strict sense for the labyrinth here is its own clue; start from the inside and there is but one road you can travel. You *must* get to the outside but you will have to walk round and round a great n° of times in one direction then in the other direction, and so on.

After a vast time we should have spider-threads of rotational separated by spider-threads of irrotational fluid. Within the small space Δr ⟨the sum of⟩ which nevertheless is supposed large compared with the infinitesimal brea[d]th of a thread, the sum of the breadths of the former being $\varrho\Delta r$ that of the latter will be $(1 - \varrho)\Delta r$ and *now* regarding Δr as infinitesimal ϱ will be a function of r. If all the energy that can be withdrawn is withdrawn, the ϱ-curve which at start was

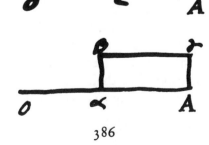

abcA becomes $O\alpha\beta\gamma$

I will stop for the present.

Yours sincerely
G. G. STOKES

1 This is Stokes's press copy of the original letter.
2 This apparently refers to an earlier letter by Stokes which has not survived. See the previous letter, note 1.

296 KELVIN to STOKES, 8 and 11 January [1873][1]
Stokes Collection, K190

Glasgow University[2]
Jany 8th 1872 [*sic*]

MY DEAR STOKES,

Thanks for your letter of the 6th. Referring to it by pages, I remark:– page 3 upper half[3] I assent to; but for complete generality define steady motion as any motion in which the stream-lines remain equal and similar. The old Cambridge definition of steady motion is motion in which the stream-lines remain fixed. In the most general natural realization of steady motion, the system of stream-lines moves with uniform ⟨translation⟩ rotation and uniform translation round an axis parallel to the ⟨round an axis parallel to the⟩ line of translation. This is, for example, the case of the simple knotted vortex when started of such a shape as shall remain permanent.

Page 4 first 8 lines,[4] I deny. Steady motion is certainly possible ⟨with a⟩ not fulfilling your condition, as, for instance, an approximately circular eccentric-

387

ally placed vortex in a cylindrical containing vessel. (For brevity I speak of circle instead of circular cylinder, and eccentric instead of exaxial, and shall continue to do so till motion not confined to one plane is considered.) The arrow-heads in the diagrams with continuous lines for shafts, represent directions of motion of the liquid, those with dotted shafts represent motion of the separating surfaces between vortex and irrotationally moving liquid,

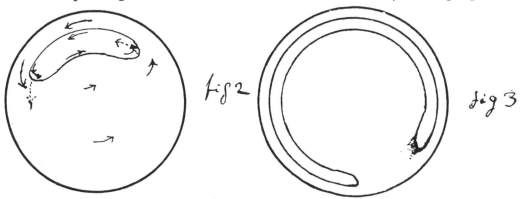

fig 2   *fig 3*

that is to say in each case, motion of a form, not of substance. My drawings are not very successful. I must get something written out for publication: Excuse my trying it on you. Either sketch may also represent a coreless vortex: but if so, the arrow-heads, except those relating to form, must be removed from the interior space. In the second sketch the motions of the substance represented by the arrow-heads ⟨represented⟩ are not the absolute motions but motions with reference to a radius of the ⟨bounding⟩ containing vessel, moving with the same angular velocity as that of the bounding surface of the vortex, that is to say, the surface separating vortex from irrotational liquid.

Page 5;[5]– I did not mean the cylindrical mass to move like a solid. Its shape only, not the arrangement of its matter remains constant. Its bounding surface must move so as to agree with the irrotationally moving liquid surrounding it. Throughout its interior its substance moves so as to fulfil the condition

$$\frac{dv}{dx} - \frac{du}{dy} = 2\zeta,$$

where ζ denotes the molecular angular velocity, and is by hypothesis constant. The second fig. roughly illustrates the kind of motion. A slight deformation such as that which you describe in page 5, will cause vibrations in the vortex. In the case of fig. 1 it is quite certain that the vibrations would remain infinitesimal. In the case of fig. 2, I believe they would remain infinitesimal. But, (as stated at the foot of page 2 and elsewhere in my former letter,)[6] a vortex with its two ends nearly meeting, is incapable of steady motion. Your illustration in page 9[7] shows a case in which, manifestly, steady motion is

⟨clearly⟩ impossible. But if, instead of the narrow separation between the two ends, you have something like that in fig. 3, the motion will probably be steady and stable. How nearly the head can overtake the tail without steady motion becoming impossible, I do not as yet see any way to find. I think my views in my letter of the 19th are on the whole correct as to what would take place, if a vortex analogous to fig. 3, with its head too near its tail for stability, were started and left to itself. I do not, however, altogether dissent from what you say on the subject although I am not sure of the reverse relative whirls being admissable.

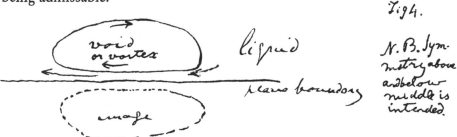

Going back to a steady stable motion, take fig 4 as an illustration of figs 1, 2 and 3, in which the radius of the vortex is infinitely small in comparison with the radius of the cylinder. Such a case of steady motion as that suggested (not represented) in fig 4. is obviously possible and stable.

(Continued January 11th 1873.)

Since writing the above I have been trying hard to see some method of finding, if not the equation, some means of approximation, graphical or otherwise to find curves which will fulfil the condition of fig 4. I have often tried it before, but hitherto, except in the case of approximate circularity, without success. I now see a plan which, with a finite amount of labour, will probably give a fair approximation to cases with not quite such long orals as those in fig. 4. These last trials have led me out of an error in which I have been ever since I thought of the subject, and which is illustrated by my reference to propinquity between the head and tail, as a circumstance on which depends the limiting form for steady motion, when the containing vessel is circular. I now see that there is in fact a limit of elongation beyond which no form can give steady motion, even when the bounding surface is plane. Consider, for example, the case of a purely irrotational vortex with void core. The dynamical condition at the boundary of the core is that the velocity, relatively to the moving figure, shall be equal at all points of this curve. Now, this condition is clearly impossible for a core infinitely long in comparison with its breadth (The dimensions I am speaking of are all in the plane perpendicular to the cylindrical surfaces we have to deal with). Consider, first, a fixed canal consisting of a pair of planes, and the system of motion of which the stream-lines and their orthoginals [*sic*] are shown in the accompanying diagram by Maxwell. (Please let me have it again at your convenience). Compound with the velocity at each point, a velocity from right to left, equal to a half the velocity in the canal, ($\frac{1}{2}V$.) Some of the resultant stream-lines are roughly indicated in the diagram with pencil. The velocity in the resultant system will be equal and ⟨parral⟩ parallel, but contrary, inside and outside the canal for all points at a considerable distance on the left hand side of the diagram, and for all points at very great distances in any direction will be equal and in the same direction as the velocity, ($\frac{1}{2}V$,) of the outside at considerable distances to the left. Now each of the new stream-lines cuts one of Maxwell's stream-lines at the point at which the letter [*sic*] is perpendicular to OX. At this point, therefore, the resultant velocity in the new stream lines is greater than $\frac{1}{2}V$, being the resultant of $\frac{1}{2}V$ and a certain velocity in the line perpendicular to it. Hence, clearly the velocity is greater in the curved parts of the new stream-lines than in their straight asym[p]totic branches from and to the left. Instead of the infinitely thin plane cores of Maxwell's diagram, imagine another such diagram constructed for two parallel planes with edges shaped to any curve whatever, as in sketch.

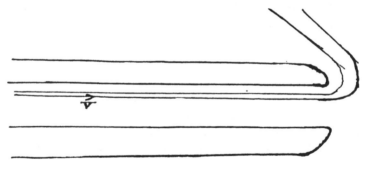

Superimpose a velocity $\frac{1}{2}V$ to the left. In the resultant system the resultant system [*sic*] the velocity will be, equal to $\frac{1}{2}V$ in the asym[p]totic portions of each stream-line, and generally along the bend will be greater than $\frac{1}{2}V$. It cannot be equal to $\frac{1}{2}V$ all along the system[8] stream-line in any such case. Hence a steady coreless vortex with its two ends infinitely distant, and the intermediate part a plane of finite thickness is impossible.

If irrotational motion ⟨motion⟩ is started with any fixed core such as that in the sketch, and the velocity $\frac{1}{2}V$ to left be superimposed, the pressure on the curved ends will be less than on the flat sides, inside and outside. Hence if a rigid core be suddenly annihilated, the coreless vortex thus instituted will speedily come to grief. But this clearly is not the case with a properly proportioned core of the general character shown in fig 4. *A fortiaori* [*sic*] a ⟨f⟩ vortex with proper rotational core, and liquid homgeneous with the irrotational external liquid, cannot have steady motion if like fig. 4, but too long in proportion to transverse dimensions. Going back to coreless vortices. One way of approximating to a pair of ovals such as fig 4, will be to take as equation systems of stream lines

$$Uy + \log \frac{DD'}{D''D'''} = c,$$

where $\quad D = \sqrt{\{(x-a)^2 + (y-b)^2\}} \quad D'' = \sqrt{\{(x-a)^2 + (y+b)^2\}}$

$\quad D' = \sqrt{\{(x+a)^2 + (y-b)^2\}} \quad D''['] = \sqrt{\{(x+a)^2 + (y+b)^2\}}.$

Then assign values ⟨of⟩ to U, c, b, so as to make the velocity equal at four different points of the curve. I believe from the diagram, and a case corresponding to $b = 0$, (Proceedings R.S.E. Session 1866–7)[9] that really finite values of b will, with really finite values of the other parametres, satisfy this condition.

Your letter of yesterday received this morning. I shall do my best about the biographical notice of Archibald Smith.[10] Please say when it will be required. Did you receive a letter from me about Latimer Clark's paper[11] on a voltaic element which I wrote in a train going to Manchester. I showed it to Joule before sending it off and he approved of it. No time for more about vortices just now as I am going to Wemyss Bay till Monday to meet Dr Lyon Playfair.[12]

Yours truly
Pro ⟨W⟩ Sir WILLIAM THOMSON
JOHN TATLOCK

1 The letter is in John Tatlock's hand. Since it is a response to the previous letter, the year must be 1873, not 1872.
2 The following is written at the top of the letter and refers to letter 292.
Corrections on my letter of 19th December 1872.
    Page 2 line 13, for 'vortical', substitute vortically. [See letter 292, note 4.]
    [Page] 2 last line, after 'has', insert an inferior. [See letter 292, note 5.]
    [Page] 3 line 2 of foot note for 'stated', substitute steady, and remark that the proposition which, for the moment, I believed to be true, as stated in first clause of foot note, is false. [See letter 292, note 7.]
    Page 4, line 3 from foot ⟨for⟩ after 'absolute', insert minimum of. [See letter 292, note 9.]
    [Page] 5 [line] 9 [from foot] for 'thrown' substitute drawn. [See letter 292, note 10.]
    [Page] 2 [line] 10 I believe I have now resolved the doubt. [See letter 292, note 3.]
3 The upper half of page 3 of letter 295 is suppose you mean. . . . to be your meaning. Letter 295 contains twenty-one pages.
4 This refers in letter 295 to: as kinematically possible . . . section of the cyl^r.
5 This refers in letter 295 to: In the case you supposed . . . that the motion will be.
6 Letter 292, dated 19 December 1872. The following passage begins on page 2 and ends on page 3 of that letter: that when the head approaches within a certain distance of the tail.
7 The first illustration in letter 295.

8 Larmor has deleted *system*.
9 Kelvin (161).
10 Kelvin (198A).
11 See letter 288, note 2.
12 Lyon Playfair (1818–98), chemist and politician, studied chemistry at Glasgow and Giessen, was professor of chemistry at Edinburgh from 1858 to 1869, was a Member of Parliament from 1868 to 1892, and was raised to the peerage in 1892 as the first Baron Playfair of St Andrews.

297 STOKES to KELVIN, 18 January 1873[1]
Stokes Collection, NB21.57

Lensfield Cottage Cambridge
18th Jany 1873

MY DEAR THOMSON,

I have not much to add about vortex motions except to correct a silly mis-enunciation of a proposition I said I had worked out and which (as I carelessly enunciated it) you rightly desired. I wrote at p. 3. of my letter of Jany 6th 'As a matter of curiosity, though not required for our problem, I worked out the condition that the compound motion should be dynamically as well as kinematically possible, and found it to be &c'. I should have said that *both* motions (the steady in the ordinary and the steady in the extended sense) were supposed to be dynamically as well as kinematically possible. Had it not been for this restriction i.e. had the proposition been true even if the steady (ordinary sense) motion which compounded with a rotation gives the actual motion were kinematically only possible, the condition I worked out, so far from being a matter of curiosity not required at [?] for our problem would have been everything for our problem. It might for example have been used instantly to disprove the possibility of steady motion in the case figured in p. 9.[2] I am not sure however but that just as I wrote the words at p. 3 my head went wool-gathering; and seeing that the kinematically possible and $\omega = $ const. ⟨motion⟩ steady (old sense) motion must also be dynamically possible, I may *perhaps* have forgotten that though this is true for each of the two parts (rotational, ω const., and irrotational) *separately* it is not true for the assemblage of the two. Be that as it may, I retract my faulty enunciation in favour of what I explained above, and which, as you see, renders the proposition of little interest.

One more explanation as to your remark on my p. 5.[3] I did not understand you to mean that the cylindrical mass moved like a solid *except initially*. I supposed that for simplicity's sake you considered more particularly the simple case of such a circular-cylindrical mass surrounded by irrotational fluid in a coaxal vessel, the sides of which afterwards jelled. The simpler case I understood you to take *merely to start with*. A good part of the investigation will be independent of any particular initial shape of the rotational part.

My supposition of the formation of corkle-noses and spider-threads was a guess; as it appeared to me a probable guess. Of course such a guess would not stand for a moment against a rigorous calculation in any case to which such a calculation may have been applied.

I return you with thanks Maxwell's diagram of which I have roughly copied one half.

The problem of waves near the surface of friction of the sliding and adjacent portions of a supposed stream [?] forms curious and interesting case of fluid motion.

I confess I am sceptical about the stability of many of the motions which you appear to contemplate. Thus in irrotational vortex motion round a core adjacent to a solid boundary, I believe that where the lines of motion open out, as at A, the motion is essentially unstable.

For irrotational motion in two dimensions within a containing vessel and round a core, I can prove that if the core be brought from rest from the side to rest near the middle the motion of the fluid is unstable.

The memoir of A. Smith[4] is not wanted by any particular day, but when ready.

Yours sincerely,
G. G. Stokes

1 This is Stokes's press copy of the original letter.
2 Page 9 of letter 295 includes the first figure and the text: *central cylinder EFGH of fluid at rest . . . . the motion of the annulus.*
3 See the previous letter, note 5.
4 Kelvin (198A).

Kelvin Collection, S404, and Stokes Collection, NB21.58[1]

Lensfield Cottage Cambridge

20th Jan[y] 1873

MY DEAR THOMSON

I have thought that the considerations as to instability of motion which I hinted at in my last might (in case they should be new to you) be of some interest. So I will write them.

For convenience I will premise a definition.

Imagine irrotational motion around a core or cores w[h] may be moving and changing their shape anyhow. Suppose a motion equal and opposite to that which would be produced in the fluid at rest by the actual normal motions of its bounding surfaces. This will be irrotational, and such that the cyclic constants (if there were [?] more [?] cores than one) or constant, are zero. Let the residue, which will have the same cyclic constants as the actual motion, and for which all the bounding surfaces are at rest, be called the innate irrotational motion. We need not say vortex motion for there can be no other such. It will be compounded of parts corresponding to motions round the several cores respectively, and each of these motions will be proportional to the corresponding cyclic constant.

Consider now motion in two dimensions, and supposing the fluid contained in an enclosing vessel, consider for simplicity the case of a single core. Let this be at first at rest with an irrotational motion about it. (fig 1) Let it be moved so as to come to the side.[2] fig (2)

In any position of the core consider the innate irrotational motion. Consider the motion conjugate to this i.e. for which the ϕ ($= \int (u\,dx + v\,dy)$) and ψ ($= \int (u\,dy - v\,dx)$) are resp[ectivel]y the $\psi\phi$ of the other. In the conjugate motion the total flux across either bounding surface is constant, and equal the cyclic constant. Translating into temperature, we may suppose that the core and the space outside the vessel are kept at constant temperatures such that the total flux = K the cyclic constant. Suppose now the core all but in contact with the side. The flux will take place all but entirely near the all but contact. Let Δ be the difference of temperature, a the shortest distance, and let x be measured from and perpendicular to the ⟨shortest⟩ line of shortest distance. When x is moderately small, the distance of the surfaces will be $a + bx^2$, where b depends on the radii of curvature of the two surfaces. The flux across dx will vary as $\dfrac{\Delta\, dx}{a + bx^2}$ and a being infinitesimal the total flux will vary as $\displaystyle\int_{-\infty}^{\infty} \dfrac{\Delta\, dx}{a + bx^2}$ or $\propto \dfrac{\Delta}{\sqrt{ab}}$ or $\dfrac{\Delta}{\sqrt{a}}$ b being supposed given. Since the total flux $= K$, $\Delta \propto \sqrt{a}$. Therefore the flux $\propto \dfrac{\sqrt{a}\, dx}{a + bx^2}$ or the velocity in either the original or the conjugate motion $\propto \dfrac{\sqrt{a}}{a + bx^2}$. The vis viva $\propto \displaystyle\int_{-\infty}^{\infty} \left(\dfrac{\sqrt{a}}{a + bx^2}\right)^2 (a + bx^2)\, dx$ or $\propto \displaystyle\int \dfrac{a\, dx}{a + bx^2}$ or $\propto \sqrt{a}$ which vanishes with a.

Now let the motion of the core be reversed, and let the core pass from infinitely near ⟨th⟩ [?] the side to the original position ⟨m⟩ [?] near the middle, and when it arrives there let it come to rest. The innate motion (which will be the only motion) will be the same as at first. But if when the core was close to the side the fluid had been at rest, then when the core was brought to near the middle (the same position as in the other case) the fluid would have been at rest, the core itself being at rest.

Hence when the core is moved from infinitely near the side to near the middle, it depends on the presence or absence of an infinitely small amount of energy whether there s[hal]l [?] be in the end a finite am[oun]t of energy or no energy at all. Of course the total work done in moving the core is finite in the first case & null in the second, but still motion which can be profoundly altered by communication of an infinitesimal amount of energy is unstable.

Yours sincerely

G. G. STOKES

---

1 NB21.58 is Stokes's press copy of the original letter, and S404 is a copy in Stokes's hand which he has marked 'copy'. Stokes no doubt prepared S404 because NB21.58 is in many places much too faint to be read. Where the two can be compared, they are nearly identical, except that S404 has many more abbreviated words than NB21.58. The text printed here is an amalgam of the two, with preference always given to NB21.58, except for the diagrams which come from S404.

2 This sentence is taken from S404. In NB21.58 it is very faint but appears to read, 'Let it be moved to close to the side'.

College, Glasgow
21st January 1872. [*sic*]

DEAR STOKES.

Many thanks for your three letters. I sent one of them to Latimer Clark, as I believe you intended that I might do so. It is likely that in one or two parts Clark['s] paper[2] may admit of abbreviation with advantage. With most of the criticisms, however, which you quote, I cannot agree. I shall speak to you about it when I see you, as I hope to be at Cambridge on Saturday to stay till Monday. I hope also then to persuade you to commence your reprint[3] instantly. It is exceedingly much wanted.

Referring to page 10 of your letter of the 18th,[4] – the motion depends solely on the cyclic constant, and on the position of the core and shape of the boundary. What you say seems to imply that the circumstances when the core is brought to rest near the middle are modified by its previously having been at rest near the side. Neither can I admit that there is instability, when a rigid circular core is placed very near the centre of a circular bounding vessel, and cyclic irrotational motion established. Let $\langle M \rangle m^5$ be the density of the core, that of the liquid being unity. The inertia relatively to the translation of the core will be[6] that of the mass $m + 1$; the kinetic energy will be that of the cyclic motion $+\dfrac{\pi c^2}{2}(m + 1)v^2$, if any velocity v be given to the core in any direction; provided always that c, the radius of the core, is very small in comparison with its distance from the next point of the boundary. (For brevity, I am speaking of masses etc as for unit length, parallel to the axis of the cylinder). Now if the core be left at rest in any excentric position, the moment of momentum of the whole motion round the axis of the bounding cylinder will remain constant. Still considering the ratio of radius of core to radius of boundary, as infinitely small, the moment of momentum of the cyclic motion when the core is at rest in any position is equal to

$$\tfrac{1}{2}(a + r)K(\langle a \rangle [c?] 1 - r) + (m + 1)\pi c^2\, rv \cos i,$$

where r denotes the distance of the core from the centre, a the radius of the boundary, i the inclination of the line of motion to the circle through the core and concentric with the boundary, and K the cyclic constant. Now it is easily proved that the kinetic energy of the cyclic motion is equal to

$$\frac{K}{2\pi} \log \frac{a^2 - r^2}{ca}$$

where (as above) c is the radius of the core. Hence the equations of motion are

$$\frac{K}{2\pi} \log \frac{a^2 - r^2}{ca} + \frac{\pi c^2}{2}(m+1)v^2 - K,$$

and

$$\tfrac{1}{2}K(a^2 - r^2) + (m+1)\pi c^2 rv \cos i = H,$$

where K and H are constants.

22nd January.

(So far I had written yesterday, intending to work out the period and the amplitude of the quasi nutation in the simple case of circular boundary and infinitely small circular core. Late in the evening I received your letter of Monday. In it you describe a method of throttling an irrotational vortex. If the core is brought slowly up till it is infinitely near the boundary, and then removed again, things will be as they were. If it is made absolutely to touch the boundary, the last spark of energy is destroyed, and the cyclic constant annihilated. But this is a discontinuity utterly to be excluded. The cyclic constant remains unchanged until the energy is infinitely small. The fact that the vortex has infinitely little energy when on the point of death is nothing against its stability when restored to pristine energy. A man who has been nearly drowned, but restored before the last spark of vital energy was extinguished, has never once lost his psyshic [sic] constant, and after restoration is as stable in his ways as ever. [)]

1 This letter is in J. Tatlock's hand, but it has several changes, most of which appear to have been made by Kelvin. The letter is misdated 1872. For the chronology involved, see the next footnote. I am grateful to P. M. Harman for bringing this to my attention.

2 See letter 288, note 2. Communicated by Kelvin, Clark's paper was read to the Royal Society on 20 June 1872. It was refereed by Maxwell and Wheatstone, the latter's report being dated 3 September 1872. (Royal Society of London, RR.7.162 and RR.7.161.) Clark had evidently been notified by 1 January 1873 of the Royal Society's decision not to publish his paper in the *Philosophical Transactions*. (Letter 293.) Kelvin mentioned the matter in two additional letters (294 and 296), and Stokes's letter to Kelvin which Kelvin reported sending to Clark obviously bore on the matter. On 23 January 1873, Clark responded to seven objections to his paper, concluding: 'I have thus endeavoured to answer some of the criticisms mentioned to me, and to thank Prof. Thomson and Prof. Stokes for giving me the opportunity of doing so'. (Stokes Collection, RS900.) See, also, note 4 below.

3 This refers to Stokes's *MPP*.

4 Letter 297. Page 10 is the last page of the letter and begins: 'the lines of motion open out, as at A ...'.

5 Kelvin has made the deletion and inserted m.

6 As it survives, this letter has two page 2s – a first version with many changes and a second incorporating the changes. The text is taken from the second, and the first is reproduced below. All the deletions and accompanying insertions were apparently made by Kelvin. Hence, Kelvin has inserted: $m+1$, $K(1-r)+(m+1)rv \cos i$, r, *distance*, the full stop following *boundary*, and i.

be that of the mass $\langle M + 1 \rangle \, m + 1$; the kinetic energy will be that of the cyclic motion $+ \frac{1}{2}(M + 1)v^2$ if any velocity v be given to the core in any direction; provided always the radius of the core is very small in comparison with its distance from the next point of the boundary. (For brevity I am speaking of masses etc as for unit length parallel to the axis of the cylinder). Now if the core be left at rest in any excentric position the moment of momentum of the whole motion round the axis of the bounding cylinder will remain constant. Still considering the ratio of radius of core to radius of boundary as infinitely small, the moment of momentum of the cyclic motion when the core is at rest in any position is equal to

$$\langle (1 - R) + (M + 1) \rangle \qquad K(1 - r) + (m + 1)rv\cos i$$
$$\langle (1 - r)() $$
$$\langle (1 - R) + (M + 1)RV\cos I, \rangle$$

where $\langle R \rangle \, r$ denotes the $\langle \text{density} \rangle$ distance of the core from the centre, and a the radius of the boundary. $\langle \text{being unity}, I \rangle \, i$ the inclination of the line of motion to the circle through the core and concentric with the boundary, and K the cyclic constant. Now it is easily proved that the kinetic energy of the cyclic motion is equal to

$$\left\langle \frac{K}{2\pi} \log \frac{1}{c} 1 \qquad \frac{K}{2\pi} \log 1 - r^2 \right\rangle$$

where c is the radius of the core. Hence the equations of
It will be noticed that there are differences between the corrected first version and the second.

300 KELVIN to STOKES, 9 May 1873
Stokes Collection, K191

Annaghmore
Merchiston
Edinburgh
May 9/73

DEAR STOKES

I was unable to get my report on Airy's paper[1] finished before leaving the Lalla Rookh and since then I have been immersed in a sea of troubles. I am on my way today to Newcastle to see the 'Hooper' cable ship, with steam up to try the transverse screw ⟨with⟩ at her moorings at the builders' yard. Trials already made are said to have promised well, throwing a great volume of water, and putting a heavy strain on the moorings.

I yesterday received the enclosed from Spottiswoode,[2] and was much surprised, as I thought the council had determined to offer the presidency to Andrews. At a meeting when I was president there seemed perfect unanimity as to Andrews being the right man for the Belfast meeting. I must say I believe it would be felt (not merely in Belfast and the North of Ireland, as a slight but) very generally, that a mistake had been made: the principles being admitted (1) that a distinguished scientific man is to be chosen, (2) that local connection is to have weight, (3) and that age, and chances of availability of a future presidency should be taken into account. On every [sic] It is not so easy (as we know) to get sufficiently high men (on the principle that a scientific man is to be chosen) from year to year, to keep up the credit of the presidency, and on this ground alone the British Association can ill spare a man like Andrews who if not president in 1874 can never be ⟨president⟩ reckoned on as available again. I am quite sure Tyndall himself ⟨wh⟩ would see all this and would agree with me. If I had been at the council meeting I should have urged that it was not a question of weighing the scientific claims of Andrews and Tyndall at all, but that in the circumstances the presidency ought certainly to be offered to Andrews. I enclose a letter from him which I had a few days ago in answer to one I had written him under impression that the council had (more than a year ago) made up its mind to offer him the presidency.[3]

Yours
W.T.

P.S. I go to Cambridge tonight or tomorrow morning (from Newcastle.) I would like to speak to you there about the B.A. presidency. I don't mean of course that what has been done by the council can be undone, but I want to hear from you how it came about.

1 G. B. Airy, 'Magnetical observations in the Britannia and Conway tubular iron bridges', *Phil. Trans.* (1873), 371–9.
2 W. Spottiswoode to Kelvin, 7 May 1873, Kelvin Collection, S290: 'I am very glad to hear a better account of Andrews' health. But as regards the Presidency of the British Assⁿ for 1874 the Council at their last meeting unanimously decided to ask Tyndall who was then present. He could not then give a decided answer; & we still wait for it'. Tyndall was president in 1874, giving a highly controversial presidential address.
3 Thomas Andrews (1813–85) was professor of chemistry at Queen's College, Belfast, from 1849 to 1879. He was a vice-president at the 1874 British Association meeting in Belfast and president in 1876 in Glasgow. See Kelvin to Andrews, 17 March 1876, Kelvin Collection, A42I, in which Kelvin urged Andrews to accept the Glasgow presidency and invited him to stay with him during the meetings.

---

301 KELVIN to STOKES, 17 November 1873
Stokes Collection, K192

Nov 17/73

DEAR STOKES

I have not yet published an account of my Tide-calculating machine ⟨, though it⟩. It was exhibited at Bradford and it will be shortly described in the Report of the Tides Committee.[1] I think of sending a more full account, with drawings, to the Royal Society.[2] Meantime here is the general plan

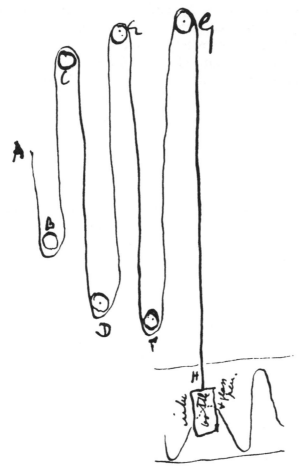

ABCDEFGH is a chain (watch-barrel chain) of which end *A* is fixed and *H* pulls the ink bottle up and down in a vertical line.

B, *C*, *D*, *E*, *F*, *G* are pulleys on the ends of cranks having adjustable radii and epochs, and each carried round in the period of one of the tidal constituents.

In the machine already made 10 constituents are included. One of these is lunar-quarter-diurnal, and another ⟨s⟩ luni-solar-quarter-diurnal. These are needed for Liverpool, and ⟨gave⟩ [?] more so for ⟨other⟩ places farther up shallow water channels. They may be set to correct the geometrical errors to a second degree of approximation, for obliquity of the line from *G* to *H* and from *F* to *G*, (*F* and *G* being the solar semi diurnal and lunar semi diurnal) were these errors sensible: but they are not in the machine as set for Liverpool giving a scale of $\frac{1}{30}$ of the actual rise and fall.

Yours (in haste)
WT

I am very glad you have given a paper[3] on refraction in doubly ref[ractin]g crystals to the French Academy.

1 The Bradford meeting of the British Association was in September 1873. There was no report by the committee on tides in 1873, the next report being in 1876 (*Brit. Assoc. Rep.* (1876), 275–307).
2 Kelvin did not publish such an account in either the Royal Society's *Proceedings* or *Philosophical Transactions*, but see Kelvin (204A).
3 Stokes (88).

302 KELVIN to STOKES, 21 November [1873][1]
Stokes Collection, K192A

Nov 21.

DEAR STOKES

It will help me very much to secure accuracy on some points regarding Smith's and Airy's work on ships' compass problem, if I can have my 'biographical sketch'[2] now nearly finished, set up in slip before being paged, and half a dozen rough proofs given to me.

If I do not hear from you to the contrary I shall send the M.SS. direct to Taylor and Francis in a few days, saying that I have made this request of you and not been refused.

Yours
W.T.

1 The year is determined by the date of the article in the next note.
2 Kelvin (198A), dated 4 January 1874.

303 KELVIN to STOKES, 30 November [October?][1] 1873
Stokes Collection, K193

Nov 30/73

DEAR STOKES

I see in the Comptes Rendus for Oct 13 – 'Abria – Verification de la Loi d'Huyghens par la Méthode du Prisme'.[2] He verifies within 1 per cent of the quantities measured, for Iceland Spar, and Quartz, and does not know of your previous publication.[3] Your result was I think much closer in accuracy. I think it would be well to write to the Secretary of the French Academy a short statement of your result, to be published in the C.R.[4] If you send it in English (written as clearly as print!) they will translate it carefully & well & publish it as a matter of course.

I hope you will *very soon* give a full description of your experiments to the Royal Society.[5]

Yours
W.T.

1 See note 4.
2 Abria, 'Vérification de la loi d'Huyghens, par la méthode du prisme', *Comptes Rendus*, 77 (13 October 1873), 814–15. *Comptes Rendus* gives no first name for Abria. The *Royal Society Catalogue* gives 'O. Abria'. However, Poggendorff identifies only Jérémie Joseph Benoit Abria (1811–92), professor of physics in the Faculty of Sciences at Bordeaux.
3 Stokes (87).
4 Stokes (88) is just such a paper. It begins with a reference to Abria's paper and was published in the *Comptes Rendus* for *17* November 1873. Kelvin's reference to Stokes (88) in this letter seems to be of an earlier date than his reference to Stokes (88) in letter 301, thus raising the possibility that Kelvin misdated this letter. Perhaps it was written on 30 *October* 1873.
5 He did not do so.

304 KELVIN to STOKES, 18 February [1874][1]
Royal Society of London, RR.7.294

Train Newcastle to Glasgow
Wed Feb 18

DEAR STOKES

I think Crookes' Paper 'on the Action of Heat on Gravitating Masses'[2] ought most assuredly to be published in the Transactions. He seems to me to have made a discovery of transcendent interest and first rate importance. The explanations and descriptions of his experiments in his paper are so clear and thorough that no room for doubt is left as to his results, and that any one may, ⟨now⟩ with access to the paper readily with moderate experimental means repeat for himself some of the most decisive and startling of the experiments.

I think the quotation ⟨of⟩ from Faye[3] might properly be omitted, because, though justly criticised by Crookes, the quotation of it gives it more weight than it seems to me to deserve.

The reference to the 'spheroidal state' p 77 might also I think be omitted with advantage ⟨because⟩ ⟨or else somewhat modified⟩. Even ⟨if ap⟩ when what might be imagined to be non-volatile bodies are shown in the 'spheroidal state' I do not think the ordinary explanation is thereby invalidated or any direct connection with Crookes' discovery proved. I think pages 83, 84, 85 might be omitted with advantage.

p 63 – I have suggested a slight change.

p 69. I think Crookes' conclusion might be confirmed and the argument strengthened by an estimate of the absolute amount of the fluid pressure which could possibly exist.

Will you accept the above as my report? Otherwise it could not reach you by tomorrow as you wish. I only received your letter on Sunday and on Monday morning left Glasgow to attend R.S.E. meeting on that day and see launch of cable-ship 'Faraday' at Newcastle yesterday.

Yours truly
WILLIAM THOMSON

1 The year is determined by the date of Crookes's paper and by Stokes's note written at the top of the letter, '1874 Crookes by Thomson'.
2 W. Crookes, 'On the action of heat on gravitating masses', *Proc. Roy. Soc.*, **22** (1873–74), 37–41. William Crookes (1832–1919) studied at the Royal College of Chemistry under A. W. Hofmann and lived in London working in his own laboratory. For the extensive correspondence between Crookes and Stokes, see the Stokes Collection (mainly letters from Crookes to Stokes) and Stokes's *Memoir*, II, 362–494 (largely from Stokes to Crookes).
3 Crookes said that Faye had introduced the hypothesis of a repulsive force of heat to account for certain astronomical phenomena. Hervé Faye (1814–1902) was educated at the École Polytechnique and taught there and at Nancy, becoming a full professor at the École Polytechnique in 1873.

305 KELVIN to STOKES, 9 March 1874
Stokes Collection, RS995

University of Glasgow
March 9th 1874

DEAR STOKES

On the long list of candidates for next election to the Royal Society is the name of my late Colleague Lewis Gordon.[1] He is a man of thoroughly scientific spirit, and although from having lost his health in cable work, and other engineering expeditions in various parts of the world, and finally from great hardships, consequent upon being shipwrecked in the Red Sea, he was obliged to retire from his engineering profession about 14 years ago, he is still devoted heart and soul to science. I can scarcely conceive any one more eligible for the fellowship of the Royal Society.

I remain
Yours Truly
WILLIAM THOMSON

Professor Stokes
P.S. I am sending copies of the above to Huxley and Hooker,[2] but if you think proper you might perhaps show it to others of the council.

1 Lewis Dunbar Brodie Gordon (1815–76) was professor of civil engineering and mechanics at Glasgow, retiring in 1855 when he was replaced by W. J. M. Rankine. He did not become a

fellow of the Royal Society. There is a correspondence of some twenty letters between him and Kelvin in the Kelvin Collection.

2 Joseph Dalton Hooker (1817–1911) was director of the Kew Botanical Gardens from 1865 to 1885 and was president of the Royal Society from 1873 to 1878.

306 KELVIN to STOKES, 13 April 1874
Stokes Collection, K194

Yacht Lalla Rookh
Largs April 13/74

DEAR STOKES

I find after all I cannot be at the R.S. meeting Thursday week but I still hope to be at the Conversazione. I go to London on Wednesday night this week, and shall probably be at the R.S. Thursday. I shall probably be able to give you the M.SS. of my Magnetic paper[1] then to be read any time you please. I ⟨sh^d⟩ did not think it would have to be taken out of turn, to be read on Thursday week. It will do quite as well in my absence as if I were present to read it myself.

Yours truly
W. THOMSON

1 Kelvin did not present a paper on magnetism to the Royal Society at this time, but his (207.1) and (209) were read to the Royal Society in May and June 1875, respectively.

307 KELVIN to STOKES, 8 March 1875
Stokes Collection, K195

The University
Glasgow.
March 8/75

DEAR STOKES,

I send you a rough proof not quite finally corrected for the press, of a communication I made last April to the Society of Telegraph Engineers on deep sea soundings.[1] Make any or no use of it as you may think proper with reference to my last letter.

If there is any communication to the Admiralty on the subject of wire soundings for the Arctic Expedition this proof, even in its rough state, might I think, be sent to them.[2]

Believe me
Yours Truly
W THOMSON

Professor Stokes.

1 Kelvin (201).

2 For an account of the Arctic expedition begun in the spring of 1875, see *Nature*, **12** (20 May 1875), 61. The Royal Society's Arctic Committee was instrumental in organizing the expedition.

308   KELVIN to STOKES [?],[1] 17 March 1875
Stokes Collection, K196

The University,
Glasgow.
March 17/75

To the Secretary of the Royal Society (Arctic Expedition)

DEAR SIR

I recently wrote to Prof Stokes regarding the observation of atmospheric electricity, and in consequence of a letter received from him I have made enquiry as to the cost of a suitable electrometer, and the time when it could be had. I enclose M^r [James] White's reply. At present the instrument cannot be had from any other maker as there has not been sufficient demand for the instrument to induce other makers, in London or elsewhere, to make it.

I think the opportunity of making observations on atmospheric electricity in the polar regions ought not to be lost. Half a dozen observations, or even a single observation, made there either in winter or summer, would give important information which cannot be had otherwise. I scarcely think the labour of making frequent observations, continuously from day to day could be recommended in the circumstances: but a few occasional observations in different localities, at different times of year, and of day and night, and in different varieties of weather (especially with reference to direction of wind) would be most valuable.

If observations are to be made at all *no time must be lost in ordering the electrometers*. I would advise four to be ordered immediately, one for use and one for reserve in each ship. I hope therefore you can decide immediately to do this. If so please let the order be given directly to Mr White, and at the same time let me know. It will be necessary for me to look after the instruments during construction (particularly as it is several years since one has been made) and to test their action when finished.

I shall draw up instructions for use as soon as I hear that the instruments are ordered.

As to tides I have little to add to my former letter to Prof Stokes. I shall try to get some short instructions written out this week or early next week as to the times to be chosen for observations when it is not convenient to make hourly observations for 24 hours or longer.

I remain
Yours truly
WILLIAM THOMSON

1 Although not addressed to Stokes, the letter appears to have been passed to Stokes.

309   KELVIN to STOKES, [March 1875][1]
Stokes Collection, K285A

The University,
Glasgow.

DEAR STOKES

I shall be obliged by your signing enclosed recommendation of Latimer Clark for R.S. and forwarding it to the Astronomer Royal[2] with request that he sends it on to M^r ⟨C C⟩ C. V. Walker[3] or if you prefer it and if you (who *ought* to be able to read any writing) can read his address from his note enclosed, send it direct to him. I understand that Airy knows Clark and I have no doubt but he will be willing to sign.

Circular motion round centre of inertia of any number >2 of particles ⟨cannot⟩ is unstable according to any law of force. No viscosity of tides or other influence needed. The motion is of course stable for two particles with $f^{ce} \propto 1/D^n$ when $n<3$.

Yours
W THOMSON

1 Latimer Clark was elected a fellow of the Royal Society on 6 June 1889 but was proposed for fellowship first in 1875 and again in 1876. See note 3.
2 G. B. Airy.
3 Kelvin has added a footnote here reading, 'I see elsewhere Tonbridge Kent as his address'. Charles Vincent Walker (1812–82), who became a fellow of the Royal Society in 1855, was electrician to the South-Eastern Railway from 1845 to 1882. The date of his death precludes 1889 as a date for the letter. Walker, Airy, and Kelvin are included in both 1875 and 1876 among Clark's supporters in the lists of candidates and their supporters prepared at the beginning of April by the society's secretaries. As Airy seems to be signing for the first time, the letter's year appears to be 1875. Clark (1822–98) began his career as a civil engineer but later was primarily concerned with submarine telegraphy.

Stokes Collection, K197

Glasgow University
May 1/75

DEAR STOKES

I had nearly finished my instructions for observing atmosph. elec^y a month ago but was forced to set the matter aside on account of the pressure of work connected with the close of our session. It came to an end only yesterday and I hope to finish the instructions[1] this evening and despatch them tomorrow addressed to you at the R.S. London. I shall mark outside the envelope,

Arctic Exped^n
Instructions for
Atmospheric
Electricity.

So perhaps you may arrange to have them sent direct to the printer. ⟨We⟩ [?] We go to London Tuesday but I fear I shall not see you this week there because of Ascension day. On Tuesday week we think of going to Cambridge where I hope to see you. The electrometers are nearly made. I have been watching progress continually at White's.

I have arranged to meet Lieut Parr[2] and show him precisely how to use the instrument next week or the week after in London.

Yours truly
W. THOMSON

1 Kelvin (206A).
2 The strategy for the expedition called for officers of the two ships to be taught science, not for scientists to be sent along. As *Nature* reported: 'Meanwhile the officers are pursuing their special studies. ... Lieutenants Parr and May are to be initiated into some special astronomical work, and two other lieutenants will receive charge of the pendulum observations'. (*Nature*, 11 (4 March 1875), 355.) Alfred A. C. Parr and William H. May both served aboard H.M.S. *Alert*.

311 KELVIN to STOKES, 14 July 1875
Royal Society of London, RR.7.415

July 14, 1875
The University
Glasgow.

DEAR STOKES

I enclose with this a copy of a letter I am sending to M^r [Walter] White.[1]

If you approve of my suggestions will you direct that one of the proofs of the short paper[2] of June 10 be sent to the referees: and that it be considered as offered to be printed in the transactions [sic] at the end of the M.SS.[3]

I hope before very long to be able to send you a fresh paper for the Transactions.[4] I have got excellent results by direct deflection of a magnetometer needle, confirming as far as they go the results I first got by the electromagnetic method: and extending to include effects of torsion, which are very remarkable. With 14 lbs hanging *on*, torsional stress diminishes greatly the magnetization by the earth's vert[l] force: with only 4 lbs, I find the same kind but much less amount of effect by torsion.

I have also experimented in the same way as before (electromag[c] induc[n]) at temperature 100°. The maximum of my curve seems shifted considerably ⟨to⟩ in the positive direction.

Yours truly
W.T.[5]

1 Kelvin's copy of his letter to White is RR.7.416 in the Royal Society and reads as follows:

14th July 1875.

Dear Sir: –

In returning for press three days ago the abstract of my Preliminary Notice 'Effects of Stress on Inductive Magnetism in Soft Iron' I requested the printers to send two copies to Professor Stokes and one to you of a final proof with my corrections made and with the diagram inserted. My reason for doing so was that I think a copy of it should be sent to the referees for my paper of May 27th for the Transactions.

I ⟨mean to⟩ am writing to Prof. Stokes suggesting that this short paper of June 10th might be printed in the Transactions at the end of my paper of May 27th and made to serve as a stepping-stone to the long continuation for the Transactions which I am preparing. This continuation will consist partly of the details of the experiments on which my Preliminary Notice of June 10th is founded, and partly of descriptions of further experiments with which I have been occupied since that date largely extending the investigation.

Yours very truly
WILLIAM THOMSON

2 Kelvin (209).
3 Kelvin (207.1).
4 Kelvin (207.2) is the continuation of (207.1).
5 Stokes has written at the bottom of the page, '1875 Sir W[m] Thomson Letter'.

312 KELVIN to STOKES, 2 November 1875
Stokes Collection, K198

Glasgow University[1]
Nov 2/75

DEAR STOKES

I think the result from Maxwell & Boltzman of which I spoke to you must be right, and it is very important. Here it is, if true. Given ⟨any number⟩ ⟨crowd⟩ any number of perfectly elastic solids emprisoned [sic] in a space bounded by perfectly hard walls. Set each in motion with any velocity. After

⟨a sufficiently⟩ an infinitely great number of collisions all the kinetic energy will have been converted into vibrations ⟨and rotations⟩. What do you think of it? It is most important, if true, & so far the more I ⟨think⟩ thought of it yesterday in the train, the surer I felt of its truth.

Yours
WT

1 Kelvin has written at the top of the letter, '(Maxwell & Boltzman)'. See the work by Brush cited in letter 249, note 2.

313 KELVIN to STOKES, 2 November 1875
Stokes Collection, K199

Glasgow University
Nov 2/75

DEAR STOKES

I am sorry I cannot undertake the biographical notice of Sir Charles Wheatstone. I am striving hard to overtake arrears of work and all I can do it must be long time before I can get my head above water in respect to things which I have promised to do with the least possible delay.

I had to refuse the same request to the Editor[1] of Nature. He applied to Barrett[2] when I could not undertake it, but I have not heard the result.

Yours very truly
WILLIAM THOMSON

I am sorry you had the trouble of coming to the train. We ⟨went⟩ came by the 7:55, for north.

I cannot think of anyone else to suggest, unless Charles Brooke.[3] Is not he an FRS and I should think he would be willing to do it. He must have known Wheatstone well I think.

1 J. N. Lockyer.
2 William Fletcher Barrett (1844–1925) was professor of physics at the Royal College of Science, Dublin, from 1873 to 1910. However, *Nature*'s obituary for Wheatstone was written not by him, but by Paolo Volpicelli (1804–79), professor of physics at the University of Rome.
3 Charles Brooke (1804–79) took his B.M. at Cambridge in 1828, became a fellow of the Royal Society in 1847, and was on the surgical staff of Metropolitan Free Hospital and Westminster Hospital. The Royal Society's obituary for Wheatstone (unsigned) is in *Proc. Roy. Soc.*, **24** (1875–76), xvi–xxvii.

The University,
Glasgow.
9th November 1875.

DEAR STOKES:–

Thanks for your letter of yesterday with Maxwell's report.[1] If Mr White would send me the whole manuscript in his hands including the note-book which the Commit[t]ee on papers wish to retain I shall undertake to return them with nothing written on them except in pencil or red ink to guide the printers. I hope to be able to take the thing up thoroughly next week and with very little delay to prepare the whole for the press, in accordance, as I hope to be able to make it, with Maxwell's suggestions. I am writing to Mr White saying you authorise me to make this request of him.

I send you copies of the first and last of my papers on the tides in the Philosophical Magazine.[2]

You have I believe the second one,[3] the one which appeared in the October number.

I shall return you Maxwell's report as soon as I have done with it, which will be when I am ready to send the paper off prepared for press.

Believe me
Yours truly
WILLIAM THOMSON

Prof. G. G. Stokes.

1 Maxwell's report on Kelvin (207.1), stating 'I therefore consider the paper as a valuable contribution to the Transactions', is in the Royal Society, RR.7.418.
2 Kelvin (210) and (212).
3 Kelvin (211).

315 STOKES to KELVIN, 11 January 1876
Kelvin Collection, S405
Printed in Stokes's *MPP*, IV, 375–6.

Cambridge 11th Jany 1876

MY DEAR THOMSON,

You have pushed me far too much forward as to spectrum analysis. Whitmell[1] sent me a syllabus of his lectures, in wh I was mentioned far too prominently, and this led me to write to him my recollection of my ideas (and it is a distinct one) when we talked about the matter. It was *you* who proposed to extend the method so much. I rather thought you were allowing your horse to run away with you.[2]

Most of the absorbing (optically not mentally) matters that then came across me were things that would not stand the fire, and I don't know that I ever asked myself the question What would take place if a coloured glass were heated? Anyhow Stewart's extension of Prevost's theory of exchanges in the Proc. R.S. X 385 form (for I was not *then* acquainted with his Edin. Phil. Trans. papers[3] though I might have been) came before me with all the freshness of a new discovery. I don't know whether you had known it before.

As to the bright D[4] of a spirit lamp with salted wick,[5] I thought the flame gave such a shake to the NaCl molecule as to make the Na bell ring, but did not think the mere[6] ethereal vibrations of D pitch could do it unless the Na were free, which I did not think of its being in the flame of a spirit lamp, though I thought the tremendous actions on the sun's surface might set it free. When later (1855) I heard from Foucault's lips of his remarkable discovery I still thought of the sodium being set free by the tremendous action of the voltaic arc of a battery of 40 or 50 elements of Grove or Bunsen.

I thought from memory that it was *when* Foucault came to receive the Copley medal that he told me of it, though all I could feel certain of from memory [was] that it was in the evening at Dr Neil Arnott's. On referring to your Glasgow address,[7] I was going to strike out the date, when I obtained proof positive that I was right. I feel *certain* I[8] should have mentioned Foucault's remarkable discovery in what I drew up for the President about his researches if I had then known of it. (Proc. R.S. VIII. 571)[9]

Yours sincerely

G. G. STOKES[10]

1 Charles Thomas Whitmell (1849–1919) received his B.A. from Cambridge in 1872, having placed in the first class in the natural sciences tripos. He was a Cambridge University extension lecturer in 1875/6 and was H.M. inspector of schools from 1879 to 1910. There are twenty-five letters from him to Stokes in the Stokes Collection, ten of which date from 1875 or 1876. The letter mentioned in this paragraph from Stokes to Whitmell, dated 23–31 December 1875, is Stokes (91) and is in Stokes's *MPP*, IV, 133–6.

2 Kelvin has drawn a horizontal line just below this paragraph and written, '? publish in Nature from this forward'. This notation was not made at the same time as those mentioned in note 10 (i.e., 1903) and probably dates from 1876.

3 For Stewart's papers, see letter 277, notes 11 and 12.

4 Larmor's printed version reads *bright line D*.

5 The printed version has a full stop instead of a comma.

6 The printed version reads *more* instead of *mere*.

7 Presumably, Kelvin (173), which was his presidential address to the British Association at *Edinburgh*.

8 The printed version reads *certain that I*.

9 In the printed version, Larmor changed Stokes's incorrect reference from volume VIII to volume VII. Lord Wrottesley's presidential address is in *Proc. Roy. Soc.*, 7 (1855), 560–77, with the presentation to Foucault on pp. 571–4.

10 Below Stokes's signature, Kelvin has written, 'Jan 11, 1876. K[elvin] Nov 30, 1903'. Below

that he has written, 'See last 4 lines of p 4. *very important.* K Dec 1, 1903'. The last four lines of the fourth page of Stokes's letter is the passage, *the Na bell ring, . . . could do it unless.*

316 KELVIN to STOKES, 27 January 1876
Stokes Collection, K201

The University,
Glasgow.
January 27/76

DEAR STOKES

I enclose the three papers[1] promised in my telegram. They are numbered II III IV because they should follow immediately after my brother's,[2] to be marked I. His integration is simply this

The disc is supported on a fixed axis inclined to vertical: the cylinder on a horizontal axis. The globe is loose, but guided by a fork touching

it at ends (or at either end) of a horizontal diameter (like a shoemaker's measurer for the length of a foot). This fork is carried to & fro parallel to the horizontal lines of the disc, so that the centre of the globe traverses a line parallel to these, during the motion of the machine. When the globe is in the axis of the disc the rotation of the disc gives no motion to globe & cylinder. When globe is on either side rotation of disc gives motion in one direction or the contrary, to cylinder.

I go to London tomorrow & bring a model with me which I shall give to Mr White so that you may have it by you when the papers are communicated. My brother's paper will be posted tomorrow, or at all events some time this week, addressed to you at Cambridge. It may be marked as communicated by me.

I shall probably have left London before this day week but if by chance not, could it be taken for these papers? I could then be present & read them myself.

Yours
In haste
W. Thomson

1 Kelvin (213), (214), and (215).
2 J. Thomson, 'On an integrating machine having a new kinematic principle', *Proc. Roy. Soc.*, **24** (1876), 262–5.

317 Kelvin to Stokes, 28 January 1876
Stokes Collection, K202

The University,
Glasgow.
Jan 28/76

Dear Stokes

Please let me have a line to say if my papers[1] on integrators can be ⟨brought⟩ communicated on Thursday evening next. If they can I shall wait in London on purpose. You have now all in writing, ready for press so Huxley will have no trouble this time, but perhaps with the machine to show ⟨I⟩ [?] it might be as well that I be there myself. I am on the wing this moment for London. Address there care of

> C. W. Siemens
> 3 Palack Houses
> ⟨H⟩ [?] ⟨Kensington⟩
> Kensington Gardens.

Yours very truly
W. Thomson

P.S. My three papers were despatched to you yesterday by letter post addressed Royal Society. My brother's[2] will be posted today or tomorrow addressed Lensfield. I enclose now a leaf accidentally omitted from yesterday's despatch.

1 Kelvin (213), (214), and (215).
2 See the previous letter, note 2.

The University,
Glasgow.
Feb 16ᵗʰ 1876.

DEAR STOKES

Considering the enormous quantity of water which may escape from a crack or from an overflow pipe in a water tank would you consider a glass tube fitted to its side (like the water gauge in a steam boiler) an untrustworthy indicator of the level of the water because of the smallness of the quantity of water that enters the gauge?

If you would then you may doubt the electrometer for contact electricity &c: if not you cannot reasonably do so.

I ought to have written this long ago; and then I forgot to say it to you when I saw you last.

The fact is the galvanometer is liable to be deceptive because of the quantity of electricity it draws off and the disturbance it thereby creates in the electrical condition to be tested.

The first essential of a gauge or test is that, if it alters the thing tested at all it shall not do so so much as to vitiate the result. The best is when the thing tested is not altered at all by the test. This is only attained when looking at the thing as in astronomical observations, or ⟨in⟩ when looking at living creatures (without vivisection) suffices for obtaining the desired ⟨result⟩ knowledge.

If the test alters the thing tested at all we must be able to take into account the amount of the alteration and it must not be so great as to alter the circumstances altogether away from those we wish to investigate. The advantage of the electrometer is that in almost all its applications and particularly in those to contact electricity, electro-chemical action &c, it does not seriously if at at [sic] all sensibly, alter the electrical condition to be tested.

Believe me
Yours very truly
WILLIAM THOMSON

Prof G. G. Stokes.

Lensfield Cottage Cambridge
19 Feb. 1876

MY DEAR THOMSON,

If by 'contact electricity' you merely mean the electrical manifestations obtained under the usual circumstances on making contact between different bodies, of course I don't deny that for [?] round numbers [?]_____ [2] you obtain by means of an electrometer. It is a mere statement of an observed fact. But the very term 'contact electricity' implies a theory for which as far as my present _____ go, I don't believe to be true – that the observed electrical manifestations are [3] conditioned [?] by the contact [?] pure and simple. The_____ of the truth this_____ this [?] point [?] by _____ an illustration. But would two perfectly pure and clean pieces of zinc and gold, if brought into contact in the inter_____ spaces manifest signs of electricity? I doubt [?] [4] it.

You say the advantage of the electrometer over the galvanometer [is?] that [?] it [?] does [?] not alter the electrical condition to be tested. My notion of the advantage of the galvanometer over the electrometer is that it renders [?] the *bringing about* of the electrical condition [5] to be tested. The two statements are not inconsistent provided the 'electrical conditions to be tested' are different in the minds of the two.

An example drawn from an actual exper[t] of Hopkinson's[2] will make this clear.

He wished to determine whether there would be [6] an electromotive force between two _____ of _____ dipped, one into a solution of permanganate of potash, the other into water, the two communicating [?]. The [?] two he poured into a a [*sic*] U-tube with a porous plug, in one leg permanganate solution, in the other leg water, or what is commonly called water; [7] and using the electrometer

_____ .

But the _____ deceptive [?] results [?]. The electrometer _____, as the galvanometer would have done, the bringing about of the electrical condition to be tested. What may have happened [?] [8] and I suspect *did* happen was this. What we *call* water in any actual experiment is really water plus an infinitesimal amount of unknown impurities. Pure water is to what we use in experiment what a geometrical line is to the thing we draw on paper, or with a [9] fine graver on a copper plate, and call a line. The so-called water in the 2nd leg was water + an infinitesimal amount of oxidizable impurities – infinitesimal it may be quoad chemical tests, but not infinitesimal quoad the charging of an electrometer by the [10] chemical action it (the impurity) can set up. In consequence of the oxidizing properties of the permanganate, the surface [?] of junction [?] of the permanganate and the so-called water became the seat of an electromotive force, by which the electrometer was charged.

[11] Now Hopkinson, from reasoning [?] from the result of the electrometer alone [?], laid down a condition which he saw when I pointed it out to him was not at all established. Supposing my explanation correct, had he used a galvanometer of high resistance instead of the electrometer, the origin of the [12] current in an infinitesimal impurity would have been revealed by the action of the current after a little time.

The substance we obtain from the best_____chemists help us to reason about pure substance just as the lines we draw [13] on paper help us to reason about abstract geometry. And just as in *experimental* geometry_____wrong by applying a microscope with _____ of 10000 to our drawings, _____ making due allowance for errors of the drawing, so it seems [14] to me in electro-chemistry we might often times go wrong by relying on the electrometer, unless we felt to our finger's ends that a pure substance is an unobtainable abstraction.

Yours sincerely,
G. G. STOKES

1 This is Stokes's press copy of the original letter. It is an exceedingly bad copy and in places completely blank. The lines in the text represent approximately the amount of material I have been unable to read. The numbers in brackets are the page numbers of the press copy which should facilitate comparison of the text with the original.

2 See J. Hopkinson, 'Certain cases of electromotive force sustained by the action of electrolytes on electrolytes', *Proc. Roy. Soc.*, 24 (1876), 183–6. John Hopkinson (1849–98) was senior wrangler in 1871, became a fellow of the Royal Society in 1878, and was professor of electrical engineering at King's College, London, from 1890 to 1898. There are forty-seven letters from Hopkinson to Stokes in the Stokes Collection, most dating from 1874 to 1877. Hopkinson and Stokes presented a joint paper in 1875: 'On the optical properties of a titano–silicic glass', *Brit. Assoc. Rep.* (1875), 26–7.

320 KELVIN to STOKES, 6 March 1876
Stokes Collection, K204

> The University,
> Glasgow.
> March 6ᵗʰ 1876.

DEAR STOKES:–

As Hopkinson has sent an abstract of his paper[1] and as the discovery of the effect of tapping which it contains is very notable I think it ought to be offered for the Transactions. I have called his attention to Kerr's discovery.[2]

> I remain
> Yours truly
> WILLIAM THOMSON

Prof G. G. Stokes.

[1] J. Hopkinson, 'The residual charge of the Leyden jar', *Proc. Roy. Soc.*, **24** (1876), 407–8, and *Phil. Trans.* (1876), 489–94.

[2] Kelvin presumably meant Kerr's discovery of what is now known as the 'Kerr effect', reported by Kerr in 'On the rotation of the plane of polarization by reflection from the pole of a magnet', *Brit. Assoc. Rep.* (1876), section 2, 40–1, and *Phil. Mag.*, **3** (1877), 321–43. John Kerr (1824–1907) studied natural philosophy with Kelvin at Glasgow and remained in Glasgow as lecturer in mathematics at the Free Church Normal Training College for Teachers, holding the position for forty-four years beginning in 1857.

321 KELVIN to STOKES, 12 March 1876
Stokes Collection, K205

> The University,
> Glasgow.
> March 12/76

DEAR STOKES

I had the enclosed from Hopkinson several days ago and ought to have sent it to you instantly. Please let it appear as note or addendum to his last paper[1] for Transactions and if you think proper let it appear in the Abstract also.

> Yours very truly
> WILLIAM THOMSON.

P.S. I hope to get some of the Toulon Tide curves roughly but usefully analysed by a wooden model machine which we have been having made as a first step from the one you saw to a proper machine for the most accurate work.[2]

[1] No part of Hopkinson's paper cited in note 1 of the previous letter is marked as an addition. However, the addition may be a paragraph on page 491 which explains that Kelvin performed

417

similar experiments for his classes several years ago, or it may be the final paragraph which discusses Kelvin's explanations of specific inductive capacity and of pyro-electricity.

2 See Kelvin (213), (214), (215), and (215A).

322 KELVIN to STOKES, 25 August 1876
Stokes Collection, K206

Yacht Lalla Rookh[1]
Lamlash, Aug 25/76

DEAR STOKES

I wish you could come and stay with us (not in the yacht but in our house in the University) during the B.A. meeting.[2] I am afraid that this is rather too late to put in an application but in case you are engaged to be with my brother-in-law [A. Crum] at Thornliebank I would ask him to let you come to us as perhaps you would find it more convenient to be *near*, and we would take you out with us at all events one day to see him at Thornliebank, if you could spare an afternoon or evening. I am writing to him just now to say that I am making this application to you, and I shall be glad to hear from you that you are not otherwise engaged and will come to us.

I have got up on Hopkins' problem of precession & nutation on the hypothesis of the earth wholly liquid, or liquid in a rigid or elastic spheroidal shell of some such ellipticity as $1/300$.[3] Precession is the same to a very high degree of approximation, on either hypothesis, as it would be if the mass were wholly rigid. The lunar 18.6 yearly nutation is increased by about $1/23$ by fluidity with any ordinary hypothesis as to thickness of shell. The solar semi annual nutation is reversed & enlarged by fluidity in proportion $61/39$ with any ordinary thickness of shell! The lunar fortnightly nutation is reverse

if the mom. of inertia of the shell is $<1/19$
it is inf. if [moment of inertia of the shell is] $= 1/19$ } of the moment of inertia
[it is] direct & enlarged [if moment of inertia of the shell is] $>1/19$[4]   of the whole

Some of these results are very unexpected. I wonder what you will think of them!

My wife[5] begs to be kindly remembered to you and Mrs Stokes and hopes you will come, and says if she will come with you so much the better.

Yours truly
W THOMSON

1 Kelvin has written at the top of the letter, 'Address University Glasgow'.
2 In 1876 the British Association met in September in Glasgow.
3 See Kelvin (217), his presidential address to Section A of the British Association.
4 Kelvin has written two exclamation marks just below these figures.
5 Frances Anna, Lady Kelvin, née Blandy (d. 1916), daughter of Charles R. Blandy (d. 1879) of

Madeira, met Kelvin when he was in Madeira in 1873 on a cable expedition and married him in June 1874.

323 KELVIN to STOKES, 16 to 19 September [1876][1]
Stokes Collection, K363

Yacht, Lalla Rookh
Weemyss [i.e., Wemyss] Bay
Sat morning
Sep 16

DEAR STOKES

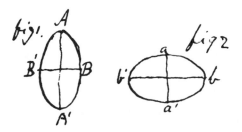

Here is a very short cut to the proof of instability for a liquid given rotating round the axis of a prolate ellipsoidal shell. Given the liquid rotating round $A'A$ in fig. 1. Keep $C'C$ (perp^r to diagram) constant in length: elongate $B'B$ to $b'b = AA'$, and shrink AA' to $aa' = BB'$. Make this distortion very slowly. The resulting motion will be steady and of less energy than the initial motion because work will be done by ['centrifugal force'][2] fluid pressure on the parts neighbouring to the ⟨*surface*⟩ points $B'B$, more than that spent against fluid pressure in neighbourhood of A', A. Now it is clear that with the given vorticity, there is no *steady* motion in the given hollow space, other than that of No 1, or of No 2. Hence there is no ⟨maxim–minim⟩ configuration of maxim–min energy with the given vorticity. Hence the energy of config. (1) is an absolute max^m, and that of fig. (2) an absolute min; and the energy of any other configuration of the fluid motion with the given vorticity, in a fixed shell of the given shape is less than that of (1) and greater than that of (2). Now let the shell be solid, with elasticity, and with viscosity giving resistance to distortion depending on velocity of distortion so that the shell cannot come to rest except in its proper figure. The slightest initial tremor disturbing from fig. (1) leads therefore to a state of things (fig. 3) in which molecular axes are on the average parallel to $B'B$: the same motion quoad the liquid as that of fig. (2), but with the shell in the same position as fig. 1. Or if, instead of the shell being slightly flexible, let it be perfectly rigid, but packed in straw. The slightest disturbance from the condition (1) will lead to a precessional motion of the liquid which will produce a couple on the shell in a rotating plane. This couple will always lead to consumption of energy in the straw, ⟨and⟩ until the configuration (3) is reached. The solution expressing rigourously the configuration (3) is easily found. (I have it but need not trouble you with it.)

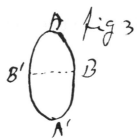

We have a different phase of marine hydrokinetics this morning from yesterday and I think you would have enjoyed it if you could have been with us – sailing rapidly with a strong breeze, and smooth water, to Largs (while I have been writing the above): inclination from 7° to 12° I guess.

I hope you have found all well at Armagh – and with kind regards to yourself and Mrs. Stokes in which my wife joins I am yours very truly

W THOMSON

The case of motion represented in Fig. (3) has energy not an absolute minimum but a maximum–min^m, with given vorticity. For with given vorticity in a closed vessel of given shape, the energy may be zero! (the different parts of the liquid may be intershuffled so as to turn the axes of molecular rotation in opposite directions in contiguous parts). Hence case of Fig. (3) is *unstable*, if the containing vessel is slightly flexible and viscous.

WT

Sep 19

1 The year is determined by the similarity of the content of this letter to that of the next and by the fact that September 16th was a Saturday in 1876.
2 Kelvin's brackets.

324 KELVIN to STOKES, 23 September [1876][1]
Stokes Collection, K207

LL[allah] [*sic*] R[ookh]
Largs Sep 23.

Consider a hollow shell of perfectly elastic solid material so far as permanence of figure when in equilibrium under any system of forces, but having (viscous) resistance to change of shape, depending on and vanishing with velocity of change. Let this be filled with perfect liquid, and set rotating as if solid, round axis of maxim. mom[ent] of inertia. The energy of this motion is less than that of any other motion of same mom[ent] of mom[entu]m. For let it be given any such other state, and let the liquid now be viscous. It will wear into a state of motion as if a solid, keeping of course same mom of mom^m, i.e. it will wear into the first supposed state, w^h therefore is of less energy than the other. Hence my last post card[2] is wrong probably: for it is probably true that the first supposed motion is absolutely stable for a perfect liquid. Consider for example a spherical hollow filled with rotating liquid. This motion is surely stable; though for a time (before and after writing last p.c.) I thought all the energy might be taken out by slight flexures of the shell.

W.T.

1 This is a post card addressed to Stokes and post marked 24 September 1876.
2 This post card has not survived.

325 KELVIN to STOKES, 9 October 1876
Stokes Collection, K208

L[allah] R[ookh]
Inveraray Oct 9/76

DEAR STOKES

Thanks for your kind note. We shall come about the 24th or 25th if that will suit you but will write beforehand.

I am much disturbed by two or three of the tubes being wrong at 11 f[atho]ms but right at 14![1] The marking is greatly improved as you will see by enclosure.

I am working out a plan by magnets used as deflectors to test the directive force on ship's compass, and then, by applying corrections to make it equal for all ⟨bearings⟩ azimuths of the ship's length, to 'correct' the compass on all points without sights of landmarks or celestial objects.[2] I think this plan promises to be readier than & as easy as the ordinary by sights or marks. I use the 'sinus-galvanometer' method: that is to say I turn the deflector (whose centre is a few inches above the centre of the compass) until its magnetic axis is perpendicular to the direction in which the magnetic axis of the deflected compass rests.

Yours truly
W THOMSON

1 See Kelvin (201), in *PLA*, III, 375–6.
2 See Kelvin (223).

The University,
Glasgow.
Nov 9/76

DEAR STOKES

I thought I missed Gordon's previous results when I went through this second paper[1] ⟨but⟩ and meant to speak to you about it but when you told me the first paper was incorporated with the second I thought I must have overlooked them. I ⟨no⟩ am decidedly of opinion that they ought not to be omitted. The result for water is even more important than that for sulphuret of carbon as water is the more important liquid. I think the results of the first paper, with just enough of detail to show how close⟨ly⟩ they probably are to the exact value, might easily be added to the paper in a preliminary paragraph or two.

I *don't* quite like the title 'Verdet's constant'![2] See Faraday's exp. Researches §2214 ⟨(or there abouts)⟩ or 2215 and you will see that Faraday expresses very clearly the idea of accurate measurement of the rotation for a given length of the substance traversed, and given strength of force of the field.[3] He does *not* indicate absolute electro magnetic measure (Does Verdet do this? ⟨)⟩ but even if he did, I think introduction of the idea of absolute measure in this connection would scarcely make it proper to call the thing measured 'Verdet's constant'!) Besides 'Verdet's constant' is not a proper way of describing a number measuring the particular value of a certain quality for a particular substance. 'Black's constant' would be a very bad way to name the latent heat of fusion of ice, or of some metal, or the latent heat of evaporation of water: though the thing measured is actually Black's discovery. In short 'Faraday's constant' would badly express the rotatory power of the magnetic action in some particular substance as water, or sulphuret of carbon but not so badly as 'Verdet's constant'.

I almost forgot about the measurement of horizontal intensity. The practical details of this process are so little known generally that I think it rather a good thing to have them put before such people as will read Gordon's paper. But ⟨perh⟩ [?] no doubt the statement might be somewhat abridged. I think enough of it ought to be left to show to what degree of accuracy the *absolute* figure may be probably relied on.

Yours very truly
W THOMSON

1 J. E. H. Gordon, 'Determination of Verdet's constant in absolute units. 1st and 2nd memoirs', *Phil. Trans.* (1877), 1–34. James Edward Henry Gordon (1852–93) took his B.A. at Cambridge in 1875 and became a highly successful electrical engineer, for example, as

manager of the electric lighting department of the Telegraph Construction and Maintenance Co. and as a founder of the Whitehall Electric Supply Co.

2 Marcel Émile Verdet (1824–66), who held a variety of professorships of physics in Paris, is noted for introducing British and German physical ideas through his lectures into French physical thought. His research cited by Gordon is in his 'Recherches sur les propriétés optiques développées dans les corps transparents par l'action du magnétisme', *Annales de Chimie et de Physique*, 3rd series, 41 (1854), 370–412.

3 M. Faraday, 'On the magnetization of light and the illumination of magnetic lines of force', *Phil. Trans.* (1846), 1–20.

327 KELVIN to STOKES, 24 November 1876
Stokes Collection, K210

The University,
Glasgow.
Nov. 24th 1876

DEAR STOKES

You will see an experimental answer to the question of your yesterday's note in §150 of my *Electrodynamic Qualities of Metals*[1] in which it is proved that iron and copper wires equally extended within the limits of elasticity have their electric resistance differently altered by the stress.

In §152 you will see something more on the subject. No one else so far as I know up to the present time has experimented upon it at all and the investigation in the paper you have received will be very valuable if it is a really good investigation.

I have often wanted to carry out the intention stated in §152 and I am very glad now to hear of anyone else doing it.

I remain
Yours very truly
WILLIAM THOMSON
per A Gray[2]

Prof. G. G. Stokes

P.S. Sir W. Thomson had to leave before this letter was written out from my notes, and asked me, therefore, to sign it for him. A.G.

1 Kelvin (92).

2 Andrew Gray (1847–1925) was Kelvin's assistant at Glasgow from 1875 to 1884 and, after fifteen years as professor of physics at University College of North Wales, replaced Kelvin as professor of natural philosophy in 1899. The year after Kelvin's death, he published *Lord Kelvin: an Account of His Scientific Life and Work* (London, 1908).

Glasgow University
Nov. 28th 1876

DEAR STOKES:–

I enclose a paper on the Residual Charge of the Leyden Jar by Hopkinson which I rather think would be suitable for the Transactions. It is marked II being I suppose a continuation of what has been already published in the Proceedings.[1] If *you* think the present paper suitable for the Transactions there might be an addition at the beginning of it containing the substance of [what] has already appeared in the Proceedings so that the whole might appear together in the Transactions.

If you think anything else should be done than publish what I now enclose in the Proceedings, shall I write to Hopkinson or will you? If, however, you think it better to publish the enclosed simply in the Proceedings it would be all right so.

Yours truly
WILLIAM THOMSON

Prof G. G. Stokes[2]

1 J. Hopkinson, 'The residual charge of the Leyden jar. – Dielectric properties of different glasses', *Proc. Roy. Soc.*, **25** (1877), 496–7, and *Phil. Trans.* (1877), 599–626. Received on 30 November 1876, the paper is a continuation of the one cited in letter 319, note 2.
2 Stokes has written on the reverse, '1876 in re Hopkinson. letter from Thomson'.

329 KELVIN to STOKES, [18 December 1876][1]
Stokes Collection, K212

See Nature July 15, 1875 (Same number as your photo.)[2] particularly top of p 218.[3] Is not this date earlier than Stoney's expl. of the 'radiometer'?[4] It is precisely that which is generally ⟨given⟩ [?] referred to as Stoney's. Tait & Dewar's communication is ill reported (as you will see) in Nature. They intended a full paper with full details of measurement &c for the Transactions RSE but owing to your action on Dewar[5] it has not yet been presented. The experiments & some measurements were however actually shown at a meeting of R.S.E.

WT

1 This is a post card addressed to Stokes and post marked Edinburgh, 18 December 1876.
2 Stokes's photograph accompanied the article by P. G. Tait, 'Scientific worthies. V. – George Gabriel Stokes', *Nature*, **12** (15 July 1875), 201–3.

3 This is *Nature*'s account of Tait and Dewar's 'Farther researches in very perfect vacua', *Proc. Roy. Soc. Edinb.*, **8** (1875), 628, in *Nature*, **12** (15 July 1875), 217–18.

4 G. J. Stoney, 'On Crookes's radiometer', *Phil. Mag.*, **1** (1876), 177–81 and 305–13. George Johnstone Stoney (1826–1911) graduated from Trinity College, Dublin, in 1848 and spent most of the rest of his life as secretary to Queen's University, Dublin. There are some twenty letters from him to Stokes in the Stokes Collection.

5 This presumably refers to the appointment of James Dewar (1842–1923) to the Jacksonian professorship at Cambridge in 1875. Dewar was also appointed to the Fullerton professorship of chemistry at the Royal Institution in 1877, and he held both professorships until his death.

330 KELVIN to STOKES, 20 December 1876
Stokes Collection, K213

The University,
Glasgow.
Dec. 20th 1876

DEAR STOKES:–

I approve of the addition of the enclosure as an appendix to Siemens's paper[1] omitting above and below the red lines according to your suggestion, so that it may not appear in the form of a letter.

At the meeting of the Government Fund Committee to be held tomorrow, will you intimate that a joint application on the part of Captain Evans[2] and myself for a grant of a certain sum for tidal investigations to be specified is intended? We have had two meetings to discuss the subject and had resolved to include an investigation of tides in the Pacific and Indian Oceans, from certain observations at present in the possession of the Admiralty particularly Swan River Australia; also an investigation of long period tides, both annual and semi-annual, which are no doubt chiefly meteorological, and lunar monthly and fortnightly declinational, which are no doubt very purely gravitational. As soon as possible Captain Evans and I will arrange the formal terms of our application. Meantime having heard from you yesterday that there is to be a meeting tomorrow I think it right to ask you to give notice that we intend to make such an application.

Yours truly
WILLIAM THOMSON

Professor G. G. Stokes

1 C. W. Siemens, 'On determining the depth of the sea without the use of the sounding line, and on an attraction meter', *Phil. Trans.* (1876), 671–92.

2 Frederick John Owen Evans (1815–85) succeeded G. H. Richards as hydrographer to the Admiralty in 1874, retiring in 1884. See Kelvin and Evans (1) and (2).

331 KELVIN to STOKES, 30 January 1877
Stokes Collection, K214

> The University,
> Glasgow.
> January 30 1877

DEAR STOKES:–

My brother and I have worked out a much improved plan for our harmonic analysing instrument[1] and I hope very soon to be able to make some trials of actual work with it although still only in the rough in a wooden model. As soon as we are satisfied with these trials we are going to have one made in brass for actual application to tidal or meteorological analysis. It would, however, be a great pity to defer such work as Stewart proposes till a machine is available.

With a moderate amount of arithmetical work such as Roberts has done for the tides I believe valuable results as to the variations of the magnetic elements may be found before we can possibly have a machine ready to economise labour.

I have not yet had time to study your letter of yesterday but hope to do so this evening. Your explanation of the non-discovery of the effect of latitude by Siemens's Bathometer[2] seems very probable. It would be easy to test it by bringing a bar magnet vertically under the instrument at such a distance as to produce a force equal to the difference of magnetic force for say 2° of geographical latitude.

Will you not suggest to Siemens to do this?

> Yours truly
> WILLIAM THOMSON
> per A. G[ray]

Professor G. G. Stokes

1 Kelvin's next paper on the subject, (227), was read to the Royal Society in 1878.
2 See the previous letter, note 1.

332 STOKES to KELVIN, 2 March 1877
Kelvin Collection, S406

> London 2 March 1877

MY DEAR THOMSON,

Was a printed paper as to the n° of copies of paper required by another sent you with the proof or revise of your paper in Phil. Trans.?[1] I rather suspect the printers neglect their duty.

I have made a few corrections.

P 16 l.2 (= 2 from bottom)
or, say ∓ 20. For . . .
    read
or, say ∓ 20, for

P 17 l.6
current still *following*
read flowing

P 18 l.1 of §194
After the conclusion . . . I have
made . . . and have obtained . . .
    read
After the conclusion . . . I made
. . . and I have obtained . . .

P 19 l.9
anomalies . . . , commencing that day . . . which
the first of them experimented on, showed . . .
    read
anomalies . . . , commencing that day . . . which
the first of the winds experimented on showed . . .

If I have done wrong there will be time to rectify it as I am to see a revise.
Yours sincerely
G. G. Stokes

1 Kelvin (207.1).

333   KELVIN to STOKES, 7 March 1877
Stokes Collection, K215

Western Club,
Glasgow.
March 7/77

DEAR STOKES

I had to leave hurriedly before getting my report on Darwin quite finished,[1] to test a compass & binnacle just about to be despatched for the German Admiralty. Since leaving I have perceived that I had inadvertently omitted ⟨two⟩ terms in the expressions for x & y. The correct expressions are[2]

$$x = c\cos \omega t + c' \sin \omega t \qquad y = -c\sin \omega t + c' \cos \omega t$$

when $t < t_0$

$$\langle \text{and } x = \int_{T'}^{T} u\,dt \rangle$$

$$x = \left(\int_{T'}^{T} u\,dt + c\cos \omega t_{\circ} + c' \sin \omega t_{\circ} \right) \cos \omega(t - t_{\circ})$$

$$y = \&c$$

when $t > t_{\circ}$

The geometrical construction which is obvious will follow tomorrow. It is of course far easier to see the actual result at first sight than it is to reduce it from the analytical solution.

Yours ($\langle$still$\rangle$ in haste again)

W. THOMSON

The binnacle & compass were quite satisfactory – for a 'Panzer Frigate' having an enormous fore & aft disturbing force, & large quadrantal.

1 G. H. Darwin, 'On the influence of geological changes on the Earth's axis of rotation', *Phil. Trans.* (1877), 271–312. Kelvin's referee's report on Darwin's paper is in the Royal Society, RR.8.14. George Howard Darwin (1845–1912), son of Charles Darwin, was second wrangler in 1868 and Plumian professor at Cambridge from 1883 to his death. There are several letters from Darwin to Stokes in the Stokes Collection, and a very large correspondence between Darwin and Kelvin is in the Kelvin Collection and the Kelvin Papers at Glasgow.

2 To the right of the word *are*, Kelvin has written in very small characters, '$\frac{dx}{dt} - \omega g$'. In the margin to the left of the equations, he has written, 'a little shab[b]iness about the signs here'.

---

334 KELVIN to STOKES, 10 March 1877
Stokes Collection, K216

The University,
Glasgow.
March 10[th] 1877

DEAR STOKES

I send the graphical construction which I had not time to write out before despatching the report for you last Wednesday. I enclose also a proof of a reprint of T and T'[1] sheet b containing some matter relating to the subject of Darwin's paper.[2]

Thanks for your corrections on my R.S. paper.[3] I have adopted them all thankfully. I appreciate your nice sense of grammar in the first line of §194. I return a copy with your corrections marked upon it with one or two more which M[r] Gray has found.

We are getting some very fine results for the effect of $\langle$lateral$\rangle$ transverse pull, by using a gun barrel subjected to hydraulic pressure. The effects are opposite to those of longitudinal pull both for the weaker and the stronger magnetizations. We find as in the case of longitudinal pull a zero with a certain degree of ⟨absolute⟩ magnetization, but have not been able to discover as yet whether it is at nearly the same degree of absolute magnetization.

Yours truly
W Thomson

1 Kelvin and Tait, *TNP*.
2 See the previous letter, note 1.
3 Kelvin (207.1).

335 Kelvin to Stokes, 21 March 1877
   Stokes Collection, K217

The University,[1]
Glasgow.
March 21/77

Dear Stokes

I received the enclosed from Jenkin this morning with much regret. I don't know if my being a member of the Committee could have made a difference in the result, but I think I could certainly have shown good reason for granting the sum applied for. Jenkin, with the assistance of J. A. Ewing, has made experiments on friction at very low speeds,[2] by a beautifully devised dynamical method, which they have carried out *very carefully* in a first investigation which has already brought out remarkable results. He showed me a paper describing the investigation so far as accomplished, a fortnight ago, and I thought it very good and important, and I advised him to send it to the R.S. (Lond.). I don't know if they have done this but if you see the paper I think you would approve of funds being granted for continuing the investigation. It is not too late I suppose for an application to the R.S. for a grant out of the £1000, but you see Jenkin himself has no idea of making another application. If however you think there might be a chance of success I would try to persuade him to put in a formal application.

I find there is a great deal of dissatisfaction in respect to actions taken by the Council of the Royal Society regarding the action of the Committee for the Government £4000. When you wrote to me the 'resolution of the Council is binding on the Committee' I understood that the government had given authority to the R.S. Council to make rules (within certain limits) which should be binding on the Committee. ⟨But unless⟩ And unless some such authority was given to the R.S. council, surely it could not legally meet and come to any resolution of any kind binding on the Committee. I find there is a

429

great deal of feeling in the R.S.E., and in the general public on the matter, and I have no other answer to give to numerous interpellators than that Stokes wrote to me that the resolution of the Council is binding on the committee. I would be very glad to hear from you how the matter stands as I feel by no means happy about it and don't feel satisfied in not having earlier asked 'how has anything been decided otherwise than *by the* Committee.'

Yours very truly
WILLIAM THOMSON

1 Kelvin has written at the top of the letter, 'Jenkin's letter Private please return it to me'. Jenkin's letter is not in either the Stokes or Kelvin Collection or in the Kelvin Papers at Glasgow.
2 F. Jenkin and J. A. Ewing, 'On friction between surfaces moving at low speeds', *Phil. Trans.* (1877), 509–28. James Alfred Ewing (1855–1935) studied at the University of Edinburgh and was professor of mechanical engineering at the University of Tokyo from 1878 to 1883. He later held professorships at Dundee and Cambridge and from 1916 to 1929 was principal and vice chancellor of the University of Edinburgh.

336 KELVIN to STOKES, 25 April 1877
Stokes Collection, K218

Ap 25/77
The University,
Glasgow.

DEAR STOKES

By all means let Darwin make any use he pleases of what I wrote regarding his paper.[1] I shall be very glad if he will adopt any part of it that he thinks could be of use incorporated with his own.

Yours truly
WILLIAM THOMSON

P.S. the calculating machine is going on and my brother & I hope soon to be able to report progress.[2] I saw it today nearly ready for trial (still in a rough wooden model) on a much improved plan from what you have already seen.

That seems a very curious thing that Hannay wrote to you about but I thought I had heard something like it from you. I enclose a letter[3] I had from him a few days ago though I suppose I need scarcely do so as I suppose he will have written the substance to you. Do not trouble yourself about returning it.

1 See letter 333, note 1.
2 See Kelvin (227).
3 James Ballantyne Hannay to Kelvin, 16 April 1877, Stokes Collection, H65. The letter makes clear that Stokes had answered Hannay's inquiry about an optical phenomenon involving

interference bands. There are forty-two letters from Hannay to Stokes in the Stokes Collection. Hannay was born in 1855 in Glasgow and had a private laboratory there. The *Royal Society Catalogue* lists several papers by him.

337 KELVIN to STOKES, 4 October 1877
Stokes Collection, K219

Yacht Lalla Rookh.[1]
Oct 4/77

DEAR STOKES

Thanks for your letter of 27th September. I wrote immediately to the printers saying I had not the slightest objection to my name appearing in the manner proposed on the proof slip which you sent.

I hope D[r] Robinson was better before you left Armagh. I presume you left on the 1st as you intended.

We are to be in Cambridge for a few days at the end of October and beginning of November, staying in Peterhouse Lodge.

I have today sent off a first instalment of 'Elasticity' for Encyclopaedia Britannica.[2] I hope it may be still in a condition available for improvements or additions when I am in Cambridge. There are many things about it on which I would like to have some instruction from you.

Yours always
W THOMSON

P.S. How about the radiometer? We have been anxiously looking for your paper.[3] When is it to appear? It is more needed now than ever, and the addition of some of the crucial experiments which have confirmed your explanations will increase its interest.

1 Kelvin has written at the top of the letter, 'We are still afloat, but leave the L.R. with much regret about Monday next'.
2 Kelvin (222A).
3 Stokes (96).

338 KELVIN to STOKES, 20 December 1877[1]
Stokes Collection, K220

The University,
Glasgow. Dec 20th 1877

DEAR STOKES,–

The period of the small oscillations shown by ripples on the tide curves is more nearly 20 or 25 minutes I think than 15 minutes. Roberts has instructions from Captain Evans and me to investigate them as far as possible from all the tide curves he has. They are to be found not merely in the Mediterranean but at Brest and Portland, and I believe everywhere where the tide gauge is delicate and correctly enough arranged to show them. Similar oscillations I believe have been observed in the Swiss lakes. I had a letter on the subject about a year ago from M. F.-A. Forel (Professeur à l'Academie de Lausanne).[2] He called them *Seiches*. In correspondence with him I thought they might depend on periods of oscillation of the lake itself. Possibly they do so. Possibly also part of the phenomenon observed in Toulon and other harbours may be due to oscillations of basins of water connected with the water in the harbour. But there is something still to be discovered. What a wonderful thing it would be if there were some tremors of the earth as a whole, or of some deep seated action influencing all the waters of the ocean and possibly waters of lakes also!

If you write to Roberts[3] he will give you the latest information available as to what the curves show.

Yours truly
WILLIAM THOMSON

Professor G. G. Stokes

1 The letter is in Andrew Gray's hand.
2 François Alphonse Forel (1841–1912) was extraordinary professor of anatomy and physiology at the Academy of Lausanne from 1870 to 1895. There are no letters from him to Kelvin in either the Kelvin Collection or the Kelvin Papers at Glasgow. He published several articles on this topic; see, for example, his 'Notes on the "Seiches" of the Swiss lakes', *Phil. Mag.*, 2 (1876), 447–9.
3 Gray has written Roberts's address at the bottom of the page: 'Nautical Almanac Office, Verulam Buildings, Grays Inn'. The Stokes Collection contains no correspondence between Roberts and Stokes around this date.

339 KELVIN to STOKES, 31 December 1877
Stokes Collection, K221

Mere Old Hall
Knutsford
Cheshire
Dec 31/77

DEAR STOKES

I hoped to have sent you by this despatch my reports of progress of Exp^{ts} on Effects of stress for magnetization,[1] and Tidal Investigation[2] carried on with assistance of Gov^t Fund but post hour has come before they are finished. I hope to finish them this evening and despatch them tomorrow which I trust will be regarded as 'reporting on or before the 31st'!

I was with Joule today who has got into a new house and is looking much better than I have seen him looking for many years. He has a much better place for his experiments than he had in his last house and seems to be setting to them with renewed vigour.

He told me that today was the last day for receiving applications for grants from Gov^t Fund, so I telegraphed two applications to the Secretaries R.S., Burlington House London (£100 for Tidal Investigation and £150 for Magnetization of Iron Nickel and Cobalt under varying stresses & at different temperatures.) I had not noticed the announcement that applications must be in by today & intended to make mine in January, after despatching my reports today. ⟨In⟩ With the reports which I despatch tomorrow I shall send statements of expenditure of the grants already received, and estimates for the continuations for which I am applying for assistance.

My wife joins in wishing you all a happy new year.

Yours very truly
WILLIAM THOMSON

1 See Kelvin (207.2), (231), and (231A).
2 See Thompson, II, 729–31, and, for example, Kelvin (249).

340   KELVIN to STOKES, 6 April 1878
      Royal Society of London, RR.8.110

The University
Glasgow, April 6 1878

Professor G. G. Stokes
DEAR STOKES,

I return Joule's paper entitled 'New Determination of the Mechanical Equivalent of Heat'.[1] I need scarcely say that it is in my opinion worthy of being printed in the Transactions. It will in fact be a contribution of great value and I am sure the Council will agree that the Royal Society is to be congratulated on having this second determination of the Mechanical Equivalent communicated to it and being the means of publishing it to the world.

I remain
Yours truly
WILLIAM THOMSON

P.S. I have written several remarks in pencil on the paper and drawings, chiefly asking for some slight additional explanations. They might be submitted to the author with the M.SS. before or after it is put into the printer's hands. I discussed the subject of the one on the last page (p 20) in Manchester shortly after Christmas with himself, and he assented that it would be better to ⟨exp⟩

⟨call⟩ take for the thermal unit the quantity of heat required to warm by 1° ⟨a pound⟩ the quantity of water which weighs 1 lb in vacuum, so he will no doubt be willing to make the suggested change in the paper.

1 J. P. Joule, 'New determination of the mechanical equivalent of heat', *Phil. Trans.* (1878), 365–83.

341 KELVIN to STOKES, 15 May 1878
Stokes Collection, K222

12 Grosvenor Gardens SW
May 15/78

DEAR STOKES

I shall, unless prevented by some unforeseen cause, send on Monday next to Mr White at the Royal Society, an abstract of my paper ⟨electrody⟩ ⟨on the Effects⟩ 'Electrodynamic Qualities of Metals Part [VII]. Effects of Stress on the Magnetization of Iron, Nickel, and Cobalt'.[1] It will include the instalment which was laid on the table at last meeting, and a continuation which is now being written out. The whole paper with curves and diagrams I hope not only to put into your hands tomorrow week but to leave in them, for reference.

Half a page or a page of abstract[2] I must write as soon as possible on the Harmonic Analyser and I hope to do this and send it to Mr White th[is][3] I am going away just now to sleep on board a yacht at Portsmouth and get an infinitesimal dose of sailing tomorrow so I ⟨am afraid I⟩ shall not be back in time for the R.S. meeting, but in any case I shall be here again by Frida[y].[4]

1 Kelvin (207.2).
2 Kelvin (227).
3 Kelvin's signature on the reverse has been clipped, thus removing much of what appears to be the word *this*, probably at least one more word, and possibly four or five more words.
4 The clipping of Kelvin's signature has also removed the *y* in *Friday*, which appears to be the last word in the letter.

342 KELVIN to STOKES, 15 June 1878
Stokes Collection, K223

Sharsted
Sittingbourne
Kent
June 15/78

DEAR STOKES

I had begun a report on Maxwell's paper[1] before I left Glasgow in the beginning of May, but stopped because I wanted to find out something on the subject referred to at the foot of p 7 of the report I now enclose. Then I was so over occupied in London that I could not touch it but kept it till I should see Maxwell in Cambridge. I think he will if you ask him add something to the paper making this matter clear. I was sorry not to be able to leave it with you at Cambridge with a report, and not to get it done at all before going to Paris ten days ago. We returned to England yesterday and I found your letter waiting my arrival here: so here is the paper and report, and I hope my delay will not retard its publication.

We go to Buckingham Palace Hotel, London SW on Monday, for two days, after which R.Y.S. Castle, Cowes will be the best general address for some time to come. We shall be living in the Lalla Rookh for the rest of the summer.

We hope to ⟨see⟩ meet you at the British Association in Dublin.

Yours very truly

WILLIAM THOMSON

1 J. C. Maxwell, 'On stresses in rarefied gases arising from inequalities of temperature', *Phil. Trans.* (1879), 231–56. Kelvin's referee's report is in the Royal Society, RR.8.123.

343 KELVIN to STOKES, [4 November 1878][1]
Stokes Collection, K224

The world will gain more by the earlier appearance of your book[2] than it will lose by the mistake. Perhaps indeed it will gain by the mistake and note correcting it. I saw the remarks of one referee, the first you allude to, but not those of the second. Could I see them both along with the proof of my paper,[3] which may go to press as it is without delay if you approve. Your letter rec^d just before we left our hotel in London this morning.

W.T. (Train to Glasgow Monday)

1 This is a post card addressed to Stokes and post marked Carlisle, 4 November 1878.
2 The first volume of Stokes's *MPP* was published in 1880.
3 Kelvin (207.2). Both reports are in the Royal Society: one by Maxwell, dated 3 June 1878 (RR.8.143), the other by George Carey Foster, dated 25 July 1878 (RR.8.144).

344 STOKES to KELVIN, 18 November 1878
Kelvin Collection, S407

Lensfield Cottage, Cambridge, 18 Nov. 1878.[1]

MY DEAR THOMSON,

I enclose the remarks of the second referee.[2] Please say whether they involve anything for which you would like to see the paper[3] before it goes to press.[4]

In the illustrations, there are a lot of figures of curves with numbers and dates. The numbers, dates, and places generally run on together, but there is one instance in which a figure is pasted lower down than corresponds to its number & date. I suppose I am safe in taking for granted that it was accidentally misplaces [sic] in the pasting.[5]

A few of my papers have gone to the press for reprinting.[6] I am thinking of introducing a slight innovation in notation. When a simple fraction or a differential coefficient is referred to in the midst of letter press, say a differential coefficient such as $\dfrac{dy}{dx}$, it certainly seems very unreasonable that the compositor should be called on to go through the troublesome process of 'justification' merely because the author wants to name the differential coefficient. Besides it breaks the uniformity of the lines of type, and spoils the look of the page. I am thinking of putting simply a slant line in the way that a halfpenny if [sic] frequently written and sometimes printed. Thus the diff. co. when occurring in letter press would be printed simply dy/dx, which could be set up as rapidly as letter press. So, when it occurred in the middle of letter press, I should write d^2s/dt^2 for $\dfrac{d^2s}{dt^2}$. The usual form would be retained in the equations, and sometimes in the case of an expression of special importance.[7]

I think the same simplification might be introduced with advantage in the case of complicated exponential expressions. Thus for

$$\frac{e^{\frac{n\pi x}{a}} - e^{-\frac{n\pi x}{a}}}{e^{\frac{n\pi x}{a}} + e^{-\frac{n\pi x}{a}}}$$

we might print

$$\frac{e^{n\pi x/a} - e^{-n\pi x/a}}{e^{n\pi x/a} + e^{-n\pi x/a}}$$

which involves very little disturbance with expressions with which the eye is familiar, while it introduces a very great saving in the time and expence [sic] of composition.[8] I am going to have some specimens of this in print, I mean of the former; and then if it looks well I should be emboldened to try it in the exponential expressions.

Yours sincerely,
G. G. STOKES

1 Kelvin has written at the top of the letter, 'Please direct two copies of Proofs to be sent me. W.T.'
2 Kelvin has written in the margin, 'Thanks I shall attend to them'.
3 Kelvin (207.2). See the previous letter, note 3.

4 Kelvin has written in the margin, 'No. They will be carefully attended to & taken advantage of when the proof comes'.
5 Kelvin has written in the margin, '*Yes*'.
6 Kelvin has underlined this sentence and written in the margin, 'very glad W.T.' Stokes's papers were reprinted in his *MPP*.
7 Kelvin has written in the margin, '[very glad. My father used to write fractions so but the first Cambridge man I ever experienced influence from told me they called 2/7 two and seven pence at Cambridge and so I ⟨got⟩ (stupidly) got laughed out of it! W.T.]' Kelvin's brackets.
8 Kelvin has written in the margin, '[highly approved. W.T.]' Kelvin's brackets.

345 KELVIN to STOKES, 20 January 1879[1]
Stokes Collection, K225

The University,
Glasgow.
Jan. 20th 1879

DEAR STOKES,

I was much obliged to you for your letter about the use of the *solidus* and proper use along with it of connecting links &c., all of which I shall try to observe correctly in the reprint of Thomson and Tait,[2] into which the *solidus* has already been introduced with excellent effect.

For about thirty-six years I have been trying to get a statement of the diurnal variations of the three magnetic elements at several places in the two hemispheres and have never succeeded. Surely this is to be had approximately from the records of our own and other magnetic observatories. I wish you could get the Meteorological Committee[3] to put together what is known or discoverable in this respect from available records of observations. A slight approximate instalment of what I ask would suffice to answer the question – Is the cause of the diurnal variation external or internal? Tolerably sufficient information as to changes in the direction of the horizontal component is given in many reports and books; but little or nothing for horizontal intensity or vertical force.

I hope Adams is now quite well and strong again. We were glad to hear from Mrs Stokes, about Christmas time, that he was in a fair way to be so. I hope when he is able to enjoy work again that he will go on with the harmonic analysis of the terrestrial surface magnetic potential. Do you know if he has already made any progress with this?

Yours very truly
WILLIAM THOMSON

P.S. A page or two of tables of numbers or a few diagrams of curves (graphic representations) would give more information than hundreds of pages of reports and statements through which one may wade without finding a grain of definite and accurate information regarding the annual and the solar and lunar diurnal variations of terrestrial magnetism. All the diurnal variations should be harmonically analysed. The curves hitherto published of them, prove them to have two largely influential harmonic terms of twenty four hours and of twelve hours period respectively.

1 The letter is in Andrew Gray's hand, and LB1.34 in the Kelvin Collection appears to be shorthand dictation in preparation for this letter.
2 Kelvin and Tait, *TNP*.
3 Actually, the Meteorological Committee of the Royal Society had been replaced two years previously, in 1877, by the Meteorological Council. Stokes was a member of the Council, resigning in 1887. (See Stokes's *Memoir*, I, 182–3, and II, 229, and *The Record of the Royal Society of London for the Promotion of Natural Knowledge*, 4th edn (London and Edinburgh, 1940), 199–200.)

346 KELVIN to STOKES, 11 April 1879
Stokes Collection, K226

The University,[1]
Glasgow.
April 11/79

DEAR STOKES

See enclosed letter. The writer wished to copy it out ⟨again⟩ but I said it would do and I would send it to you. The paper will follow if it does not come to you along with this. He has just been with me and has taken it with him to add a photograph.

The pencillings on the letter are his own, not of my suggestion! The correction on the envelope is mine!!

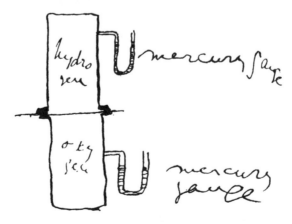

Fawsitt is an embryo discoverer.[2] He seems to be always thinking and experimenting. I have just been encouraging him to go on with an experiment he tells me he has made proving or seeming to tend to prove that at ordinary temperatures occlusion of hydrogen and oxygen causes them to meet and combine in thin platinum foil. In a fortnight the mercury had sunk an inch in the gauge connected with the hydrogen and half an inch in the other. Should I encourage him to apply for assistance from R.S. fund or Gov^t Grant, to allow him to probe into this or other investigations more effectively than his means (which are no doubt limited) allow him?

Yours very truly
WILLIAM THOMSON

1 Stokes has typed at the top of the letter, 'Ansd. 14 April 1879'.
2 Charles A. Fawsitt of Ibrox, Glasgow, was an amateur experimenter who apparently sought Kelvin's opinion whenever he found something of interest. His short note, 'Strange properties of matter', *Nature*, **19** (5 December 1878), 98, reported the results of two experiments which he had shown to Kelvin who had suggested explanations of them. So far as I know, Fawsitt's research which Kelvin and Stokes discussed was not published.

347 STOKES to KELVIN, 14 April 1879[1]
Kelvin Collection, S408

Lensfield Cottage, Cambridge, 14 April 1879.

MY DEAR THOMSON,

I had some conversation with Spottiswoode about your application to the Royal Society ⟨relative to the machine you contemplate for the solution of simultaneous differ simple equations. He had it seemed heard remarks from mote [*sic*] more than o?e [*sic*]⟩[2] [fo]r a grant for your machine for the mechanical solution of simul[ta]neous simple equations.[3] It seems that Spottiswoode had heard [f]rom more than one remarks as to the number of grants made to [yo]u, who are not in the same condition as many others as to [de]pendence upon these grants for carrying on the investigations you have in your mind.[4] Of course it is not as if we had the disposal of funds limited only by the possibility of expending them with real advantage.

Having mentioned this, Spottiswoode left it entirely to me whether to bring forward your application to the council. There is it seems a balance in the donation fund just about sufficient to meet it.

Under the circumstances, though you had asked me to bring forward the ap[p]lication, ⟨to the council,⟩ I did not like to take the responsibility of doing so without consulting you, more especially as if you still wished to bring it forward my writing to ascertain your wishes would only interpose a month's delay. I did not at all know what your feeling about it might be. On the one hand you might not at all wish to bring forward the application if any such feeling were entertained; on the other you might feel strongly that no consideration should be entertained of a man's personal circumstances, or of other grants which he may have had; that nothing in fact should be looked to but the probable yield of the grant in results of value to science.

I took it upon myself to postpone the bringing forward of the application till I should have had an opportunity of communicationg [*sic*] with you. I should be glad to know, after what I have told you, whether you are still of the same mind.

– A few lines on an other subject –

Yours sincerely,
G. G. STOKES.

1 This is Stokes's copy of his letter to Kelvin.
2 This deletion is in pencil and was probably made by Larmor.
3 See Kelvin (232).
4 The five previous additions in brackets result from the edge of the letter being torn away.

348 STOKES to KELVIN, 17 April 1879
Kelvin Collection, S409

Lensfield Cottage, Cambridge, 17 April 1879.

MY DEAR THOMSON,

I have read over Fawsitt's paper.[1] It gives me the idea of an earnest but quite young worker, who was not yet well acquainted with what others had done. He is I should say most deserving of encouragement, but I have some doubts whether the paper is suitable for publication by the Royal Society. It may be, and I think is very likely to be the case, that those who have worked much with alloys are familiar with a good many of the facts mentioned by Fawsitt. I am not in that condition myself, and therefore cannot judge. It strikes me that the paper, meritorious though it be, has a little too much the character of a set of laboratory notes, and contains too little of principle or methodised conclusions to be suitable for the Royal Society. But as I said I am not a competent judge. I would suggest taking the opinion of some ⟨s⟩ chemist who has worked with alloys, say Roberts of the mint.[2] It may be that the facts are sufficiently novel to make it desirable that the paper should be published.

As one instance of what is new to the author not being new to the world, I may mention what he says of the use of sodium in promoting the amalgamation of metals. It happens that Dr. Robinson mentioned to me that in the manufacture of the so-called galvanised iron it was found that the addition of a little sodium to the zinc enabled the coating readily to take place.

I shall not send the paper on to Mr. White till I hear from you. I do not know whether you know Roberts personally, or whether you could suggest some better man. Dr. Percy[3] would be an admirable man, but it is difficult to get him to express an opinion. What do you think of the suggestion of asking some chemist who has worked much with metals to look over the paper?

I am coming now to a part of my reprint when I must decide whether or no to reprint the notes on hydrodynamics whic[h] appeared in the Mathematical Journal.[4] They did not profess to contain original matter. I doubt if they are worth reprinting.

Yours sincerely,
G. G. STOKES

P.S. If Fawsitt's apparent discovery of the amalgamation of hydrogen with platinum at ordinary temperatures be confirmed, that would be a very different matter.

1 See letter 346, note 2.
2 William Chandler Roberts-Austen (1843–1902), who acquired his additional surname in 1885, studied at the Royal School of Mines and became a private assistant to Thomas Graham, master of the mint. When Graham died in 1869, Roberts-Austen received an official post at the mint, and, when Percy resigned his professorship at the Royal School of Mines in 1879, Roberts-Austen replaced him, still retaining his position at the mint.
3 John Percy (1817–89) was lecturer and then professor at the Royal School of Mines from 1851 to 1879 and wrote *A Treatise on Metallurgy*, 4 vols. (London, 1864–80).
4 Stokes (16), (19), and (28), reprinted in Stokes's *MPP*, II, 1–7, 36–50, and 221–42, respectively.

349 KELVIN to STOKES, 19 April 1879
Stokes Collection, K227

The University,
Glasgow.
April 19th 1879

DEAR STOKES,

I shall be very glad if the opinion of Roberts be taken before Fanssit's [i.e., Fawsitt's] paper is communicated to the Royal Society. Will you send it to him direct? or, if you prefer it, send it back to me and I will forward it to him. The phenomena described were new to me but I think it very possible they may not be new to Roberts and it is desirable at all events to make sure that they have not hitherto been published. Did you notice Fanssit's little communication to Nature about cohesion between solids at different temperatures? The phenomena were new to me and I recommended him to send a short account of them to Nature.[1]

Yours truly
WILLIAM THOMSON

Prof. G. G. Stokes

1 See letter 346, note 2.

May 4, 1879[1]
The University,
Glasgow.

DEAR STOKES

Thanks for your letter announcing the grant for my equation-solver. Will you thank the council also for me. It will be a great lift to help me to finish the machine.

Can you tell me anything of 'optical contact', particularly as to the forces required to produce it. I remember of course your experiment on this in relation to metallic reflection. I have been looking a little into Newton's rings in this respect. Don't you think particles of dust or shreds, account for the shortest distance being in any case greater than the small fraction of the quarter wave length indicated by central blackness? However small the force pressing the two together surely they will *touch* (or come nearer together than 1/300000 of an inch) unless kept asunder by particles of dust or shreds.[2] I was startled by Maxwell's Royal Institution lecture[3] on action at a distance, and I think I spoke to you about it at Cambridge last October year. But the more I have though[t] of it the more I am convinced that dust is the explanation.

Would not this be a good way of observing

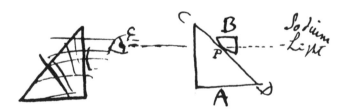

A, B two right angled prisms B (which might be as large as A) convex; ⟨as is⟩ (the prism of a prism compass would do).

A bright sodium light in the position shown might be studied by an eye at E, while B is gradually brought into optical contact, or carried away from optical contact through a fraction of a wave length, by aid of a micrometer screw. When the distance is less than (? how much? ? 1/160000 of an inch?) the light would be seen as if through a fine hole. This we are more or less familiar with in rough experiments, but has any one done it deliberately with a screw, and do you think anything which we cannot learn from theory (with the exponential function for disturbance outside a ⟨to⟩ transparent solid in the case of total internal reflection is to be learned by experimenting? Instead of a micrometer screw I mean to try with the weight of D partially supported by a thread, the surface CD being made horizontal for this purpose. Has the area of optical contact been measured in any case, in relation to the mutual force? This is interesting ⟨in relation⟩ as an illustration of equilibrium of elastic solids;[4] but I suppose we could find by a theoretical solution as much as by experiment.

I have sent Roberts' report ⟨from⟩ to Fansitt [i.e., Fawsitt] but not heard from him yet. I am sure he will be obliged to you for taking so much trouble to get his paper[5] into a fit state for the R.S.

Yours very truly
WILLIAM THOMSON

1 Stokes has typed at the top of the letter, 'Ansd. 7 May 1879'.
2 Kelvin made this point in his (262) in 1883.
3 J. C. Maxwell, 'On action at a distance', *Proc. Roy. Inst.*, 7 (1873), 44–54.
4 A line in pencil has been drawn, probably by Larmor, down the left margin, marking the passage, 'as an illustration of equilibrium of elastic solids'.
5 See letter 346, note 2.

351 KELVIN to STOKES, [4 May 1879][1]
Stokes Collection, K229

Is the dynamics of reflection and refraction of distortional waves at a surface of separation of two homogeneous incompressible solids united so as to allow no *slip*, worked out completely? It is of course very easy, and it must ⟨include⟩ lead to definite formulas for the intensity and phase of reflected and refracted rays in cases of vibration in, and perpend[r] to the plane of incidence. Two suppositions to be considered (1) the two mediums of same density, but different rigidities; (2) different densities, but same rigidity. The complete working out would give the resu[l]t for any relations of density & rigidity. Has this been done.

1 This is a post card in Kelvin's hand addressed to Stokes and post marked Glasgow, 4 May 1879. Stokes has typed on the front of the card, 'Ansd. 7 May 1879'.

352 STOKES to KELVIN, 7 May 1879
Kelvin Collection, S410

Lensfield Cottage, Cambridge, 7 May, 1879.

MY DEAR THOMSON,

First as to your question about reflection. I presume you mean to confine the investigation to plane waves reflected at a plane surface. I suppose too, but of this I am not sure, that you refer to isotropic media.

The problem for this has been virtually solved by Green, ⟨Camb.⟩ Camb. Phil. Trans. vol. 7, p. 1, reprinted at p. 245 of his works.[1] The relation he supposes between the constants would not affect the difficulty of the work.

The work might be shortened by employing an artifice much used by Cauchy, namely representing the disturbance by an exponential with an imaginary index instead of ⟨an expone⟩ a circular function. In this way the number of arbitrary constants to be determined is just halved, and on arriving at the end it is easy to preserve only the real parts of our expressions, and so represent the formulae in the more usual shape.

In this way for the case of vibrations in the plane of refraction we should have just 4 arbitrary constants to determine by 4 linear equations. In the case of vibrations ⟨in⟩ ⊥ to the plane of incidence we should have 2 unknown constants to determine by 2 simple equations. So for an isotropic medium the work is not heavy. I think I worked out the thing a long time ago, but I don't know whether the papers still exist.

The problem I had in my mind is that of two isotropic elastic solids each with its two constants; including therefore as a particular case that in which the two media are incompressible. This is the case specially considered by Green.

Cauchy in some of his later papers made a mess about this in relation to light by introducing his alleged 'principle of continuity', the 'pretended principle of continuity' as MacCullagh justly designated it.[2] This casual expression of MacCullagh's occurring incidentally in a controversial article, and not showing the reasons why he so designated the principle, seems to have attracted little attention, and several writers have used the principle as if they had no idea of its hollowness. I had sometimes thought of writing a short paper about it. One does not like to be needlessly bellicose, but when an error seems to have gained currency it should be noticed.

As to the Newton's rings,[3] as long as one only observes them when the curvature of the lens is sufficient, that is sufficiently small, to show them on a good scale, the hypothesis that it is only dust &c. that keeps the glasses from coming into contact seems vary [sic] plausible. But when the cirvature [sic] is so great that the rings are so small that you require a lens to see them, and find this apparent repulsion a constant phenomenon; that pressure is uniformly required to develop the black spot, or all but a trace of it; that it disappears when the pressure is removed; and when we consider the extreme smallness of the patch of glass where the glasses are nearly in contact, and the extreme improbability that in spite of cleaning dust should always be present in the variety of little patches tried; when I say all this is watched and considered, I think the conviction grows upon one that the repulsive force is a reality, whatever may be the cause of it.

Yours sincerely,
G. G. Stokes

P.S. The time is approaching when I must make up my mind finally whether or no to include the 'Notes on Hydrodynamics' which I wrote in the Math. Journal in my reprint or not.[4]

1 G. Green, 'On the laws of reflexion and refraction of light at the common surface of two non-crystallized media', *Trans. Camb. Phil. Soc.*, 7 (1842), 1–24 and 113–20, reprinted in *Mathematical Papers of the Late George Green*, ed. N. M. Ferrers (London, 1871), 245–69.
2 I have not found this particular criticism of Cauchy by MacCullagh. However, for a paper highly critical of Cauchy, see MacCullagh's 'Notes on some points in the theory of light', in *The Collected Works of James MacCullagh, LL.D., Fellow of Trinity College and Professor of Natural Philosophy in the University of Dublin*, eds. John H. Jellet and Samuel Haughton (Dublin and London, 1880), 194–217. MacCullagh (1809–47) graduated from Trinity College, Dublin, and became professor of mathematics in the university in 1833 and of natural philosophy in 1842.
3 Kelvin has drawn a line down the left side of this entire paragraph and written in the margin, '[Important and interesting. K. Nov 30, 1903]'. Kelvin's brackets.
4 Stokes (16), (19), and (28), reprinted in Stokes's *MPP*, II, 1–7, 36–50, and 221–42, respectively.

353 KELVIN to STOKES, [8 May 1879][1]
Stokes Collection, K230

Many thanks for your letter. Do please *instantly* write out and publish the whole affair of reflection and refraction of waves of distortion at the separating surface of two isotropic homogeneous incompressible elastic solids. It is curious that so straight forward a thing should have been bemuddled by Cauchy. In public interests you should refer to this because no doubt the confusion still lives, banefully. If things are as you say are they so, certainly?) in [*sic*] respect to Newton's rings the repulsion must be investigated.

1 This is a post card in Kelvin's hand addressed to Stokes and post marked Glasgow, 8 May 1879. Kelvin has written near the top of the card, 'Address till Monday, Northfield Largs, by Greenock'.

354 STOKES to KELVIN, 9 May 1879
Kelvin Collection, S411

Lensfield Cottage, Cambridge, 9 M£y [*sic*] 1879

MY DEAR THOMSON,

It is not to be supposed that Cauchy went wrong in the problem of determining reflection at the common surface of two elastic media where the transition from one medium to the other is very rapid, so that it may be treated as abrupt. In his later papers he seems to have abandoned the idea of attempting to explain the phenomena of light by regarding the ether in bodies as a single elastic medium, and to have taken to the supposition of two mutually interpenetrating media. He does not appear however to have made anything out of it worth mentioning. It was in attempting to evade the difficulties of this problem that he threw out the 'principle of continuity', a wholly fallacious principle as I deem it.

As to writing a paper on reflection at the common surface of two isotropic media where there is no slip, the whole thing is virtually contained in Green's paper,[1] though the work might be shortened by employing Cauchy's artifice. Before writing it I should have to look up the literature of the subject, and see that the thing has not been done explicitly already, which is likely enough. At present I am engaged with a daily lecture.

It is however, I take it, of more importance to point out explicitly the fallacy of the so-called 'principle of continuity'. It appears to be pretty generally current, as if there were no doubt about it.

Yours sincerely,
G. G. STOKES

1 See letter 352, note 1.

355 KELVIN to STOKES, 20 May 1879
Stokes Collection, K231

The University,
Glasgow.
May 20th 1879

DEAR STOKES,

Darwin's papers[1] will be returned to you by himself. I am sorry to have kept them so long but I really did not lose a single day in attacking them and with the exception of Osborne Reynolds' paper[2] only allowed matters that I had undertaken years before to delay me from doing so. I hope you will explain to the Council that my keeping the paper so long was not through any neglect on my part and that I regret very much the necessity for it.

I forgot when I wrote to you last about your notes on Hydrodynamics.[3] I hope you will not on any account omit them from your reprint. They supply what is very much wanted and what is not to be found anywhere else by learners in the subject and to a vast proportion of your readers will I am sure be most valuable.

I am going to London tomorrow and hope to be at the Royal Society on Thursday night and to meet you but cannot say for certain.

Yours very truly
W THOMSON

1 G. H. Darwin, 'On the precession of a viscous spheroid, and on the remote history of the Earth', *Phil. Trans.* (1879), 447–538, and 'Problems connected with the tides of a viscous spheroid', *ibid.* (1879), 539–93. Kelvin's report on Darwin's papers is in the Royal Society, RR.8.153, dated 13 May 1879.

2 O. Reynolds, 'On certain dimensional properties of matter in the gaseous state. Part I. Experimental researches on thermal transpiration of gases through porous plates and on the laws of transpiration and impulsion, including an experimental proof that gas is not a continuous plenum. Part II. On an extension of the dynamical theory of gas, which includes the stresses, tangential and normal, caused by a varying condition of gas, and affords an explanation of the phenomena of transpiration and impulsion', *Phil. Trans.* (1879), 727–845. Osborne Reynolds (1842–1912) was seventh wrangler in 1867 and professor of engineering at Owens College, Manchester, from 1868 to 1905. The Royal Society contains four referee's reports by Kelvin on Reynolds's paper: RR.8.189, dated 13 May 1879, and letters 357, 367, and 368, reproduced below.

3 Stokes (16), (19), and (28), reprinted in Stokes's *MPP*, II, 1–7, 36–50, and 221–42, respectively.

356 STOKES to KELVIN, 5 June 1879
Kelvin Collection, S412

Lensfield Cottage, Cambridge, 5 June, 1879.

MY DEAR THOMSON,

When I was at the R.S. one day Mr. White asked me if there was any objection to change the title of Mr. Roberts's paper[1] in a manner which he showed me, saying you wished the title changed in that way. I could not see what the object of the change was; it seemed to me a very mild and unobjectionable one. I said I did not see that there was any objection to the change. I was utterly surprised by hearing from Mr. White that Mr. Roberts strongly objected to the change; that he considered that it was *his* machine. It had never entered my head to suppose that any one regarded it as other than your machine. I do not know whether Mr. Roberts's abstract is in type. I have asked Mr. White if it be to let me have a copy. It is possible that it may be made all right in the body of the paper, though if Mr. White has not over-stated Mr. Roberts's views I fear it is hardly likely. Mr. White would certainly not *knowingly* make an over statement; but it is possible that his statement of Mr. Roberts's views is partly derived from his own interpretation of them.

If Mr. Roberts would not like his paper to appear with the changed title, *a fortiori*, I should suppose, he would not like it to appear with the ⟨title⟩ note added that you have sent me,[2] unless he were allowed to add another of his own, and then it becomes a matter of controversy, which we try to avoid as far as possible in the Proceedings.

I am going to London on Monday morning, and I will try and call at the R. S. so as to have a talk with Mr. White on the matter. I hope Mr. Roberts may be induced to make a satisfactory acknowledgement in the body of the abstract, and then it would not signify about the title of the paper.

If Mr. Roberts is so tenacious of the modifications of detail – I do not know what they may have been – which he has introduced, he can I presume state them in the abstract, acknowledging the foundation on which he worked; and then the reader would be in a condition to judge for himself to whom the machine should be attributed; and if Mr. Roberts should have one opinion on the subject and the reader another, that would not signify. However I may get some further light on the subject at the R. S.

Yours sincerely,
G. G. STOKES

1 E. Roberts, 'Preliminary note on a new tide-predictor', *Proc. Roy. Soc.*, **29** (1879), 198–201.
2 The published paper contains no note by Kelvin, but Roberts, after describing a machine he said he had designed, concluded with the statement: 'To Sir William Thomson the author's thanks are due for the improved parallel slide and other details, and also to Mr. Légé (the maker of the instrument) for the design of the wheel-gearing'.

357   KELVIN to STOKES, 6 June 1879[1]
      Royal Society of London, RR.8.190

DEAR STOKES

Use my report[2] as you please. Any part of it, or the whole if you please, may be shown to Prof Reynolds. I think he will understand that I mean nothing offensive or derogatory in any respect and am as anxious for his own credit as for any one's else when I say he ought to refer very explicitly to Clausius, Maxwell, Loschmidt, Tait & Dewar, and Stoney as to *fact of dimensions* even if his (Stoney's) particular mode of using the *dimensional* idea in explaining the radiometer be not admitted as correct.[3]

Yours truly
W. THOMSON

Cambridge June 6/79[4]

1 This letter begins at the bottom of and continues on the reverse of a letter from Stokes to Maxwell, dated 3 June 1879. The letter reads:

Lensfield Cottage, 3 June, 1879.

My dear Maxwell,

As to Reynold's paper, the committee of papers have passed a resolution to print the first – the experimental – part in the Trans. subject to the author's consent, leaving the question of the second part, which in any case would seem to require a good deal of alteration, yet to be decided about.

I have not yey [*sic*] written to him, as the[r]e were several suggestions made by the referees, and I am not quite sure of what I had best propose to him. Thomson is quite willing that you shoul should [*sic*] see his report, and I have already had your leave for him to see yours. He is coming however today to

Cambridge and perhaps you could confer with him, and advise me as to a as to the [*sic*] recommendations I should forward on to him. Perhaps I had best send all. I could easily alter them into my own language.

I have been writing against time, and so I suppose I have made a good many mistakes.

Yours sincerely,
G. G. Stokes

2 See letter 355, note 2, for Kelvin's report and Reynolds's paper.

3 Of the works by the men mentioned here, Reynolds's paper cites only three papers by Maxwell: 'On the viscosity or internal friction of air and other gases', *Phil. Trans.* (1866), 249–68; 'On the dynamical theory of gases', *ibid.* (1867), 49–88; and 'On stresses in rarefied gases arising from inequalities of temperature', *ibid.* (1879), 231–56. Relevant papers by the others include: R. Clausius, 'Ueber den Satz vom mittleren Ergal und seine Anwendung auf die Molecularbewegungen der Gase', *Sitzungsberichte der Niederrheinischen Gesellschaft für Natur- und Heilkunde zu Bonn* (1874), 183–231, and *Phil. Mag.*, **50** (1875), 26–46; J. J. Loschmidt, 'Experimental-Untersuchungen über die Diffusion von Gasen ohne poröse Scheidewände', *Sitzungsberichte der Mathematisch-Naturwissenschaftlichen Classe der kaiserlichen Akademie der Wissenschaften*, **61**, Abth. 2 (1870), 367–80, and **62**, Abth. 2 (1870), 468–78; P. G. Tait and J. Dewar, 'On a new method of obtaining very perfect vacua', *Proc. Roy. Soc. Edinb.*, **8** (1875), 348–9, and 'Farther researches in very perfect vacua', *ibid.*, **8** (1875), 628; and G. J. Stoney, 'On Crookes's radiometer', *Phil. Mag.*, **1** (1876), 177–81 and 305–13, and 'On the nature of what is commonly termed a "vacuum"', *Phil. Mag.*, **4** (1877), 222–3. Johann Joseph Loschmidt (1821–95) turned to a career in science after business failures, holding posts in Vienna from 1856 and becoming associate professor of physical chemistry at the University of Vienna in 1868. Reynolds's paper did cite four papers by T. Graham, for which see letter 367, note 4.

4 Below Kelvin's letter, Stokes has written, 'Stokes to Maxwell 3 June '79 also Thomson to Stokes 6 June '79'.

358   KELVIN to STOKES, 10 June 1879
Stokes Collection, K232

12 Grosvenor Gardens
London SW
June 10, 1879

DEAR STOKES

I only received your note of the 6th yesterday evening on arriving in London from Tunbridge Wells where we had been after Cambridge.

The model analyser was not arranged to give round numbers for any particular scale of curves. The cylinders and cranks were I think as nearly as may be equal, and therefore the scale which would give round numbers with one ⟨curve⟩ cylinder would give round numbers with the others also. I intended to estimate the values of the cylinder readings by theory from measurements of the ⟨radii of the⟩ ranges of the slides, and the diameters of the cylinders, and to verify them by analysing carefully drawn simple harmonic curves: also broken lines such as

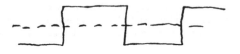

and

and comparing the results with the Fourier-analysis. I mean to do this way with the large tidal harmonic-analyser which is now finished in Glasgow except a counter for days and years which I mean to add to it.

I enclose correspondence[1] (which you may put in the fire if you have at hand this season, after glancing at them). They relate to an offered communication 'On a Tide-predicting machine constructed for the Indian Government by Messrs Légé & Co. By E. Roberts Esq. of the Nautical Almanac Office. Communicated by Sir W. Thomson.'[2] Will you accept it as a communication for Proceedings, for the meeting of the 19th and let me have a line to say if as much as $\frac{1}{4}$ h[our] or 20 m[inutes] at most will be allowed for it. It will be a written paper, and might be read within the time by Roberts himself if you please. The machine itself would be exhibited and curves drawn by it (which come out splendidly) would be shown as proposed by Roberts. I would be there but I suppose there will be no time for discussion. I think people would see the machine with interest, and the curves too.

Will the above title do? If you do not approve of it, alter it please, ⟨as⟩ to what you think proper.

Will you also take the following title

Preliminary Report of Experiments on the Effects of long-continued stress on the Elasticity of Metals. By J. T. Bottomley ⟨communi⟩ MA, F.R.S.E., communicated by Sir W.T.[3]

for ⟨a⟩ a communication for the Proceedings, for 19th. I have it in writing from Madeira where Bottomley posted it ten days ago from a ship in which he was going to the Cape and I am only keeping it to read through it before I send it to you.

Yours truly
W THOMSON

Bottomley's paper may be merely laid on the table if time does not suffice to read it. It is not very long.
P.S. I am writing to Roberts asking him to send his paper direct to you.

1 See E. Roberts to Kelvin, 7 June 1879, and W. White to E. Roberts, 6 June 1879, both in the Stokes Collection, RS1417 and RS1417a, respectively. Also, of the several letters from Roberts to Kelvin in the Kelvin Collection, six date between January and May 1879.

2 See letter 356, note 1, for Roberts's paper, which was listed as 'communicated' by Stokes.

3 J. T. Bottomley, 'Preliminary experiments on the effects of long-continued stress on the elasticity of metals', *Proc. Roy. Soc.*, **29** (1879), 221–6. James Thomson Bottomley (1845–1926), who became a fellow of the Royal Society in 1888, was Kelvin's nephew and long-time assistant.

359   KELVIN to STOKES, 14 June 1879
Stokes Collection, K233

June 14/79
12 Grosvenor Gardens
S.W.

DEAR STOKES

I enclose J. T. Bottomley's paper.[1] (Elasticity of Metals) I think it may be for the Proceedings, with the prospect of sending a more detailed account, (with drawings of apparatus) of the exp[ts] already made and those in prospect, and with some (still preliminary!) results on the secular wires, for the Transactions next session.[2]

Excuse the roughness of the present paper in consideration that it was written on board ship in order to be in time for communication this session.

I think a note should be added to Bottomley's previous paper[3] (thermal conductivity of Water) to say that the question of how much the results can be influenced by convection in the liquid will be the subject of future exp[t]. As soon as he gets back from the Cape, Bottomley intends to commence exp[ts] on this matter. Your suggestion of a screen will I think be the easiest to carry out. I should think a complete cylinder of thin canvas or other cloth, on a slight wooden cage-frame, would settle the question very satisfactorily.

Yours
W THOMSON

1 See the previous letter, note 3.

2 Bottomley did not publish such a paper.

3 Bottomley, 'On the thermal conductivity of water', *Proc. Roy. Soc.*, **28** (1879), 462–3, and **31** (1881), 300, are abstracts of the full paper in *Phil. Trans.* (1881), 537–45, which contains a note added in December 1880 concerning possible errors due to convection.

360 KELVIN to STOKES, 4 July 1879[1]
Collection of Francis Bottomley

4 July 1879

DEAR STOKES

Roberts desires to have his paper withdrawn from the Proceedings rather than allow it to appear with a corrected title which I sent to him and to Mr White last week.[2] As he objects to the change of title it may if you think proper appear as it is, but if so, as it is communicated by me, please let the accompanying note be added to it.[3]

I enclose Légé's final account for the first instrument completed for practical work (the one now in South Kensington) the heading of which is a curious comment on Roberts' objection to my correction of the title of his paper.

Yours truly
(Signed) WILLIAM THOMSON

1 This is a copy of Kelvin's letter in his wife's hand.
2 See letter 356, notes 1 and 2.
3 The 'accompanying note' (also in Lady Kelvin's hand) reads:

Note on Mr Roberts' paper
by Sir William Thomson.

July 4. 1879

After the reading of Mr Roberts' paper I requested him to alter the title to the following: 'Preliminary Description of Sir William Thomson's Tide Predicter constructed for the Indian Government' By E. Roberts &^c &^c communicated by Sir William Thomson.

It seemed to me that Mr Roberts' paper without an amended title, or title without amendment of the paper, might give a false impression regarding the origin of the instrument described, and I was surprised when he objected to the change of title which I proposed.

(sgd.) W.T.

361 KELVIN to STOKES, 9 July 1879[1]
Collection of Francis Bottomley

Largs, by Greenock,
July 9/79

DEAR STOKES,

Your letter came to me here yesterday. Do as you think best about Roberts' paper.[2] It is enough that it is on record that I asked him to change the title and he refused.

However I think you should know from me directly about the origin of the tide-predicter.

I had long wished to make a machine to utilize the results of the harmonic analysis without the great labour of calculating ⟨of⟩ on which I had an experiment made by Roberts for the 1872 Report[3] and which, even with his

452

great skill, proved to be even more serious than I had anticipated. On returning from Gibraltar in my yacht at the beginning of August 1872 I asked Roberts to come and stay with me onboard at Cowes for a few days to finish the Report and while he was with me I talked a great deal about my plans no doubt with him and Mr Tower (a friend of Mr Froude's who had been with me to Gibraltar for his health and who was still with me onboard.) When Roberts left ⟨me⟩ us ⟨and I left along with Tower for Brighton⟩ no workable plan for combining the constituent tides had occurred, and ⟨the⟩ on my journey, with Tower alone, to Brighton, I was at work the whole way in the train from Portsmouth on plans like those of Preece and Stroh[4] and speaking of them to Tower, when he said why don't you use a chain and pulleys as in Wheatstone's ⟨letter showing instr⟩ ABC telegraph instrument. I had known this arrangement but when Tower explained it to me I jumped at it and instantly knew it was the very thing for me. Before I left the train my plan was complete, as realized in the ⟨S.K.⟩ machine now in S.K. I wrote this to Roberts some time after that, and before the end of August ⟨'He (Tower) suggested also a plan with pu [?]⟩ as ⟨coming from⟩ derived from a suggestion I had had from Tower, and I told him that I had instructed White to commence a partial model for trial. This model, in wood, was ⟨merely wooden⟩ made I believe before my arrival in Glasgow. It was ⟨wooden [?]⟩ merely to serve for planning the positions of cranks and counter points; ⟨and hollow [?]⟩ When I was on the point of ⟨putting it into⟩ setting White on to make a working machine in brass I had occasion to come to London ⟨on the occasion⟩ and finding Roberts exceedingly anxious to get the work for Légé I let him do so, and gave very particular instructions to have the pulleys centred directly on the cranks. ⟨I was and the plane of⟩ and I was much displeased afterwards, on coming to London again, sometime in the spring of 1873 I believe, to find ⟨an utterly unw⟩ ⟨grievously⟩ an intolerably frictional arrangement of slides ⟨with⟩ in a horizontal plane, made instead of what I had ordered. I felt that what they had done was a grievous waste of time and of money, and I directed the whole thing to be changed ⟨back to my original⟩ so as to be in accordance with my first instructions to them. ⟨I was exceedingly sorry I had not car [?]⟩ A great [end of draft]

1 This letter is in Kelvin's hand, and he has written at the top of it: 'd[ra]ft commenced, but not finished. Shorter letter (of w^h copy by F. kept) is actually sent today'. The next letter is the copy.
2 See letter 356, notes 1 and 2.
3 'Report of the committee appointed for the purpose of promoting the extension, improvement, and harmonic analysis of tidal observations', *Brit. Assoc. Rep.* (1872), 355–95. The report was 'drawn up by Mr. E. Roberts, under the direction of the Committee'.
4 See W. H. Preece and Augustus Stroh, 'Studies in acoustics. I. On the synthetic examination of vowel sounds', *Proc. Roy. Soc.*, 28 (1879), 358–67.

Largs, by Greenock
July9/79

DEAR STOKES,

Your letter came to me here yesterday. Do as you think best about Roberts' paper.[2] It is enough that it is on record that I asked him to change the title and that he refused.

My great difficulty with him & Légé has been to have my own ideas carried out, and I have often regretted very much that I did not have the whole work done by White in Glasgow. With his genius to help, the details would have been much more satisfactorily carried out and I should have had *infinitely* less trouble.

I have never had a suggestion from any human being that has helped me except one very important one from a Mr Tower, a friend of Froude's, who had been with me to Gibraltar and back in my yacht for his health. He made it to me in the train from Portsmouth to Brighton on our way to attend the B.A. when I was hard at work on plans like those of Preece and Stroh[3] for combining simple harmonic motions. It was to take a chain and pulley as in Wheatstone's A.B.C. telegraph instrument. I had never known the insides of this instrument, but when Tower explained it to me, I jumped at it and said, 'That is the very thing for me.' All the rest followed, as you will see, with ease from that.

Roberts has been most excellent and useful in all the tidal calculations, and I left wholly to him the determination of the numbers of teeth fo[r] the periods ⟨of⟩ in the machine and to him & Légé the planning of the shafts to bring the motions to the cranks in the positions in which I placed them; but every other detail I fought out *against them* in each case in which it was novel. They did their best but their dynamical intelligence was not superior to that of ordinary instrument makers, and, on that account, not from any wish on their part to obstruct me, & because they were 400 miles from my home, I had infinitely more trouble and a less satisfactory result than I should have had with White.

Yours very truly,
(signed) WILLIAM THOMSON

P.S. I enclose an old letter which is a fair specimen of the kind of assistance I had from Roberts in respect to the machine. Address University Glasgow.

1 This letter is in Lady Kelvin's hand and is the copy referred to in the previous letter, note 1.
2 See letter 356, notes 1 and 2.
3 See the previous letter, note 4.

363 KELVIN to STOKES, 11 July 1879
Stokes Collection, K234

July ⟨12⟩ 11, 1879
The University,
Glasgow.

DEAR STOKES

I have received this evening a second letter from you of date 10th, and had previously answered the former of same date which came this morning.

I hope to write an account of the Tide-predicter for communication to the R.S. in time for its first meeting of next session.[1] I shall probably send with it the original model disinterred today from [James] White's, which will serve to illustrate the principle, not carried into effect in the S. Kensington machine, of counterpoising the forces on the cranks. It is possible also that I may send a new working instrument which I am thinking of making for my own use, both for tide-predictions and (with an easy change of wheels) for illustrations of Fourier-series in solutions of conductivity and cable problems, and vowel sounds. I have been setting White on to it today and with his assistance I hope to have at moderate expense a more useful instrument than either of those hitherto made. I don't see why (now that the horizontal quick motions of the ink bottle to mark the hours are done away with, which limited the speed of the S. Kensington machine) more than 2 seconds need be given to the 12 h[ours] (calculate centrifugal force with $\omega = \pi$). At this rate a year's curve will be run off in 24 min.

Yours truly
WILLIAM THOMSON

1 Kelvin did not do so, but see his (249) and (249A), both published in 1881.

364 STOKES to KELVIN, 14 July 1879
Kelvin Collection, S413

Lensfield Cottage, Cambridge, 14 July, 1879.

MY DEAR THOMSON,

I return you Roberts's letter,[1] which I forgot to do before. I wrote to him addressing to the Nautical Almanac Office, but probably he is away for his holiday. However I anticipate no further difficulty.[2]

I am very glad that you are going to read an account of your machine.[3]

Yours sincerely,
G. G. STOKES

1 Perhaps Roberts's letter cited in letter 358, note 1. There is also a letter dated 5 July 1879 from

Roberts to Stokes (Stokes Collection, RS1425) in which he explained his version of the development of the tide predicting machine.

2 See letter 356.

3 See the previous letter, note 1.

365 STOKES to KELVIN, 20 August 1879
Kelvin Collection, S414

Lensfield Cottage, Cambridge, 20 August, 1879.

MY DEAR THOMSON,

Your series of papers 'Electrodynamic Qualities of Metals' are numbered, Part I, Part II, Part III, ... [1] the last being Part ⟨V⟩ VI.[2] Should not the present one[3] be called 'Electrodynamic Qualities of Metals – Part VII. Effects of Stress on the Magnetization of Iron, Nickel, and Cobalt'? Or perhaps it should be Part VI continued.

If you wish it put in, please write at once to the printers. I have directed them to wait 4 days for a letter from you, after which if they had not hear[d] they might proceed as you left it. I think one of the two ought to be put in, merely as a matter of correct printing arrangements; but as I can hardly suppose you forgot it, and therefore I assume as most probable that you had some reason for the omission, I have not altered it.

It will not do to quote a paper in the Philosophical Transactions by the date of reading, simply because it is throwing upon every reader who wishes to consult the paper a perfectly gratuitous amount of trouble which you have no right to impose upon him. A reader seeing a paper referred to as Phil. Trans. May 25 1875 might send his servant to a library a mile off to get the Phil. Trans. for 1875, and when he got it he would not find the paper there. I don't like it even in the Proceedings, though I would not alter it in that if the author wished to have it so. But in the Transactions it is intolerable, because you never know in what volume to find a paper ⟨published⟩ read in a given year. There is of course no objection to adding the date of reading if the author wishes for it. As you appear to wish to preserve in the present paper the date of reading of Part VI, I have *added* it in parentheses the first time the reference occurred.

I found in one place a ⟨mm⟩ 'magnetomer' which I have changed into 'magnetometer', a change to which I presume you will not object.

You may be now in the middle of the Atlantic for aught that I know, so it is doubtful if I shall get the sanction I should wish for before the paper is printed off.

Yours sincerely,
G. G. STOKES

1 Kelvin (92).
2 Kelvin (207.1).
3 Kelvin (207.2).

366 STOKES to KELVIN, 27 August 1879
Kelvin Collection, S415

4 Windsor Terrace, Malahide, Co. Dublin, 27 August, 1879.

MY DEAR THOMSON,

It is to me perfectly inconceivable that if you will think about it you can for a moment maintain the propriety of referring to a paper published in the Philosophical Transactions by the date of reading instead of for example 'Phil. Trans. for 1873, p. 245.' Given this, a reader can turn to it in a moment, and cannot possibly confound it with anything else. Given merely the date of reading, he has to turn to the indices of a set of volumes till he finds it. Thus a paper read say 29 May 1873 may not be published till the Phil. Trans. for 1877. What then does the reader do? He says to himself, well, it can't be earlier than Phil. Trans. for 1873; let us try that. He takes down the volume for 1873, turns to the index, looks out Thomson, or whoever the author may be if he knows the author's name, or otherwise hunts out two or three of the most likely words under which to find it; not there; he repeats the process for the Phil. Trans for 1874, no go; for 1875, the same; for 1866, [*sic*] the same, for 1867, [*sic*] at last he finds a reference to p. so & so. Then he says to himself c o n f o u n d that author; why could he not at once have put Phil. Trans. for 1877, p. so & so, and I could have turned to the paper referred to in a moment.

If the Phil. Trans. was even quoted by volume instead of year there would be some force in your objection; though even then I cannot admit that the objections on the other side are not far stronger. But as it is, what you object to do for the Phil. Trans. is the *very same thing* that you so strongly urge the doing of for the Phil. Mag. You say, the time is the only independent variable. Granted; then say I, arrange according to the time. But what time? You say date of reading; I say date of printing. Date of reading is what we want for questions of priority, or of tracing the mental history of an individual, but for reference it is horribly inconvenient *unless* the order of publication follows that of the date of reading. Such is the case with the Proceedings of the Royal Society, except as regards papers which are occasionally ordered to be printed in extenso in the Proceedings after an abstract has already appeared; but such is *not* the case with the Transactions. In that there is only an extremely rough approximation to an agreement of order as to reading and publication; so rough that nobody thinks of attending to it.

I don't know whether you have countermanded the alteration of the reference to the Transactions by the date of reading; or rather I should say the substitution of the date of reading *for* a reference; for I cannot allow that it is any proper reference at all. To me the mode of reference you propose seems so manifestly and tra[n]sparently wrong as regards the *Transactions* that I cannot write to the printer to restore it to what you left it. I don't think there is any question of references in your paper except to the Transactions, or if there be to the Proceedings I have not altered what you put, though I should myself have put the volume & page.

Thanks for the specimen of the printing with the tide calculating machine. It seems to be a great success.

I should be glad to know what you think of what I said in a former letter as to the formationn [*sic*] of a surface of discontinuity in the case of ⟨al⟩ an all but sharp reentrant angle in an all but perfect fluid, I said that the limit of the motion when the two independent small quantities – the defect of sharpness & the defect of perfect fluidity – were supposed to vanish might be indeterminate, depending on the order in which the small quantities were supposed to attain their limits. And that if we supposed the edge first to become sharp, and the fluid then to become perfect the result might be altogether different from what it would be ⟨in⟩ if we supposed the fluid first to become perfect, and the edge then to become sharp. I have promised to put a note about it in a part of my reprint[1] which I am now approaching.

I am much obliged by your kind invitation, but we have come over to Ireland for the summer. My wife, Arthur & Isabella left Cambridge on the 31st of July. I was not able to follow them till after a series of meetings of the Commission beginning the 12th of August. I came here last Friday, on a visit to a sister of mine,[2] and intend going to Armagh tomorrow where my family are. My address will be Observatory, Armagh, Ireland.

Yours sincerely,
G. G. STOKES

1 See the note added to Stokes (21) in *MPP*, I, 311–12.
2 Elizabeth Mary Stokes (1811–1904), who lived in Malahide.

367 KELVIN to STOKES, 3 September 1879
Royal Society of London, RR.8.194

Sept 3. 1879
Netherhall.
Largs.
Ayrshire.

DEAR STOKES

Maxwell has sent me the papers regarding Osborne Reynolds which I return to you enclosed. I have carefully read Reynolds' two letters,[1] and re-read my own report,[2] in which I have made a slight change in ink on page 16, and have dated and initialled it. I knew when I wrote it that Reynolds had controverted Stoney's theor⟨em⟩y and I have no doubt but that the *Stoney Stratum* is quite wrong. Therefore my statement 'gave the true theory of the radiometer' requires limitation. He gave the great essential of the true theory; that is the dimensional condition. This was the one thing that was important in respect to my report on Reynolds' paper, and this was all I thought of when I wrote 'the true theory.' In referring to Stoney, as Reynolds undoubtedly ought to do, (his having been in controversy with him is no reason for his not referring to him on this very essential point in respect to the very title of his paper,) it would of course be quite right that he should ⟨point out⟩ say that he did not admit the correctness of Stoney's details.[3] I have pencilled some remarks on Reynolds' letters to you, which are also enclosed. Can it be that R. does not understand the principle he is dealing with? It seems as if it was so from his statement on page 6 of his letter of the 18th of August which I have marked. Certain it is that he has confounded Graham's transpiration and effusion.[4] According to Graham's language what Reynolds calls transpiration could not be called transpiration. (See page 19 of my report). It ought more properly to be called effusional though there is no one word of Graham's that corresponds exactly to it. In page 3 of his letter of 22nd July, in the second passage marked with pencil, he shows while accusing the first referee of confusion an utter want of apprehension of 'effusion' and 'transpiration', which it is to be presumed he thinks he is using in Graham's sense. I ⟨have⟩ can only repeat to you my letter of the 6th of June written on yours to Maxwell of June 3, one of the present enclosures.[5]

Yours truly
WILLIAM THOMSON

Prof Stokes

P.S. I have also made a change on p 17 of my report, and would gladly say more & stronger in praise of this one of O.R.'s two discoveries, which are both of them beautiful & important, and lose credit only by the [two or three illegibly deleted words] faults of the paper referred to in my reports.[6]

---

1 The Royal Society has three letters from Reynolds to Stokes dating from the summer of 1879: RR.8.191, dated 22 July 1879; RR.8.192, dated 18 August 1879; and RR.8.193, dated 21 August 1879. Kelvin has annotated RR.8.192.
2 See letter 355, note 2.
3 See letter 357, note 3.
4 Reynolds cited four papers by T. Graham: 'On the law of the diffusion of gases', *Trans. Roy. Soc. Edinb.* (1834), 222–58; 'On the motion of gases', *Phil. Trans.* (1846), 573–632, and (1849), 349–92; and 'On the molecular mobility of gases', *Phil. Trans.* (1863), 385–405.
5 Letter 357.
6 Stokes has written on the reverse, 'Thomson to Stokes Sept 3, '79'.

368 KELVIN to STOKES, 10 September 1879
Royal Society of London, RR.8.195

Sept 10th 1879
Netherhall.
Largs.
Ayrshire.

Prof. Stokes
Observatory
Armagh

DEAR STOKES

I find a reference in Poggendor[f]f's Annals page 302 vol 148 year 1873[1] to thermal diffusion which it w^d be well to call Osborne Reynolds' attention to.

I have not had time to go into the thing but it seems to be related to Reynolds' 'thermal transpiration'.

Yours truly
WILLIAM THOMSON

1 W. Feddersen, 'Ueber Thermodiffusion von Gasen', Poggendorff's *Annalen der Physik und Chemie*, **148** (1873), 302–11. Berend Wilhelm Feddersen (1832–1918) received his doctorate from Kiel in 1858 and lived the rest of his life in Leipzig. Kelvin (119) is an account of photographs taken by Feddersen which supported Kelvin's theory of the oscillatory nature of the discharge of a Leyden jar. (See Thompson, 1, 237–8.)

369 STOKES to KELVIN, 19 September 1879
Kelvin Collection, S416

⟨Lensfield Cottage⟩
Observatory, Armagh, 19 September, 1879.

MY DEAR THOMSON,

I still owe you a letter about surfaces of discontinuity, but it is not that that I am going to write about just now. The proof sheets of the first volume of my book[1] accumulated on my hands till at last Mr. Clay[2] wrote to me asking me to get on as the book was being delayed. So I have had to look through them. That alone would not have taken long, but I wished to make some additions.

I have just returned three sheets for a revise, and I have asked Mr. Mason at the Pitt Press to send you duplicate revises of two of the sheets that you may see, if you care to do so, the new matter I have introduced. It will be at pp. 219–29,[3] and 231–5.[4]

The first relates to oscillatory waves. I find on looking into the matter that Rankine's solution[5] in finite terms for a particular case of wave motion was given by Gerstner so long ago as 1802. I began to read Gerstner's paper, as given in Weber's Wellenlehre,[6] when preparing for my report on hydro-

460

dynamics in the Brit. Ass. Rep. for 1846.[7] I came however to an assumption which I saw to be false, namely that the stream lines – when the motion is converted into steady motion – are lines of constant pressure, which I saw to be false, and having cursorily examined one of the results, which I supposed to be wrong from mistaking the notation, I concluded that the whole was wrong and took no further trouble about it. But I see now that that result with the notation rightly interpreted is right; and though the assumption I have mentioned is wrong, that is, there is no such necessary proposition, still there is one particular case in which it holds good, which is that of the solution in finite terms, in which I find that Rankine was anticipated by Gerstner. I thought it well to point out that irrotational waves form the really interesting case, because some mathematicians, both English and French, at least one of each, have been run away with by the simplicity of the solution.

I have further shown that Rankine was in error in saying that the highest irrotational waves had crests of 90°.

I have partially supplied also the detail of the motion of two spheres which we worked together in 1847, but which hitherto had not been published beyond the short notice in the Reports of the British Association for 1847,[8] and your little paper on a system of magnetic curves in the 2nd vol. of the Cambridge & Dublin Mathematical Journal, p. 240.[9] I should be glad of a line when you see the sheet to say whether you approve of the mention I have made of you.

The thing has been worked quite independently by Hicks in a paper[10] which I believe is now in your hands. I had intended in contemplation of my book to supply the demonstration, but I feel a little difficulty in consequence of the presentation of Hicks's paper to the Royal Society. So I have steered a sort of middle course, giving the process by which I found out the existence of an image in that particular case, and explaining a little more fully the method, but not going into detail as to spheres outside each other, or one wholly within the other, which Hicks has fully done, but working out the result for the case of two spheres intersecting at right angles, which to judge by the abstract he appears not to have given.

Perhaps when you get the sheets you would kindly tell me if there is anything you would wish altered without much delay, as I shall want to return the sheets to press, as I am blocking up a good deal of their type.

Yours sincerely,
G. G. Stokes

1 Stokes's *MPP*.
2 Charles John Clay (1827–1905), who took his B.A. at Cambridge in 1850 as third classic, was a partner in the firm of Richard Clay and Sons and was the university printer from 1854 to 1894, when he was succeeded by his son, John Clay (1858–1916), who held the position

until 1916. Although the letter mentioned here has not survived, there is correspondence involving both John and Charles John in both the Stokes and Kelvin Collections.

3 This is an appendix to Stokes (29).

4 This is an addition to Stokes (12).

5 W. J. M. Rankine, 'On the exact form and motion of waves at and near the surface of deep water', *Phil. Trans.* (1863), 127–38.

6 Franz Joseph von Gerstner (1756–1832) was professor of mechanics and hydraulics at the Polytechnic Institute in Prague from 1806 to 1832. His theory of waves was presented in E. H. and W. E. Weber, *Wellenlehre auf Experimente gegründet; oder, über die Wellen tropfbarer Flüssigkeiten mit Anwendung auf die Schall- und Lichtwellen* (Leipzig, 1825), 238–361. Ernst Heinrich Weber (1795–1878), elder brother of Wilhelm Eduard, was professor of human anatomy (including physiology from 1840 to 1865) at the University of Leipzig from 1821 to 1871.

7 Stokes (6).

8 Stokes (12).

9 Kelvin (28).

10 W. M. Hicks, 'The motion of two spheres in a fluid', *Phil. Trans.* (1880), 455–92. Kelvin's referee's report on the paper is in the Royal Society, RR.8.228. William Mitchinson Hicks (1850–1934) was seventh wrangler in 1873 and became professor of mathematics and physics at Firth College, Sheffield, in 1883. When it became a University College in 1905, Hicks became its first vice-chancellor.

370 STOKES to KELVIN, 22 September 1879
Kelvin Collection, S417

Observatory, Armagh, 22 September, 1879.

MY DEAR THOMSON,

I asked Mr. Mason at the Pitt Press to send you duplicate revises of two sheets of my book,[1] partly that I thought that perhaps it might be of some interest to you to glance over pp. 219–229,[2] about which we had some talk once; partly that you might see what I had said about you at pp. 231, ⟨233⟩ 234.[3] I got however today copies called revises of the two sheets, but in which the corrections were not yet entered, but only some additions I sent in the mean time. I don't know whether these so-called revises were sent to you or not; but partly lest you should be puzzled by them if they were and you had looked at them, partly that you might see the thing earlier than if you waited for the true revises, I send you duplicates of the false revises now.

I have made corrections where the sense seemed to be altered, but not changed mere printer's errors.

I should be glad if you would just glance over what I have said of you, and tell me if you have anything you would like altered. I should like also to know if you have any alteration to suggest in what I said of Rankine.

Yours sincerely,
G. G. STOKES

1 Stokes's *MPP*.
2 Appendix to Stokes (29).
3 Addition to Stokes (12).

371 STOKES to KELVIN, 23 September 1879
Kelvin Collection, S418

Observatory, Armagh, 23 September, 1879

MY DEAR THOMSON,

I have written to Mr. Mason at the Pitt Press to alter p. 234, l. 6[1] thus:–

for

applicable even in this case in certain instances; for though in general the method fails. . . . .

read

not limited to the cases in which each sphere is complete; and although in general it fails. . . . . .

I wished to avoid an ambiguity; for as it stands it might be taken to mean, either that you had suggested to me the whole affair of applying it to intersecting spheres, or only that you had shown me that although the method fails in general in this case from non-convergence, yet that in certain cases a result could be obtained in finite terms.

It is curious how these things bring back our work together in 1847.

Yours sincerely,
G. G. STOKES

P.S. Perhaps you will say that the ambiguity is not absolutely excluded now. There can however I think be no reasonable doubt which is meant. If you can suggest a better form of expression I shall be happy to adopt it if I get it in time.

1 Addition to Stokes (12) in his *MPP*, I, 230–5.

372 STOKES to KELVIN, 24 and 25 September 1879
Kelvin Collection, S419

Observatory, Armagh, 24 September, 1879.[1]

MY DEAR THOMSON,

Can you tell me whether the following mode of inversion is new?

Let ϕ, ψ be two conjugate functions satisfying the equation

$$\left(\frac{d^2}{dx^2} + \frac{d^2}{dy^2}\right)(\phi \text{ or } \psi) = 0, \text{ so that}$$

$$\frac{d\phi}{dx} = \frac{d\psi}{dy} \quad \frac{d\phi}{dy} = -\frac{d\psi}{dx}:$$

For example ϕ may be the function so denoted in hydrodynamics, and $\psi = \int (u\,dy - v\,dx)$, or ϕ may be a temperature, and ψ a flux of heat, &c.; then if instead of regarding x, y as the independent variables of which ϕ, ψ are functions, we make ϕ, ψ the independent variables and regard x, y as functions of them, we shall have by changing the independent variables

$$\frac{dx}{d\phi} = \frac{dy}{d\psi} \quad \frac{dx}{d\psi} = -\frac{dy}{d\phi}$$

Hence for any solution to the equation $\nabla^2 \phi = 0$ (from which the conjugate function may be obtained by integrating a perfect differential), we may obtain another solution by interchanging either of the two ϕ, ψ with x and the other with y.

In a similar manner with polar coordinates the equation for ϕ or ψ is of the same form as before if we take $\log r, \theta$ for the independent variables. The inversions obtained from the same ϕ will not be the same when we invert by the coordinates $\log r, \theta$ as by x, y.

I was led to think of this as possibly useful from trying to obviate an objection to the mode of treatment I gave of oscillatory irrotational waves when the waves are very high. Take for simplicity the case of deep water; but the same applies to water which is not deep. Reducing the motion to steady motion, the expression I used for ϕ is of the form

$$\phi = -cx + \Sigma\, A_n e^{-nmy} \sin nmx.$$

The motion being continuous, this expression must by the theory of periodic series be convergent for any value of y which gives a line lying within the water. It will however be divergent if y be ⟨positive⟩ negative and large enough. But it might also be divergent for a value of y corresponding to a line lying below the crests but above the troughs of the waves. Yet the singular points which render it divergent might be situated outside the water, though at a lower level than the crests. The series would therefore fail within the limits of the values of y for which we want to employ it. But this is not from anything inherent in the motion, but from a faulty method of expansion. It is just as if we wanted to express for points external to an ellipsoid the potential of an internal point, and were to employ polar coordinates and expand in Laplace's Functions. If the internal point were at a distance from the centre greater than the least semi-axis, the expansion applicable to a sufficiently distant point would fail from divergence ⟨from⟩ for points within the space that we want to deal with. But this divergence arises, not from anything inherent in the problem, but from a faulty mode of attacking it.

But suppose that in the wave problem instead of expressing ϕ and thence ψ in terms of x and y, we express x and y in terms of ϕ and ψ. We shall have, supposing for greater generality that the depth is finite, (see below)

$$x = -\frac{\phi}{c} + \sum_{1}^{\infty} B_n\, e^{+nm\psi} \sin nm\phi$$

$$y = -\frac{\psi}{c} + \sum_{1}^{\infty} B_n\, e^{nm\psi} \cos nm\phi$$

Sept. 25.

I wrote down without thinking of what I had written just before the formulae for an infinite depth; those for a finite depth are

$$x = -\frac{\phi}{c} + \sum_{1}^{\infty} B_n\, (e^{nm\overline{\psi+ch}} + e^{-nm\overline{\psi+ch}}) \sin nm\phi$$

$$y = -\frac{\psi}{c} + \sum_{1}^{\infty} B_n\, (e^{nm\overline{\psi+ch}} - e^{-nm\overline{\psi+ch}}) \cos nm\phi$$

The advantage of this is that whereas formerly the fluid extended from $x = \infty$ – let that stand for machine infinity[2] – negative to positive, and from $y =$ an unknown function of x determined by the solution of the problem to $y = h$, now ϕ extends from $-\infty$ to $+\infty$ and ψ extends from one constant value to another. (For the stream line of the surface we may take $\psi = 0$, which determines the origin of y, and for the stream line of the bottom we have $\psi = -ch$), and that at the same time that we secure the advantage of constant limits for the independent variables, which itself alone could be done by the use of parameters in an infinite number of ways, we have the now dependent variables x, y determined by conjugate solutions of the same partial differential equation as before, namely $\left(\dfrac{d^2}{d\phi^2} + \dfrac{d^2}{d\psi^2}\right)(x \text{ or } y) = 0$

The solution of the wave problem cannot actually be effected, save by approximation, for the same reason as before, namely, that the equation of condition at the free surface is not linear. It is that we must have simultaneously $\psi = 0$ and $gy - \frac{1}{2}(u^2 + v^2) = \text{const.}$ The components of the velocity are determined by

$$u = \frac{1}{R}\frac{dx}{d\phi}, \quad v = \frac{1}{R}\frac{dx}{d\psi}, \quad R = \frac{dx}{d\phi}\frac{dy}{d\psi} - \frac{dx}{d\psi}\frac{dy}{d\phi} = \left(\frac{dx}{d\phi}\right)^2 + \left(\frac{dx}{d\psi}\right)^2$$

$$\therefore \quad u^2 + v^2 = \frac{1}{R}$$

The advantage is the theoretical one that we do not encounter series rendered divergent by sources not situated within the limits of the fluid.

It is only a couple of days or so ago that I thought of this method, and I have been very busy with various things, and have not worked out the actual approximations on this system even to the second order.

I should be glad to know if the mode of inversion is new to you.

Yours sincerely,

G. G. STOKES

1 Kelvin has written the following in the margin near the beginning of the letter:

$$\nabla^2 v = \frac{d^2 v}{d\psi^2}\left(\frac{d\psi^2}{dx^2} + \frac{d\psi^2}{dy^2}\right) + \frac{d^2 v}{d\phi^2}\left(\frac{d\phi^2}{dx^2} + \cdot\right) + \frac{d^2 v}{d\phi^2}\left(\frac{d\phi^2}{dx^2} + \frac{d\phi^2}{dy^2}\right)$$

$$\frac{dv}{d\langle\psi\rangle x} = \frac{dv}{d\psi}\frac{d\psi}{dx} + \frac{dv}{d\phi}\frac{d\phi}{dx}$$

$$\frac{d^2 v}{dx^2} = \frac{d^2 v}{d\psi^2}\left(\frac{d\psi}{dx}\right)^2 + \frac{dv}{d\psi}\frac{d^2\psi}{dx^2} + \frac{d^2 v}{d\phi^2}\left(\frac{d\phi}{dx}\right)^2 + \frac{dv}{d\phi}\frac{d^2\phi}{dx^2}$$

$$\frac{d\psi}{dx}\frac{d\phi}{dx} + \frac{d\psi}{dy}\frac{d\phi}{dy} = 0$$

$$\frac{\dfrac{d\psi}{dx}}{\dfrac{d\phi}{dx}} = -\frac{\dfrac{d\psi}{dy}}{\dfrac{d\phi}{dy}} =$$

2 This is a typewritten letter, and Stokes meant that this was as close as he could come to the symbol for infinity with his typewriter.

373 STOKES to KELVIN, 27 September 1879
Kelvin Collection, S420

Observatory, Armagh, 27 September, 1879.

MY DEAR THOMSON

Thanks for your letter and the return of the proofs.[1] I did not however want them as they were duplicates, and you can keep the proofs you have though they are not quite correct, though nearly so.

I do not see that the transposition of 'in general' alters the sense, but I think the order you propose is rather an improvement in the English.

I recollected perfectly the facts you mentioned as to the convergence, and that when the spheres touched the ratio⟨n⟩ of consecutive terms of the series was ultimately a ratio of equality. But I don't agree with you that that necessarily or even probably prevents numerical calculation. The first series you mention, namely

$$1 - \tfrac{1}{2} + \tfrac{1}{3} - \tfrac{1}{4} + \tfrac{1}{5} - \ldots$$

admits of easy ⟨mun⟩ numerical calculation by summing to a certain number of terms and completing the series by the formula

$$U_n - U_{n+1} + U_{n+2} - \ldots = \tfrac{1}{2}U_n - \tfrac{1}{4}\Delta U_n + \tfrac{1}{8}\Delta^2 U_n - \ldots$$

I calculated yesterday the series

$$S = \frac{1}{1^2} + \frac{1}{2^2} + \frac{1}{3^2} + \ldots$$

from the same formula, having previously put it into the form

$$S - 2\frac{S}{4} \; (= \tfrac{1}{2}S) = \frac{1}{1^2} - \frac{1}{2^2} + \frac{1}{3^2} - \frac{1}{4^2} + \ldots$$

The calculation was very easy with the aid of Barlow's Table of Reciprocals.[2] Working with decimals to 7 figures, and not rejecting any decimals in the end, I got for the sum 1.6449340, $\frac{\pi^2}{6}$ being 1.6449341. It is a chance of course that the omitted decimals balanced so well.

I can foresee that the same method would apply to the calculation for equal spheres in contact, and I feel little doubt and I feel little doubt [*sic*] that either it or a modification of it would apply to unequal spheres in contact. But I have lots of other things to work at, and I must not steal time to try at present. I shall keep back I think sheet 15, and send 14, 16, 17, 18 to press.

I feel curious to know what you think of the inversion. I believe that as applied to oscillatory waves it will be a distinct improvement as to facility of approximation, and not merely remove a theoretical blemish which may or may not exist, I cannot prove which, I mean the[3] ⟨possibility of⟩ encountering divergent series before we have reached the steepest possible wave.

Yours sijcerely, [*sic*]

G. G. STOKES

---

1 Proofs for the reprint of Stokes (12) and (29) in his *MPP*. (See letters 369–71.)

2 Peter Barlow, *New Mathematical Tables, Containing the Factors, Squares, Cubes, Square Roots, Cube Roots, Reciprocals, and Hyperbolic Logarithms of All Numbers from 1 to 10000* (London, 1814). Barlow (1776–1862) was assistant mathematical master and later professor of mathematics at Woolwich.

3 Stokes apparently intended to delete *the* also.

374 KELVIN to STOKES, 29 September [1879][1]
Stokes Collection, K235

Sep 29.

Your letter of 27th and post card received. The case of relative motion of two spheres with infinitely small distance between them is very interesting. No doubt the case of no relative motion & the two in contact is calculable easily enough as you say.

I don't quite like the word 'resistance' as you use it. I forgot to say so when I wrote last. It would certainly be misleading & w[d] imply (to anyone not quite conversant with the affair) that there is resistance to uniform motion. You don't talk of resistance [of (?essence of inertia?) anything][2] to the motion of a solid through vacuum. Yet there is exactly the same resistance to it as there is 'resistance of a fluid to the motion of two sphere[s]' or of any solid body. It is effective inertia-equivalent that is the idea to be conveyed.

W.T.

1 This is a post card addressed to Stokes and post marked Greenock, 29 September 1879.
2 Kelvin's brackets.

375 STOKES to KELVIN, 29 September 1879
Kelvin Collection, S421

Observatory, Armagh, 29 September, 1879.

MY DEAR THOMSON,

I found my ideas as to the greatest height of oscillatory irrotational waves gradually clearing up, both before and after I had written what you have seen in print, but which I am keeping back from printing off, though I have sent subsequent sheets to the press.[1] I convinced myself that there could be no sharp angle, and imagined that at what I called the greatest possible wave the root of an equation depending on the condition at the surface became imaginary, and had thought something about an instability of the motion about the limit. On reading your letter my ideas were still further cleared, and I felt convinced that there was a gradual transition from a stable to an unstable form. But what do we get when we have gone well on into the latter? I feel satisfied it is not a shape like this – Fig. A. – but like this – Fig. B. – and that the answer to the question, what is the greatest possible height? if we include the unstable forms is, there is no limit to the height. The nature of the motion will be I think more readily understood by first considering stationanr [i.e., stationary] oscillations. – Fig. C. – The red and black forms[2] will come alternately. From this we may pass without difficulty to the conception of a progressive wave, or of [sic] we prefer taking it so, to steady motion. In such extreme forms, potential is more rapidly converted into kinetic energy if the wave falls over to one side than if the descending fluid steers so straight that it gets flattened out. The motion is consequently unstable.

Yours sincerely,
G. G. Stokes

For figures see the back of the page.[3]

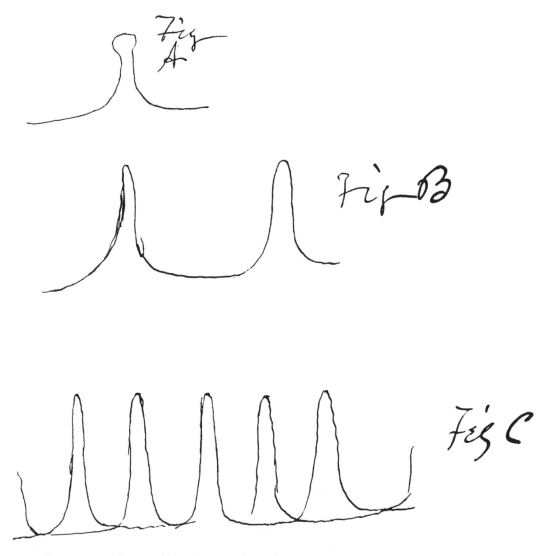

1 This refers to Stokes's addition to his (29) in *MPP*, 1, 219–29.
2 If we begin numbering the five waves in figure C from either end, then Stokes has drawn the second and fourth in red ink.
3 Stokes has drawn the figures on the reverse of the letter.

Observatory, Armagh, 29 Sept. 1879.

MY DEAR THOMSON,

It had occurred to me before I got your letter that very likely I might find the 'inversion' in Lamé's curvilinear coordinates. I must look into the matter when I get access to books.

As to the highest waves, what seems to me the most probable is this. When the wave length is given, and also some other element, I am not prepared at present to say what, – I suppose the depth given; the 'other element' is some function of the constant which I called a – there are two conjugate solutions,

the lower probably stable, the higher unstable.[1] When the lower is very low, the higher is probably very high. As the height of the lower increases, the two approach, and ultimately coalesce. This corresponds to what I called the maximum wave; which however is only the highest possible *stable* wave.[2]

I must not attempt to work the thing out by the new method, I mean to carry out the approximation; for I hardly expect it will lead to a perfect solution of the maximum wave matter; just at present, for I have other matters pressing which must be attended to.[3] But I can foresee I think that it will very greatly lighten the labour of proceeding to a high order of approximation.

Your method of images would undoubtedly lead to an easy numerical solution of the problem of finding the total charge on a pair of insulated conducting spheres, equal or not, in contact, and charged up to a given potential. If I am to infer from what you wrote about convergency that the method is in this case a pp [*sic*] 'practical failur[e]', I should say, for 'practical failure' read 'perfect success'. I feel satisfied from certain general considerations that it could also be applied[4] that it could also be applied [*sic*] to find the portion of the charge on one only of the spheres without driving us to the direct summation of an infinite series in which the ratio of consecutive terms is ultimately a ratio of equality; but to make sure of bringing it into this form requires more consideration than I can give it at present. Perhaps you will think of the proverb about carrying coals to Newcastle; but really what you wrote seems as if you were not fully aware of the power of your own method.

There is no question about being in time as regards Bottoml[e]y's paper;[5] when it was brought before the committee of papers the decision was to pos[t]pone it till Bottoml[e]y had had an opportunity of clearing up in some way or other the point which remained in some doubt, or at least which might be thought to remain in some doubt, about the possible communication of heat dowm [sic] the sides of the vessel.

I am to leave this on Thursday at 6 p.m. for London, and expect to be in Cambridge on the fourth.

Yours sincerely,
G. G. STOKES

P.S. As to waves, the critical height probably corresponds to a minimum periodic time.

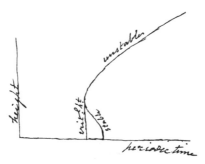

It would certainly be interesting to try whether an approximation could not be made in actual experiment to the wave of 120°.

1 Stokes has drawn the two higher waves in the figure in red ink.
2 Stokes has drawn the higher wave in red ink and has written in the margin, 'The highest stable would doubtless be much higher than that drawn if the water is deep'. Larmor has written in the opposite margin, 'cf. Poincaré's rotating fluid forms'. See Henri Poincaré, 'Sur l'équilibre d'une masse fluide animée d'un mouvement de rotation', Comptes Rendus, 100 (1885), 346–8, 1068–70, and 101 (1885), 307–9.
3 The punctuation of this sentence has been altered, apparently by Larmor. He has inserted dashes after the words method and matter and changed the semicolon after approximation to a comma.
4 Larmor has written in the margin, 'Maxwell Treatise 1872 [sic]!' James Clerk Maxwell, Treatise on Electricity and Magnetism, 2 vols. (Oxford, 1873).
5 J. T. Bottomley, 'On the thermal conductivity of water', Proc. Roy. Soc., 28 (1879), 462–3; 31 (1881), 300; and Phil. Trans. (1881), 537–45.

377 STOKES to KELVIN, 30 September 1879
Kelvin Collection, S423

Observatory, Armagh, 30 September, 1879.

MY DEAR THOMSON,

I have worked a little at the equation of the surface, just to see what sort of length it would run to. It will be long enough, though I think not by a good deal so long as if I had worked with x & y as the independent variables.

The motion may, likely enough, become unstable somewhere about the height for which the velocity of propagation is a maximum, but I don't see that there is any authority for saying that that is the particular height for which the motion becomes unstable. I feel pretty well satisfied now that the solution may be pushed to an infinite height, becoming at the same time infinitely unstable. There is therefore no need to suppose that the equations themselves will indicate any critical height. I should think it probable that they would given numerical results, without going to any enormous trouble in the approximation, (at least in the simpler case of an infinite depth) leading up to or beyond the height at which a wave would become unstable, and consequently break, but I don't think that they would give any indication when the critical point was arrived at.

Yours sincerely,
G. G. STOKES

378 STOKES to KELVIN, 30 September 1879
Kelvin Collection, S424

Observatory, Armagh, 30 September, 1879.

MY DEAR THOMSON,

I got your p. card this afternoon.[1] I hardly think that the mere use of the term 'resistance' will give rise to misapprehension, especially as I refer to my paper on some cases of fluid motion,[2] where the thing is fully explained, and besides mention the thing explicitly in this very same paper at p. 235,[3] about one third of the way down.

A further light seems to have come upon me as to oscillatory waves, at least for the case of shallpw [*sic*] water. I went to a second approximation in that zase, [*sic*] and remarked that unless *a* were very small, the second term of the series might be much larger than the first. I thought then that there was a limitation of some kind as to the height of the waves which could be propagated without change of form, and that the greatest height for very shallow water was very small. But considering now that there is no limit, when the question of instability is set aside, I thought what would be the approximate form of the expansion in periodic series of such extravagant waves as those I drew. From the well known properties of the series

$$\tfrac{1}{2} + \cos x + \cos 2x + \cos 3x \ldots$$

I inferred that for a good way the coefficients of the terms would be nearly equal. What then are we to infer from finding a second term much greater than the first? Why, supposing for a moment that the other terms are not large, that the wave consists approximately of two nearly equal waves; that the series does not much differ from a larger (i.e. higher) series of half the wave length. If other terms are large as well, then the whole wave is made up of a group of waves, presenting two, three, or more maxima and as many minima in one complete period.

When $\frac{h}{\lambda}$ is very small the velocity of propagation is but little short of its limiting value $\sqrt{gh}$, I mean the velocity of propagation for infinitely low waves. It increases somewhat with the height of the wave. Consequently a wave of moderate elevation with wave length $\frac{\lambda}{2}$ would travel as fast as a very low wave with wave length λ. This serves to explain how the compound wave can travel with one uniform velocity and without change of form, though consisting of a fundamental and of overtone waves. In a small wave-trough, a single disturbance is very apt in experiment to break into a group.

Yours sincerely,
G. G. STOKES

1 Letter 374.
2 Stokes (13).
3 Addition to Stokes (12) in his *MPP*, I.

379 KELVIN to STOKES, 1 October 1879
Stokes Collection, K236

Oct 1, 1879
Great Western Hotel
London

DEAR STOKES

We were summoned here by telegraph on Monday by very sad intelligence. My father-in-law[1] had been ill for about ten days but the last letters we had, even those we received on Monday morning told us that he was getting better. Almost immediately after receiving them a telegram came that he was gone. When we came here we found that he had been much better on the Sunday evening and talking cheerfully with friends till 10 or 11 o'clock. He died quite suddenly early in the morning. An examination has shown that the cause of death was rupture of the heart itself, which had become thinned in one part on account of ossification of the coronal artery. It was a very sad shock to us all as we hoped there were many years of life with good health, in store for him.

Your letter of the 29th came to me here this morning. I hope you will go on with the highest-wave problem. It will be most interesting and I think you will be able to work it out. The idea of minimum periodic time is certainly very instructive and most probably I should think true.

As to images, I knew that the method leads to a true solution for every variety of case when the two surfaces don't cut, including actual⟨1⟩ contact ⟨or⟩ and infinitely nearly contact. I considered that the calculation by *mere* summation[2] of such a series as $1 - \frac{1}{2} + \frac{1}{3} - \&c -$ by mear [i.e., mere] summation as a practical failure because of the slowness of the convergence – ten thousand terms necessary to come within 1/20000 of the correct result. I knew that the series to be summed could be summed easily by definite integrals[3] such as those that Poisson gave, and you will find that I used this plan for, if I remember right, the repulsion between two spheres in contact in an article (contained in my Reprint of Electrostatics &[c] of which I hope you got a copy from me) on mutual forces betw. electrified spheres (of about 1853.)[4] I don't think I ever attacked the question of the approach to infinities in the solution for two spheres infinitely near one another and not infinitely nearly at the same potential: ⟨The⟩ (which is very interesting and *important*). The corresponding problem in fluid motion is very interesting – two spheres with relative motion, – in the line joining their centres infinitely nearly in contact. But ? will it too involve infinities?

I have not had time to read Hicks' paper,[5] referred to me, yet, but I thought on glancing through it that it seemed *not* confined to motions in line of centres. If it is not really, it will have special interest of its own, as going much beyond what we knew how to do so well without it.

I am afraid I have kept Ayrton & Perry's paper[6] too long.[7] I have read it I think quite all through lately, and nearly all ⟨I⟩, at first, I am ashamed to say how many months ago – but there were some difficulties connected with the main question, which I wanted to try to digest before reporting. I have no doubt of reporting in favour of its publication in the Transactions, and in any case I must send it to you without farther delay. I hope to do so on Monday or Tuesday next when we expect to be again at Netherhall.

I am leaving here, in the Hotel because it does not fit itself for post or a parcel, – two large photographs mounted on card board of my large tidal harmonic analyser for the Royal Society. I don't know if you would think them worth hanging up in the library or elsewhere. Will you let a messenger come from the Royal Society here for them unless I bring them there myself this week? They will be addressed to M[r] White R.S. I hope early in the session to send a particular acc[t] of the instrument, and results of its application to Lisbon tide curves which I have in hand at present, – part of a year already received from M[r] Capello[8] & the rest to come soon I hope.

We probably leave this for Largs on Friday evening but may remain two days longer. If so could you come here to see me or shall I find you on Friday ev^{g9} at the R.S.?

Yours
W Thomson

P.S. I think we shall remain here till Sunday night. Will you come & see me on Friday ev^g or Saturday morning before you go to Cambridge?[10]

1 C. R. Blandy.
2 Kelvin has interlined the phrase, 'by *mere* summation', duplicating a phrase already in the sentence. He has added a footnote here reading, 'I was quite prepared to look for shortcuts for approximating to the *remainder* after calculation of a moderate number of terms'.
3 Kelvin has added a footnote here reading, 'All this is to show you that I am not and have never been, wanting in faith in the method'.
4 Kelvin (66) in *PEM*, 86–97.
5 See letter 369, note 10.
6 W. E. Ayrton and J. Perry, 'Contact theory of voltaic action', *Phil. Trans.* (1880), 15–34. Kelvin's referee's report is in the Royal Society, RR.8.147. William Edward Ayrton (1847–1908) and John Perry (1850–1920) both held professorships in Japan in the mid- to late-1870s, before taking positions in London. The *Royal Society Catalogue* lists sixty-seven joint papers by them.
7 Kelvin has added a footnote here reading, 'I have had to spend every moment I could get, on "Heat" for Encyc. Brit^a. I ought to have finished it by now but alas it is not $\frac{1}{2}$ done'. See Kelvin (243A).
8 João Carlos de Brito-Capello (b. 1831) was director of an observatory in Lisbon and published a few papers, including two joint ones with Balfour Stewart, on magnetic and meteorological observations.
9 Kelvin has added a footnote here reading, 'or Saturday morning'.
10 Kelvin has written on the envelope, 'We are decided to remain here till Sunday night. So I hope either to see you here on Friday ev^g or Saturday morning or to find you at the R.S. before you go to Cambridge'.

380 STOKES TO KELVIN, 5 October 1879
Kelvin Collection, S425

Lensfield Cottage, Cambridge, 5 October, 1879.

MY DEAR THOMSON,

When I arrived yesterday evening I went to Maxwell's house, to try if I could hear anything further. The housekeeper had heard of his illness, but did not seem to know anything very definite about it. She told me he was to return to Cambridge tomorrow in an invalid carriage if he was able to travel. Today I overtook Dr. Paget, and asked him if he had heard of Maxwell's illness. He heard of it yesterday for the first time, and evidently his information about it was very meagre. He evidently seemed to think it was likely to be most serious. I will let you know if I hear anything definite.

As to the wave difficulty, I am very strongly inclined to think that I was wrong in throwing overboard the edge of 120° on merely artistic grounds. There is no need to suppose that the points of inflexion in the flanks run to the top when the top becomes a singular point, so that the flanks may be inclined to the horizon at an angle much greater than 30° even though it comes down again to 30° at the top, without being for all that an inclination changing continuously through zero to negative. When waves break on a sandy beach, such a transitional form might be hardly noticed, as the lasting forms of a smooth swell before the maximum and a steep and ultimately curling wave after it would dwell on the memory.

I recollect noticing from the deck of a steamer an inconspicuous breaking of swells at the top when their bluntness seemed to give them no right to break. I recollect also in watching sweels [*sic*] breaking on a sandy beach noticing that just about the time when they got sharp, and before they actually broke, there seemed to be a rapid increase in the rate of propagation. According to my present views, this would be just after the transition from uniform propagation to propagation accompanied by change of form.

Yours sincerely,
G. G. STOKES

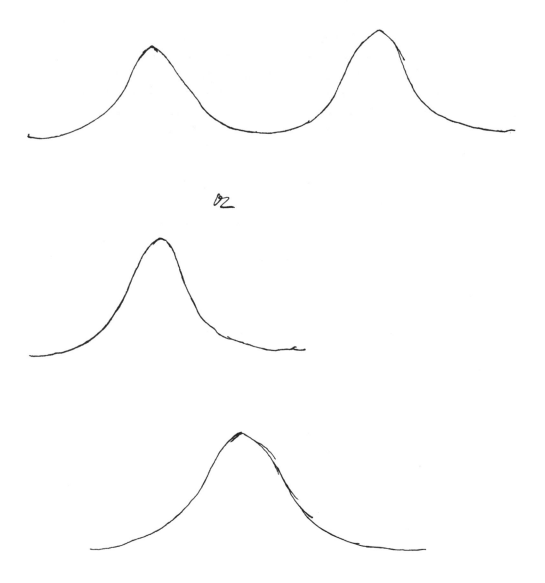

381 STOKES to KELVIN, 6 October 1879
Kelvin Collection, S426

Lensfield Cottage, Cambridge, 6 October, 1879.

MY DEAR THOMSON,

I did not mention my views about the case of a very long wave. Although the expansion for finite depth went to the second order only, it already showed the tendency for a set of periodic waves to become a set of solitary waves. When the ratio of l the wave length to d the depth is very great, the second term of the series for $\langle phi \rangle$ ϕ is large compared with the first, unless the wave be excessiv[e]ly low. But we are not to infer from this that the wave is necessarily very low; that if it were otherwise the series would be divergent. Suppose $l = 100d$. $l = 100d$ [sic] We have approximately a series of solitary waves at intervals of $100d$. But the main part of each may be comprised in a length of say $3d$. Hence the early terms of the expansion will be small compared with some later terms, and some way beyond that again the terms will decrease again. They will be greatest when we get to the part where the submultiples of l are comparable with $3d$. The sum approximates in character to an integral from 0 to ∞, and the parts of the integral for very small or very large values of the variable are but trifling. For a strictly solitary wave the proper expression would be doubtless an integral and not a sum. The maximum height is doubtless not by any means insignificant compared with the depth; but the proportion of the height represented by the coefficient of the term of the first order, in the case of one wave of a series, not quite a solitary wave, is very small.

For an infinite depth, and also for a finite depth but with more labour, the maximum wave would be determined approximately numerically by seeing for what ratio of the constant a to l the series passed from convergent to divergent. For the separating case, giving the maximum wave, the series for the height for instance would be of the convergency of

$$\frac{1}{1^2} + \frac{1}{3^2} + \frac{1}{5^2} \cdots$$

For lower waves it would be of the convergency of a geometric series with a ratio less than 1. So I feel pretty well satisfied the thing could be solved numerically if one took pains enough. It is pretty clear that for deep water the maximum height would be somewhat less than the l by 2 pi of Gerstner & Rankine.[1]

Yours sincerely,

G. G. Stokes

P.S. Contrary to an opinion expressed in my report,[2] I am now disposed to think there is such a thing as as [sic] a solitary wave which can theoretically be propagated without degradation.

1 See letter 369, notes 5 and 6.
2 Stokes (6) in *MPP*, ii, 157–87, especially p. 170.

Kelvin Collection, S427

Lensfield Cottage, Cambridge, 7 October, 1879.

MY DEAR THOMSON,

I have worked out oscillatory irrotational waves by the new method to the fifth order for the case of deep water.[1] In the former paper[2] I went to the third order only. It required some patience, but in going to a high order it is far easier by the new method. Here is the result I got.

$c = $ vel^y of prop^n, $\quad m = \dfrac{2\pi}{\lambda}, \quad$ a a const^t approximately the height from mean level

$$ma \left(= \frac{2\pi a}{\lambda} \right) = r, \quad x \text{ hor}^l \text{ measured from trough}, \quad y \text{ vertical \& downwards.}$$

$$c^2 = mg(1 + r^2 + \tfrac{7}{3}r^4)$$

and for the implicit eq^n of the surface $\left(\dfrac{m\phi}{c} = \Phi \right)$

$$mx = -\Phi + r\sin\Phi - (r^2 + \tfrac{1}{3}r^4)\sin 2\Phi + (\tfrac{3}{2}r^3 + \tfrac{19}{12}r^5)\sin 3\Phi$$
$$- \tfrac{8}{3}r^4 \sin 4\Phi + \tfrac{125}{24}r^5 \sin 5\Phi$$

$$my = r\cos\Phi - (r^2 + \tfrac{1}{3}r^4)\cos 2\Phi + (\tfrac{3}{2}r^3 + \tfrac{19}{12}r^5)\cos 3\Phi$$
$$- \tfrac{8}{3}r^4 \cos 4\Phi + \tfrac{125}{24}r^5 \cos 5\Phi$$

October, 8.

I was staggered last night when I had got this result, and suspected an error in the work, but on looking over it I could find none. The reason why I was staggered was that I had found by the old method that as far as the third order the surface was a trochoid, and I expected that the coefficients of the second and third orders would have vanished. But on carefully looking over my work I could find no error, and the velocity of propagation agrees to the third order with the old result. Moreover I verified as far as the second order that the form of the surface comes the same. The fact is that Φ is not the angle of rolling, but only a function of the angle of rolling, with which it agrees at every half turn. The relation between the two angles would be similar to that between mx and Φ.

Already the series gives a rude indication of the height of the maximum wave. If we put $r = 1$ we get for the coefficients

$$1, \quad 1.500, \quad 3.083, \quad 2.667, \quad 5.208,$$

where there is an evident divergence. It is to be observed that the odd terms form one order of sequence and the even another, so that in considering the convergence one should compare the odd with the odd and the even with the even. For $r = 0.5$, the coefficients divided by the first are

$$1, \quad 0.562, \quad 0.479, \quad 0.333, \quad 0.342,$$

where there appears to be an indication of convergence, though less distinct than that of divergence before. If we take $r =$ two-thirds, we shall probably not be far off from the mark for the maximum wave. The height from crest to trough would be twice the sum of the odd terms into $\dfrac{\lambda}{2\pi}$. Twice the first coefficient would be four-thirds, and the double sum of the odd coeffs. perhaps eight-thirds or more. Two thir[d]s for r is doubtless too high; to get anything more than a rude idea of the limit we should have to include a good many more terms. I may perhaps work it further; anyhow I mean to work out to the third order at least for finite depth. In the old way I did it only to the second.

Yours sincerely,
G. G. Stokes

P.S. The Maxwells came back late last night. I called there today but only saw Mrs Maxwell.[3] Dr. Paget was with him. I have not seen Dr. Paget since he saw Maxwell.

1 See Stokes (99A).
2 Stokes (29).
3 Katherine Mary Clerk Maxwell.

383   Stokes to Kelvin, 9 October 1879
Kelvin Collection, S428

Lensfield Cottage, Cambridge, 9 October, 1879.

My dear Thomson,

Allow me to make a correction. I said that in the limiting case the series for x & y had ultimately the convergency of

$$\frac{1}{1^2} + \frac{1}{3^2} + \frac{1}{5^2} + \dots$$

It should be that for $\Phi = \pi$ they have ultimately the convergency of

$$\frac{1}{1^{\frac{5}{3}}} + \frac{1}{2^{\frac{5}{3}}} + \frac{1}{3^{\frac{5}{3}}} + \dots$$

Yours sincerely,
G. G. Stokes

$\frac{dy}{dx}$ $\langle$becomes infin$\rangle$ changes discontinuously, but $\frac{dx}{d\phi}$, $\frac{dy}{d\psi}$ become infinite.

384 STOKES to KELVIN, 10 October 1879
Kelvin Collection, S429

Lensfield Cottage, Cambridge, $\langle 9 \rangle$ 10 October, 1879.

MY DEAR THOMSON,

I fear that Maxwell's case is hopeless. It appears to be dropsy. I have not seen Dr. Paget, and I know that physicians do not like to be asked about their patients, but I hear that Dr. Paget spoke vary [*sic*] badly about the case. I called yesterday, and heard that Maxwell had not left his room. I met Dr. Guillemard[1] today, who told me that he had been with him. Dr. Guillemard you know is the clergyman of his parish. Maxwell was in bed today.

Yours sincerely,
G. G. STOKES

---

1 William Henry Guillemard (1815–87) took his B.A. at Cambridge in 1838 and became a fellow of Pembroke the same year, Stokes's second year as an undergraduate at Pembroke. He was head master of the Royal College, Armagh (where Stokes's wife's family lived), from 1848 to 1869 and was vicar of St Mary the Less in Cambridge from 1869 to 1886. There are many letters from him to Stokes in the Stokes Collection, dating from as early as 1842.

385 KELVIN to STOKES, 10 October 1879
Stokes Collection, K237

Train to Glasgow Oct 10/79

DEAR STOKES

Your letter of the 7th reached me just as I was leaving Netherhall for a day in laboratory, Glasgow. I return this evening and Netherhall, Largs will find me for another week. I am much interested in it & $\langle$the two$\rangle$ [?] your two preceding letters. Can it be that for even the smallest value of r the series becomes ultimately divergent, and thus that your solution is for a wave-form of oscillatory wave which is more and more approximately steady the smaller is r, but not rigourously [*sic*] steady in any case. You see that for $r = \frac{1}{2}$ the

481

evidence supporting supposition of convergence is less decided than of divergence for $r = 1$ ⟨⟩⟩ (is really not decided, perhaps even negative).

The more I think of it the more I am disposed to conclude that there is no such thing as a steady free periodic series of waves in water of any depth. I can't believe in the solitary wave.

I strongly suspect that there is just one rigourous solution of the case of motion represented in the diagram, (supposed to be steady, irrotational, and in two dimensions – i.e. the bottom ⟨cylindrical⟩ generates by motion of a straight line parallel to itself & the motion of each particle ⟨parallel⟩ perp^r to this direction). There certainly is one solution – that of minimum energy, (for a given horizontal momentum, or some such condition as that). For the case of plane bottom ⟨the⟩ this solution is that the free surface is plane & the motions in straight lines.

I can't imagine steadiness got by such a form as above. I would scarcely object to the form as 'unartistic' however.

I am afraid Maxwell must be very ill. I hope you will be able to give me a favourable report however when you have seen Dr Paget.

Yours
W.T.

386 STOKES TO KELVIN, 11 October 1879
Kelvin Collection, S430

Lensfield Cottage, Cambridge, 11 October, 1879.

MY DEAR THOMSON,

I feel satisfied that there *is* steady wave motion possible in water of infinite depth, or of finite depth if the bottom is plane. The calcul[a]tion leads to a process which can be carried out to any order, and the only question is that of the convergence of the series. The calculation gives the equation of the surface in the form of a periodic series, and if this be divergent, we must be aiming at a something which presents an infinite or imaginary ordinate however small r be. This I feel satisfied is not the case. The equation of the surface will be convergent, and more so than if the nth term contained the inverse ith power of n, where i is a given constant however great, till a height is reached where some one of the differential coefficients of y becomes infinite or discontinuous.

482

Now for the supposed disproofs. First for the analogy of a sound wave in air. Observe that if we proceed by approximation the impossibility of uniform transmission without change shows itself already in the second order, whereas in waves we have a process which can be carried out indefinitely, and which gives no indication of any change.

The physical difference is that in waves of water the motion at any point is influenced by what takes place at a distance from that point. In sound, when we make abstraction of the dimensions of & finite intervals between the molecules, the motion at one point depends only on the state of things infinitely near that point. If we were to take account of the finiteness of the mean interval between the molecules, then I have no doubt we should avoid the occurrence of that discontinuity which is indicated by the interpretation of the integral without approximation first given by Poisson.

For a corrugated bottom, motion irrotational & steady, I agree with you that there is only one form of steady motion, and that that becomes a motion in parallel horizontal lines when the bottom becomes plane. I am supposing as you do that the upper surface is free. But I say a corrugated bottom essentially excludes in general a wave motion. In order that a wave motion should be derivable from a steady flow, the surface conditions must be unchanged when you superpose a horizontal velocity, which in the case of finite depth cannot be the case unless the bottom be a horizontal plane. Now the limit of a ⟨wave⟩ motion from which a wave motion is essentially excluded does not become a wave motion merely because in the limit the surface conditions become such as would have been compatible in the first instance with a wave motion.

To illustrate this let us take a problem I considered in my paper on the steady motion of incompressible fluids.[1] If we ask what steady motion, if any, can take place in similar & coaxal elliptic cylinders, we find that there is one and but one kind of steady motion possible – I suppose the motion in two dimensions, in planes perpendicular to the axis of the cylinders – namely one in which the particles in a plane through the axis remain in a plane through the axis. The limit of this when the eccentricity vanishes is a motion of rotation in which the fluid moves as a solid, revolving uniformly about the axis. Are we to infer that there is no kind of steady motion except this possible in which the fluid moves in coaxal circular cylinders? Assuredly not. In this particular case the velocity may vary as any arbitrary function of the radius vector. The motion is not by any means restricted to be the limit of the unique motion which alone is possible when the cylinders are ⟨circular⟩ elliptic, and this is shown by the equation itself which answers the question in the general case, but would not be shown by considering [sic] merely the particular problem of the motion in similar coaxal cylinders.

It is just so with waves. A corrugated bottom excludes in general wave motion. That is to say the unique case of steady motion belonging to it (unique when depth & momentum are given) is not in general one which is capable of conversion into wave motion. If we suppose the fluid, instead of resting on, that is, flowing over, the corrugated bottom to rest on other fluid, we may 'produce', to use a Euclidian word, the motion downwards, but on going far enough we shall in general arrive at sources or sinks. Before going so far, we may select a lower stream line and make it a new corrugated bottom. For very special forms of bottom, which would be determined by the solution of the wave problem, before arriving at a source or sink we should find a stream line at a finite depth which would be straight, or else without there being any sources or sinks the stream line would tend indefinitely to a horizontal line as we descend. In the first of these cases we may make the straight line the bottom, and then superposing a horizontal velocity, which the straight bottom permits, we may convert the steady ⟨w⟩ motion into wave motion. It is similar in the second case, only that the depth is infinite.

The state of the c[a]se then I feel convinced is this. For a straight bottom we have in [sic] infinite number of possible wave forms, for the length is arbitrary, and the height too provided it do not exceed a certain limit. Any one of the wave motions may be converted into steady motion, and thus for a flat bottom we have an infinite number of possible kinds of steady motion with free surface. For any one of these we may select a stream line above the bottom, and make it a corrugated bottom, and we shall get a corresponding possible form of steady motion. For a given corrugated bottom with given mean depth and given mean momentum, there is but one form of steady motion with free surface possible. But in general this steady motion is not one which is capable of conversion into wave motion, for in general not to speak of possible sources below the bottom when we produce the motion, no one of the stream lines is straight and horizontal. It is only accidentally that we pitch upon a bottom which with suitable depth & momentum yields a steady motion which is capable of conversion into wave motion.

As to the limiting form, I am inclined to think that it does not bulge so much as I drew, and you following me drew in your last letter. Though I think that the points of inflexion in the sides don't run to the summit when that becomes a singular point, I think the bulging, if any, ⟨is left⟩ less. I have a mind when I have occasion to go to ⟨Brighton⟩ ⟨go to⟩ London to take a run down to Brighton if a rough sea should be telegraphed, that I may study the forms of waves about to break. I have a sort of imperfect memory that swells breaking on a sandy beach became at one phase very approximately wedge-shaped. This was some little time before the final breaking; in fact before or at the very commencement of the curling.

Cayley told me he had seen Dr. Paget today, who said that Maxwell was no better since he came, but neither was he worse. He told me also that he had heard that Dr. Paget said a day or two ago that he did not know what was the matter with him. If this be correct, it is plain that the case is not one of dropsy, or at least is not clearly one of dropsy, so that possibly it may not be hopeless as I supposed. That he is very ill is clear, though it seems the nature of the illness is not clear.

Yours sincerely,
G. G. STOKES

1 Stokes (1).

387 KELVIN to STOKES, 15 October 1879
Stokes Collection, K238

Oct 15, 1879
Netherhall.
Largs.
Ayrshire.

MY DEAR STOKES

I am much grieved to hear such sad reports of Maxwell's illness. If you or Mrs Stokes see him or Mrs Maxwell will you say how much my thoughts are with them. I am afraid it might disturb them if I were to write to either. I shall be much obliged if you will write or ask Mrs Stokes to write, just a line to say what accounts you have. I can scarcely bring myself to think we are to lose him so soon, with so much of pleasant intercourse as we hoped to have, and so much to do for science before we all go.

Yours very truly
WILLIAM THOMSON

388 KELVIN to STOKES, 15 October 1879
Stokes Collection, K239

Netherhall.
Largs.
Ayrshire.
Oct 15/79
(No 2)

DEAR STOKES

Your letter of yesterday came by second delivery and with it one from Porter[1] also giving a better report. I do hope the more favourable symptoms will continue, and I shall anxiously expect further reports.

I quite see how I may have been quite on a wrong groove in respect to part of what I wrote last regarding waves, and that there may be multiple-

rigourous [*sic*] solutions for the case of plane bottom though but one for corrugated. The minimum problem is curious and when well understood may be important. Given a fixed plane bottom, vertical parallel sides, and a (cylindrically) plastic surface S ⟨First with no gravity⟩ and given a uniform velocity V in parallel lines. Mould S to any shape plane or other. First consider no gravity. The plane shape is one that makes energy *not* an absolute minimum but I suppose a minimum–maximum. The same thing is true when there is gravity. Then, the plane configuration gives minimum energy for all ⟨simple-harmonic⟩ curve-of-sines configuration of ⟨the plane⟩ S, with wave length greater than *l* in the equation

$$\sqrt{\left\{\frac{gl}{2\pi}\frac{1-\epsilon^{-\frac{4\pi D}{l}}}{1+\epsilon^{-\frac{4\pi D}{l}}}\right\}} = V$$

and it will be a configuration of max^{m} energy for all ⟨sinu-sinoidal⟩ simple harmonic deviation of figure for which the wave length is $<l$. Still, when there is no resistant film at the surface the plane figure is obviously stable ⟨(provided the bottom be infinitely smooth⟩ But if there be a perfectly flexible surface film given at rest, with inertia, the plane figure will be certainly unstable: for instance if there be a thin layer of lighter liquid given at rest, on the surface of the plane – flowing liquid below.

I shall be greatly pleased if you can prove that there are steady finite wave forms & quite think you may ⟨I am not quite⟩ though I see great difficulties as to the highest-possible-wave question. I am not quite educated up to the solitary wave yet but would be very glad if you can prove his reality.

Yours truly
W THOMSON

See Camb. Cal 1874 p 562, last Senate house quest of Fri^{d} Jan 23/74 9 to 12.[2]

1 James Porter (1827–1900) was ninth wrangler in 1851 and master of Peterhouse – Kelvin's college – from 1876 to 1900. Although some correspondence between Porter and Kelvin has survived in the Kelvin Collection from the 1880s and 1890s, this particular letter has not. Porter's brother, William Archer Porter (1825–90), third wrangler in 1849 and fellow of Peterhouse, corresponded with Kelvin in the 1840s but was in India from 1863 to 1885.
2 Kelvin was additional examiner for the mathematical tripos in 1874, responsible for questions on heat, electricity, and magnetism. The question cited follows one on electricity and one on magnetism, so probably was posed by Kelvin himself. The question is:

Verify that the value of

$$\int (u\,dx + v\,dy + w\,dz)$$

for a case of steady irrotational motion of an incompressible fluid may be

$$Ux + (A\,\epsilon^{my} + B\,\epsilon^{-my})\cos mx,$$

where U, A, B, m are constants. Shew that for this case the integral of the differential equation of the stream lines is

$$Uy - (A\,\epsilon^{my} - B\,\epsilon^{-my})\sin mx = C.$$

Supposing the axis of x to be horizontal, give an expression for the pressure at any point of the fluid [fundamental propositions of hydrokinetics assumed]. Supposing the disturbance to be everywhere infinitely small, and U to be given, find A, B, and m, so that the upper surface of the liquid may be free and the lower a fixed corrugated bottom at depth a, having for equation

$$y = h\,\sin\frac{2\pi x}{l},$$

h being of course infinitely small in comparison with l.
Illustrate the (analytically) failing case of

$$U = \sqrt{\left\{\frac{gl}{2\pi}\frac{1 - \epsilon^{-\frac{4\pi a}{l}}}{1 + \epsilon^{-\frac{4\pi a}{l}}}\right\}}$$

by reference to observed phenomena in tide-races, mill-courses, or other aqueducts; and prove that the velocity of propagation of waves of length l in water of depth a is equal to the preceding value of U. (*Cambridge Calendar* for 1874, pp. 561–2. The brackets are in the question.)

389 STOKES to KELVIN, 20 October 1879
Kelvin Collection, S431

Lensfield Cottage, Cambridge, 20 October, 1879.

MY DEAR THOMSON,

I have just got your post card.[1] I wrote to you last night, but as I addressed to Glasgow you will not get the letter for some time.

I am afraid you have built too much on what I said about Maxwell. He is rather better than he was when he came, in the sense of being more free from from [*sic*] the accessory and non-essential ailments connected with his complaint, but he is also weaker, and dreadfully emaciated. I do not think that either he himself or those about him expect that he will get over it. Perhaps Mrs Maxwell may be building something on these slight improvements, but if so, I think she stands alone of those about him in thinking he may ⟨well⟩ get well. I don't think Dr. Paget has pronounced his case hopeless; possibly he may even have a ray of hope, but I should suppose that is the utmost that could be said.

Lady Thomson told me that if you were both coming you felt engaged to the Robinsons.[2] I gathered however from what you told me that if you should be coming alone to the college meeting you would like to come here. We shall be very glad to have you; but as I said in my letter to you under the circumstances I will not have a party to meet you. I am to go to London tomorrow morning, to stay the rest of the week, at least till Friday afternoon or rather evening. I shall be engaged every day from about 11 to 6 with the Commission,[3] but I dare say we can manage to meet. We could breakfast together for instance any day at the Athenaeum.

I feel pretty clear in my mind now as regards oscillatory waves on the point of breaking. I have little doubt that if the approximation were worked out to a considerably higher order of approximation, we should get with tolerable precision the value of r for the highest possible wave. As a rule, when such things are carried out to a fair number of terms, there is a regular sequence in the values of the coefficients. In the early terms they jump about. As far as I have gone, I find for the logs. of the coefficients, keeping the odd and even terms distinct.

	Odd			Even	
Logs.	Diffs.			Logs	Diffs.
0.0000					
	0.6198			0.0000	
0.6198					0.5007
	0.2100			0.5007	
0.8298					

The differences of the logs. taken in order, are 0.6198, 0.5007, 0.2100. The coefficients appear to increase at a decreasing proportionate rate of increase. If we could find the limit, l, to which the differences of the logarithms tend, and that we probably could do by going on further in the approximation, l would be the logarithm of the squared reciprocal of r for the highest possible wave.

I should have explained that the coefficients I mentioned are those of the powers of r not those of the successive cosines. I take $\dfrac{m\phi}{c} = \pi$ which gives all the cosines equal to -1, corresponding to a crest, where there is greatest tendency to divergence, that is, where finite difference formulae become unavailable to help out the numerical calculation.

Yours sincerely,
G. G. STOKES

1 The post card has not survived. Letter 374 is the most recent post card before 20 October 1879 from Kelvin to Stokes that has survived, and Stokes answered it in letter 378.
2 Probably Charles Kirkby Robinson (1826–1909) who was master of St Catharine's College from 1861 to 1909.
3 Stokes was a member of the Statutory Commission appointed in 1877, for which see D. A. Winstanley, *Later Victorian Cambridge* (Cambridge, 1947), 307–57.

Stokes Collection, K240

118 Ebury Street
London SW
Nov 16, 1879

DEAR STOKES

I wish very much that I could write the obituary notice of Maxwell[1] but I feel so over burdened with work already undertaken that I could not possibly write it now, and I see no prospect of being free-er any time before the middle of next summer, if then, that much as I would wish to write it, I feel that it would be wrong of me to undertake it. Would not Lord Rayleigh[2] write it? I am sure he would do it well, in all respects and he would thoroughly appreciate Maxwell's scientific work. But much better still – would not you do it yourself? I know you of all people are always under pressure of work, but I think you would write it much more easily than I ever could and no one knows as well as you Maxwell's real character and at the same time could write of it so well. I hope you will think of this, and may see your way to writing the notice yourself. Will you ⟨sen⟩ [?] write on my letter enclosed the name of a photographer (in answer to the question in the other letter enclosed) and post my letter?

Yours very truly
WILLIAM THOMSON

I am sorry not to have answered your letter sooner. I only got back to London from the 'Northampton' on Friday night. We go to Glasgow on Tuesday.

1 The unsigned obituary of Maxwell appeared in *Proc. Roy. Soc.*, **33** (1881–82), i–xvi.
2 John William Strutt, Third Baron Rayleigh (1842–1919) was senior wrangler in 1865 and was the Cavendish professor of experimental physics at Cambridge from 1879 to 1884. He won a Nobel Prize in 1904 and was president of the Royal Society from 1905 to 1908. There are numerous Rayleigh letters in the Stokes and Kelvin Collections, and there are six from Kelvin to Rayleigh in the Kelvin Papers at Glasgow. For a description of the Rayleigh archives, see J. N. Howard, ed., *The Rayleigh Archives Dedication*, Air Force Cambridge Research Laboratories special report no. 63 (Bedford, Massachusetts, 1967).

391 KELVIN to STOKES, 28 January 1880
Stokes Collection, K241

The University,
Glasgow. Jan 28, 1880

DEAR STOKES,

I agree with Balfour Stewart's recommendation that Ellis's paper[1] should be published when the points of priority indicated by him are put right. I should myself have made the Same [*sic*] condition in respect to points of priority if I had myself been properly learned in the subject. I return my own report.

Yours truly
WILLIAM THOMSON

Prof. G. G. Stokes Secr^y R.S.

1 W. Ellis, 'On the relation between the diurnal range of magnetic declination and horizontal force, as observed at the Royal Observatory, Greenwich, during the years 1841 to 1877, and the period of solar spot frequency', *Phil. Trans.* (1880), 541–60. William Ellis (1828–1916) joined the staff of the Royal Observatory in 1841 and from 1875 to 1893 was superintendent of its magnetical and meteorological department. Kelvin's report on Ellis's paper is in the Royal Society, RR.8.221, dated 6 January 1880.

392 STOKES to KELVIN, 22 March 1880
Kelvin Collection, S432

Lensfield Cottage, Cambridge, 22 March, 1880.

MY DEAR THOMSON,

I got your letter about Ayrton, which I shall bear in mind, and perhaps read to the Council when the manes [*sic*] are being discussed. I was aware that he was a good man.[1]

You ask about the finite waves. I have not looked into the thing for perhaps 3 months. My hands have been full of other matters, and then, which perhaps you may not have heard, my wife has been seriously ill, with inflammation in the lungs. She is now convalescent, but has not yet been down stairs.

I enclose you an uncorrected proof of a paper[2] I presented to the Royal Society. I hope I was right in doing so. There was a good deal in it that was new *to me*, but perhaps it is an old story to you. I was particularly struck with the strong current produced in the surrounding helix by a pull tending to lift off the keeper, utterly surpassing what might be produced by the mere mechanical strain, even though the keeper did not sensibly move. This *magnetic pull*, as I may call it, contrasted altogether with the effect of a push, which I suppose was mainly mechanical. Also the demagnetization of a magnetic ring by moving a surrounding helix with ends connected backwards and forwards along the ring was quite new to me. The increase of the power of a magnet by gradually loading it I had known before.

Please let me know whether the whole thing was known already, as in that case I think that in the event of any future papers being sent in by the same authors I had best submit them to you before they are presented.

Yours sincerely,
G. G. STOKES

P.S. I should correct what I wrote as to the effect of increasing the magnetic power by hanging on increasing weights being known to me. It was with reference to permaneny [sic] magnets that I had seen. [sic] it.

1 Although the letter has not survived, it no doubt recommended Ayrton for fellowship in the Royal Society, a distinction he achieved in June 1881.
2 C. W. Vincent and Lord Elphinstone, 'On magnetic circuits in dynamo- and magneto-electric machines', *Proc. Roy. Soc.*, **29** (1879), 292–7, and **30** (1880), 287–93. The two parts were received on 26 July 1879 and 10 March 1880, respectively. Charles Wilson Vincent was a fellow of both the Royal Society of Edinburgh and the Chemical Society. William Buller Fullerton (1828–93) became the fifteenth Baron Elphinstone in 1885.

393   STOKES to KELVIN, 10 April 1880
Kelvin Collection, S433

Lensfield Cottage, Cambridge, 10 April, 1880.

MY DEAR THOMSON,

Would you kindly look over the enclosed,[1] and say whether you think there is anything in what I have written that requires alteration?

The original draft was a little porcupinish, and I used in my note a stronger expression than you will now find in it. But I got Reynolds to modify what he had written, and I modified on my part what I had written, and I think that in the present state there is nothing unpleasant.

Yours sincerely,
G. G. STOKES

Might I ask for an early reply, to avail myself of it before the thing is printed off.

1 Stokes (100A), a note in defence of Maxwell added to O. Reynolds's letter to Stokes, dated 23 October 1879 and published as 'Note on thermal transpiration', *Proc. Roy. Soc.*, **30** (1880), 300–1. Stokes's addition is on pages 301–2.

394   KELVIN to STOKES, 11 April 1880
Stokes Collection, K242

April 11/80
Glasgow University

DEAR STOKES

I think your ⟨letter⟩ Note on Osborne Reynolds' letter is quite satisfactory.[1] You have I think kept quite free from any thing that could make a cause for bad feeling.

Did you look up the German reference which I gave?[2] Maxwell cannot have known of it, as it anticipates Reynolds in the discovery of the thing, though so far as I could judge by a very slight dipping into it, the author (? F Neumann?)[3] was in a very unadvanced state of mind in respect to true theory of gases, and as to the relation between what he had discovered, and such things as the Peltier effect in Thermoelectricity.[4]

I was so overpowered by my 'Heat' article[5] and kept at bay by the printers that I only got half through the proof you sent me of Lord Elphinstone and Mr Vincent's article,[6] at the time I received it from you and so I delayed writing to you. I thought it very interesting, and think this still more just now when I have read the remainder. You need not be at all concerned in imagining 'the whole thing' to be 'known already'. It certainly is very new and suggests much interesting matter for investigation. We were very sorry to hear of Mrs Stokes having been so poorly, and hope that she is now quite recovered. My wife joins in kind regards.

I hope you will really get on⟨e⟩ with the steep waves again very soon and with your book.[7] Is it going on?

Yours very truly
WILLIAM THOMSON

We are to be in Cambridge about the 21st of May, staying in Peterhouse Lodge.

1 Stokes (100A).
2 Apparently the article by Feddersen mentioned in letter 368.
3 As stated in the previous note, the author was apparently Feddersen, not Neumann. I find no such paper by the well-known German physicist, Franz Ernst Neumann (1798–1895), but there is a much less well-known Franz Neumann (b. 1837) who did publish a paper involving heat: 'Beobachtungen über die specifische Wärme verschiedener, namentlich zusammengesetzter Körper', Poggendorff's *Annalen der Physik und Chemie*, **126** (1865), 123–42. Perhaps this paper, published in the same journal as Feddersen's, caused the confusion.
4 Jean Charles Athanase Peltier (1785–1845), in measuring 'the temperature distribution along a series of thermocouple circuits. . . . discovered that a cooling effect can take place at one junction and excessive heating at the other'. (*Dictionary of Scientific Biography*.)
5 Kelvin (243A).
6 See letter 392, note 2.
7 Stokes's *MPP*.

395 KELVIN to STOKES, 14 May [1880][1]
     Stokes Collection, K243

12 Grosvenor Gardens SW London
Frid May 14.

You must instantly write a short paper[2] for the next R.S. meeting giving the theory of phosphorescence. It is sure to ooze out, and get published by

Kirch[h]of[f] or some one else and nobody will know to whom it was due. It is perfectly clear, simple and complete (or nearly enough complete to show the essentials) as you told me it yesterday ev^g.

WT.

1 This is a post card addressed to Stokes and post marked 14 May 1880.
2 Stokes did not present such a paper at this time, but see his (105), presented to the Royal Society in 1882, which contains 'some introductory remarks on phosphorescence'. But see especially Kelvin (262) in which he described Stokes's dynamical theory of phosphorescence and presented a mechanical model to illustrate it. (Kelvin's *PLA*, 1, 211–14.) In letters 435 and 449, Kelvin again asked Stokes when he would publish his theory.

396   KELVIN to STOKES, [22 May 1880]^1
      Stokes Collection, K371

DEAR STOKES,
    Will you dine with us in Peterhouse hall at 7.15 this evening?

Yours truly
WILLIAM THOMSON

Peterhouse Lodge
Saturday

1 The date of this letter is suggested by the last line of letter 394. May 22nd was a Saturday.

397   KELVIN to STOKES, 14 July 1880
      Stokes Collection, K244

Yacht, Lalla Rookh. Largs^1
July 14, 1880

DEAR STOKES
    I think it will be best to let the few additional pages of explanations offered by Darwin, be given.^{2} It is a delicate and very interesting question, and many a reader might read and appreciate this addition who had not been able to make the whole mathematical process his own consciously & completely enough to see at once the explanation for himself.
    I return Darwin's letter.^{3}
    We sail in a quarter of an hour for the South of England via Dublin.
    Will you not come and have a sail with us and see & *feel* waves. We would take you away out to the west of Scilly for a day or two if that would suit best.
    ⟨Address R Y⟩

Yours truly
WILLIAM THOMSON

P.S. Are you coming to the British Association Swansea? If so I hope you will take a passage with us from Cowes. Or will you come from Swansea up channel with us to Dublin or the Clyde, or both? I wish you would, and I hope it would be very good for you, besides useful for study of waves.

1 Kelvin has written at the top of the letter, 'Address R.Y.S. Castle Cowes Isle of Wight'.
2 G. H. Darwin, 'On the tidal friction of a planet attended by several satellites, and on the evolution of the solar system', *Phil. Trans.* (1881), 491–535. The last few pages present a non-mathematical summary of the highly mathematical paper. Kelvin's referee's report on the paper is in the Royal Society, RR.8.283.
3 G. H. Darwin to Stokes, 27 June 1880, in the Royal Society, RR.8.219. Stokes has typed on Darwin's letter the first paragraph of letter 397.

398 STOKES to KELVIN, 9 September 1880
Kelvin Collection, S434

Observatory, Armagh, Ireland, 9 September, 1880.

MY DEAR THOMSON,

It is not easy to say where to find a man who owns a yacht, but I write on spec, and at any rate you will soon I suppose be back in Glasgow.

I either wrote or intended to write to ask if you had any evidence to show whether the indications of your quadrant electrometer as applied to the observation of atmospheric electricity, when it is collected as usual at only a very moderate elevation, are other than extremely local. Does it give at all truly, do you think, the rate per foot of change of potential in ascending, truly meaning as applicable to a fair amount of space around, or are the changes of potential from place to place like drifting clouds? What would you consider the requisite height for the collecting point in order that the indications should be fairly representative?

These are important practical questions to answer in relation to observations being carried on. I see you were at Swansea.[1] I remain here probably till the first of October, and then start for Cambridge.

Yours sincerely,
G. G. STOKES[2]

1 In 1880 the British Association met in Swansea at the end of August.
2 Kelvin has written at the end of the letter:

283
Q2.
392

These are references to Kelvin's *PEM*. (See letter 400.)

> Sep 10, 1880
> Netherhall.
> Largs.
> Ayrshire.

DEAR STOKES

I have a paper (and abstract of it) by Shida[1] on magnetization ready to send to you for the R.S.[2] It has tables of results, and curves, which I am very anxious to keep at hand for my own use, to guide in respects to future work and work I have in hand at present, and it would be a great labour to get it all copied out. Could it be set up in type, and the curves lithographed, by your printers, and printed copies ⟨bu⟩ put into the hands of the referees, if I become responsible to pay the expense, supposing it is not accepted for the R.S., and any expense incurred by keeping up in type longer than usual? I would be very glad to undertake this, for my own convenience.

I shall send you the paper immediately on hearing from you, that in any case you may see it before it goes to the printers, and that you may send it to them with instructions if you accept my proposal.

How about the high waves? I hope you are getting the thing done, or have got it. It will be tremendously interesting.

I suppose you are somewhere from home (? in Ireland) but I write to Camb. for address. I hope you have all been well & my wife joins in kind regards.

> Yours
> W THOMSON

1 Kelvin has added a footnote here reading, 'Rinzaburo Shida, a Japanese student who has been with me nearly two years. He is a splendid worker, and *neat* in [h]is curves &ᶜ to a remarkable degree. [Illegible deletion of four or five words.] His patience and thoroughness are far greater than I have yet had experience of in students'.

2 R. Shida, 'Experimental determinations of magnetic susceptibility and of maximum magnetisation in absolute measure', *Proc. Roy. Soc.*, **34** (1883), 285–8, and **35** (1883), 404–54. *The Royal Society Catalogue of Scientific Papers* lists only four other papers by Shida, all in the 1880s and all on electricity or magnetism. Shida is identified in the *Proceedings* as 'Thomson Experimental Scholar, University of Glasgow'.

Sep 13, 1880
Netherhall.
Largs.
Ayrshire.

DEAR STOKES

I *did* get your previous letter asking the electric question and I have had it on my mind all this time to answer it but each day was prevented by something urgent. I am sorry you have had the trouble of writing again.

You will find in my Reprint of Papers on Electrostatics and Magnetism §283Q2 and §392,[1] all I know in answer to your question. I hope a copy of the book was sent to Dr Robinson,[2] but (in case it is not at hand) the answer is that the indications are greatly affected by local masses of air. Visible clouds have no monopoly of electrification. The smallest height is fairly representative of something. A greater height of something considerably different. It happens that at present I am resuming observ^{ns} to test the ⟨condition⟩ electrification of circumambient air, by electrometers & water-dropping collect^{rs} with nozzles at different heights outside the University tower, and some of them in rooms inside. It is certain that a considerable part of the potential measured by an electrometer in connection with a water-dropper with nozzle at N (projecting from a window of an ordinary house) is due to air both above it and below it, and that air within a radius of 50 feet of it (above and below) contributes sensibly to the whole pot^l. If the nozzle be at N' it is possible that the contribution from air within 100 feet of the ground may be more than half the whole.

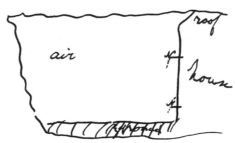

For at least 18 years I have intended to make measurements of atmospheric potential in some large hall (or church on a week day, or railway station on a Sunday) with a nozzle as nearly as may be in the centre of the enclosed air. Your enquiry is a stimulus and I hope this winter will not pass without my getting something done.

I think a meteorological ⟨shed⟩ observatory ought to have two water droppers and two electrometers: the nozzle of one up above the roof (two or three feet enough): the other under an iron shed, or a wooden or stone empty building with enough of metal in roof to make sure of no sensible difference of potential from the ground. Air blowing freely through this shed, would have its electrification tested by electrometer connected with nozzle in its centre. The other would show more fairly that due to the higher regions of air or the general electrification of the earth's surface within half a mile or a mile.

⟨The enclosed observations (made by a Japanese⟩

I thought of enclosing some observations made a few weeks ago in my laboratory by a Japanese student,[3] but I see they do not help.

I have long been wanting to hear from you if you have been doing more about waves. I hope you have. Do you see more light as to the highest possible wave?

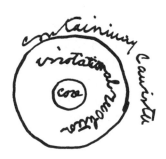

I have been working again at the old vortex problem of transition from maximum to minimum energy in two-dimensional fluid motion, and have at last got to a perfectly clear, very surprising conclusion.[4] Commencing with this, and leaving the fluid to itself in an imperfectly elastic canister, the core first swells into *vortex sponge* (by mixture of irrotational with rotational fluid) and ultimately the sponge gets squeezed outwards leaving the irrotational fluid at rest in a central cylinder and the rotational fluid in a cylindrical shell revolving rotationally round it. I shall send you an abstract. I can no more now as I am finishing hurriedly on board L[alla] R[ookh], late after a day's sail to Arran & trials of sounding machine in 92 fathoms and less depths, all very satisfactory.

Yours always truly
WILLIAM THOMSON

---

1 These are numbers of sections of Kelvin (108) and (117), respectively, as reprinted in *PEM*, 208–26 and 316–20.

2 That is, since Stokes was visiting T. R. Robinson in Armagh (see return address on letter 398), Kelvin hoped Robinson had a copy of *PEM* for Stokes to consult.

3 R. Shida.

4 See Kelvin (242) and (244).

Observatory, Armagh, 15 September, 1880.[1]

MY DEAR THOMSON,

Many thanks for your letter. If I were sure you had got the first letter and had not forgotten it, I should not have troubled you with the second, as the matter was not at all pressing. What you tell me quite agrees with what I recollected hearing from you as we were walking together one day. You told me that one day as you were lecturing at Glasgow a thunder storm came on, and you stopped your lecture to show your class how the electrometer danced about as 'puffs of electrified air came in.'

It seems to me that not much good can come from the permanent regitstration [sic] of phenomena so exceedingly local. The interest of such observations is rather physical that [sic] meteorological; or more properly is of the nature rather of experiment than observation. It strikes me that observations made with electricity collected at a considerable height, and apart from a building, suppose by an electrical kite, or a captive balloon, would be more likely to connect themselves with meteorological elements.

Another element of variability attending the use of a collector attached to a house seems to me to be the very different conditions of the house itself according as it is dry or wet, or at least moist. In the former case it would have to be regarded as a non-conductor, in the latter as a conductor; and the difference of potential between the end of the collector and the ground might be very different, though the electric charge of the atmosphere might be the very same, according as the house was to be regarded as a conductor ⟨of⟩ or a non-conductor.

I enclose a foot note added to my reprint,[2] taken from a spare proof which you need not return. It bears on the subject we discussed in section A at the meeting of the British Association at Glasgow. I sent it to Tait, asking him to send it on to you if he knew where you were; but at the time you were on the wide wide sea, and were not accessible to bores in the shape of postmen. I wanted to send the sheet to press, so I could not wait. The first vol. is now out of my hands, and I hope a copy will soon be in yours. It is thin, only 328 pages, and takes me only to 1847. In one case, see p. 314, (enclosed) I have added something more than a note.[3] I have carried the approximation by the new method to the 5th order for deep water, and to the third for water of finite depth.

You ask if I have done anything more about the greatest possible wave. I cannot say that I have, at least anything to mention mathematically. For it is not a very mathematical process taking off my shoes and stockings, tucking up my trousers as high as I co[u]ld, and wading out into the sea to get in a line with the crests of some small waves that were breaking on a sandy beach. I stayed for a week at Malahide on my way here, but there were no good waves during my stay. I tried to make out something from what I could get, but they were paltry ones. However it did seem to me that the waves began to break while their sides still made only a blunt angle, a good deal less than 90°. I feel pretty well satisfied that the limiting form is one presenting an edge of 120°.

If waves in general may be pushed to this limit, then making the wavelength infinite we pass in the limit to a solitary wave. It appears then that a solitary wave can be propagated without change of form, and that the highest wave which can be so propagated is one with a ridge of 120°. It may not be easy to generate a solitary wave of the requisite form for travelling unchanged. It seemed to me that the highest solitary wave had a height equal to half the d[e]pth of the water; and indeed I wrote out a passage to be added to by [sic] book to this effect, but did not feel sufficiently certain about it to put it in. I will copy it out however.

In a report[4] published in 1846, I expressed the opinion that probably degradation in height was an essential charecteristic [sic] of a solitary wave (ante p. 170). I now think that it *is* possible for a solitary irrotational wave to be propagated without change of form. For I see nothing to limit the generality of the investigation regarding oscillatory waves, so long as the height is below the limit mentioned at p. 226.[5] And when we suppose the length of wave to increase indefinitely each elevation becomes in the limit a solitary wave, and the different elevations become independent of each other, so that we may imagine them all suppressed but one.

It would seem too that the greatest height of such a wave is half the depth of the fluid. For when the wave motion is converted into steady motion, the velocity at any point at the surface is equal to that due to the depth of that point below the crest, or ridge of 120°. As shown at p. 226. At a distance from the elevation the velocity in question will be that of propagation, which therefore is equal to that due to the height of the wave. On the other hand, considering the wave motion as it actually is, it would seem that the outer portions of the wave, where the elevation is very small, must be propagated with the velocity of a long wave of small elevation; and as by hypothesis the whole is propagated together, the velocity of propagation must be that of a long wave, or that due to half the depth of the fluid at a distance from the elevation.

The doubtful point is, whether on receding laterally from the vertical plane through the crest, the horizontal motion may not decrease according to so rapid a law that we nowhere arrive at a place where the vertical motion can be neglected in comparison with the horizontal, so that the formula for long ⟨ve⟩ waves may be applied.[6]

Since I sent off my paper[7] I have drawn a figure for the case of depth = 0.3 of wave length, and coefficient in first term of height = 3-8ths about, or ⟨0.275⟩ 0.375 of depth. I drew the approximations to the 1st, 2nd, and 3rd orders separately. We see how the approximation gradually approaches the correct form, and by interpolating by the eye we are able to get not far from the true form. The figure however shows that the coefficient .375 of depth is considerably above that for the highest wave. I should think half that would be nearer the thing.[8]

We know that the swells of the ocean break over a shoal even when the depth is very considerable.

My first volume will ⟨soo now ss⟩ soon now be out. I have already sent some copy for the second volume, telling them that if it were thought well it might be set up in slip, as I had not quite decided whether or no to include a paper which if it did come at all would come before the paper I sent for setting up. The papers I am doubtful about are the series of papers I wrote entitled 'Notes on Hydrodynamics'.[9] As some were written by you[10] and some by me, my share would be rather fragmentary, and I sho[u]ld be rather disposed to leave them out. On the other hand, some of my Cambridge friends seemed to think they would be useful for the students. But I hardly think that students will care to get my book. I think Tait was of opinion that they might as well be left out. I should like to know your opinion if you happen to have formed one. I should be glad also to know whether you are satisfied with the foot note at p. 311.[11]

The result you mention as to the motion which results from an infinitesimal deformation of an initial state in which you have a core of fluid of the form of a circular cylinder revolving about its axis surrounded by a coaxial cylinder of fluid revolving irrotationally is very curious, and is not what one would have anticipated.

I do not know whether you have heard of the very serious illness of our good master.[12] From the last accounts he is not likely to survive for many weeks.

Yours sincerely,
G. G. STOKES

1 Kelvin has drawn the following figure and written the following above, beside, and just below the first paragraph of the letter:

Certain impulse given: min^m energy.

$E'' = cm^{\frac{1}{2}}$

$mv = I = \sqrt{2E'} \cdot \sqrt{m}$

$\frac{1}{2}mv^2 = E'$

$$E' = \frac{I^2}{2m}$$

$$cm^{\frac{1}{2}} + \frac{I^2}{2} m^{-1} = a[?]$$

$$+ \tfrac{1}{2} cm^{\frac{1}{2}} = \frac{I^2}{2m^2}$$

Given the energy, make the mom[entum] a max no. mom[entum] may be ∞.

2 Note added to reprint of Stokes (21), in *MPP*, I, 311–12.
3 Stokes (99A), published for the first time in *MPP*, I, 314–26.
4 Stokes (6), in *MPP*, I, 157–87.
5 Stokes (29), in *MPP*, I, 197–229.
6 Larmor has written in the margin, 'The result would in fact disagree with Michell's conclusions (see Papers v. [V] p. [159]) and moreover it would imply that all solitary waves of whatever height travel at the same speed'. Larmor's reference is to a note added by him to Stokes (137), published posthumously in *MPP*, v, 146–59. Larmor's note is on pages 158–9. John Henry Michell (1863–1940), senior wrangler in 1887, was lecturer and later professor of mathematics at Melbourne from 1891 to 1928.
7 Stokes (99A).
8 Larmor has written in the margin, 'Michell's value is [.142]'. Larmor gives the value in Stokes's *MPP*, v, 159 (see note 6). Michell first gave the value in his 'The highest waves in water', *Phil. Mag.*, **36** (1893), 435.
9 Stokes (16), (19), and (28).
10 Kelvin (29.1), (29.2), and (40).
11 See note 2.
12 John Power (1818–80) and Stokes were undergraduates together at Pembroke, both becoming wranglers in 1841 – Power eighth, Stokes senior. Power pursued a college career as tutor at Pembroke from 1852 to 1870 and master from 1870 to 1880. There are a dozen letters in the Stokes Collection from Power to Stokes, dating from 1848 to 1880.

402 Kelvin to Stokes, 21 September 1880
Stokes Collection, K247

Fergus' Photographic Studio
Largs, Sep 21, 1880

Dear Stokes

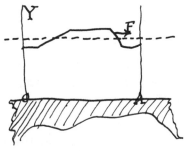

Waiting here with a friend to be be [*sic*] photographed I have found something that I tried for last year about waves unsuccessfully and to which your last letters have set me on again. Motion confined to two dim^{ns}. Given a perfect liquid spread over an infinite plane under influence of gravity. Displace the surface to any arbitrary shape, periodic, (wave-length OA). Keeping this form rigid apply force F to each wave of it, and keep it applied till a momentum M has been given; then leave it to itself. It will go on forever as a wave kept in shape by the rigid form at its surface. Now let this form lose rigidity and have instead a flexural resistance-couple at every point proportional to rate of change of curvature with time. The wave will begin to change shape, unless it has been rightly shaped by the rigid form to begin with. In this change, energy energy [*sic*] is lost but momentum remains constant; and the motion is at each instant the same as if it were started from rest by giving the surface its actual form, and normal velocity at every point. The shape to which the surface will subside is determinately the wave of which the length is the given length and the momentum the given momentum. Thus we see that a wave of constant form is determinately *the* configuration of motion of which with given momentum the energy is (a?) minimum (? a minimum or the minimum?) subject to the condition of the l-periodicity. The minimum which is the solution of the ⟨question⟩ wave problem is not the ⟨smallest⟩ motion in which the energy is least possible: for this is clearly uniform motion of the whole water, with the given momentum; and is infinitely nearly that which would be produced if the initiating form were that of Fig 2. This is not a proper 'minimum' in math[l] language, I suppose. There certainly is a proper minimum unless the given momentum be too much. The result of giving too much momentum to the initiating ⟨w⟩ form to allow subsidence to a ⟨steady⟩ constant wave, is curious and difficult to follow off hand. I should say it must lead to something spongy. If the momentum be not too great there is one true minimum. A smaller momentum will permit two minimums ($l =$ wave length in one of them $\frac{1}{2}l$ in the other). Still smaller will permit three minimums (l, $\frac{1}{2}l$, $\frac{1}{3}l$) and so on. In every case the motion will subside into one or other of the minimums, according to the character of the initiating form.

Given the resultant motion due to two true waves, (l and $\frac{1}{2}l$) superimposed. (Let them be infinitely small if [?] you please). Let there be a massless, viscously flexible surface. The motion will subside into the l or $\frac{1}{2}l$ wave.

Yours W.T. (obliged to stop short, to go out for an afternoon sail and use a good breeze to test relative merits of globular and elongated sinkers (16 lbs). Which do you think best?

Observatory, Armagh, 22, September, 1880.

MY DEAR THOMSON,

Thanks for your interesting letter about waves. In reading it an idea struck me which I think would be worth mentioning to you, though I don't know but that it may have occurred to you already, and perhaps it was that you had in your mind when you wrote about the sponge.

Suppose a series of waves travelling uniformly along, of course having the proper shape to enable them to do so. Suppose now gravity suddenly to diminish considerably. The momentum is now much too great. What will take place? Clearly the crests, where the motion of the particles was forwards, will shoot forwards, and the waves will curl over and fall down on the anterior side. Now at any rate 'surfaces of discontinuity' will be formed, though not of the kind we have been considering, but such as are formed by a portion of what was common surface of water and air, or say and vacuum, coming to be in contact with another portion of the same surface, so that there is a breach of continuity in the conditions. But that is merely by the way, and is not what I meant to write about. *That* is this. Instead of supposing gravity to alter, suppose the depth to receive a secular decrease, as when waves come in on a shelving sandy beach. Presently the momentum will be too great, and then the waves must begin to shoot forward at the crests.

I have devised a method by which I think I shall be able to draw the form of the maximum wave. It applies best to the extreme cases of deep water, or else of a solitary wave. When length and depth are both finite, I am obliged to leave it in the shape of harmonic series, which in the two extreme cases admits of summation or integration. The method is one involving trial and error. An approximate form of the surface and approximate velocity of propagation – this last only in case the wave is short of the maximum, for for [*sic*] the maximum the thing is connected with the form, – are taken for trial, and then by a particular process a second curve is deduced from the first, which will coincide with it if the trial curve be true, and otherwise, I expect, will indicate how the trial curve should be corrected, so that after two or three repetitions of the process I hope to get the outline sensibly exact. I have not yet tried it.

As to the foot note I introduced about discontinuity,[1] I think we must wait till we meet to discuss the matter. If what I have advanced, not as a thing demonstrated, but one to which I was stro[n]gly inclined, be capable of being shown to be wrong, it is too late to correct it for the book. I should not wonder however if it should be found that the difference between us is apparent only, depending upon our proposing different problems for solution. I have had some curious instances of instability, I should rather say curious indirect evidences of instability, in some other cases in which viscosity is concerned.

You don't say anything about the notes in hydrodynamics,[2] so I suppose you have no decided feeling one way or other.

Yours sincerely,
G. G. STOKES

P.S. I did not mean to imply that the trial method I mentioned would fall to the ground in case the length and depth were comparable, only it would be more laborious, and in the case of the maximum wave, or very near it, might not be very exact, ay [sic] least without more labour than the thing was worth.

2nd. PS. I see you have a paper of Niven's,[3] sent you June 4.

1 Note added to the reprint of Stokes (21), in *MPP*, I, 311–12.
2 Stokes (16), (19), and (28).
3 C. Niven, 'On the induction of electric currents in infinite plates and spherical shells', *Phil. Trans.*, **172** (1881), 307–53. Kelvin's referee's report is in the Royal Society, RR.8.237, dated 4 November 1880. Charles Niven (1845–1923) was senior wrangler in 1867, professor of mathematics at Queen's College, Cork, from 1867 to 1880, and professor of natural philosophy at Aberdeen from 1880 to 1922.

---

404 KELVIN to STOKES, 22 and 23 September 1880
Stokes Collection, K248

Lalla Rookh at sea
Clyde Sep 22/80

DEAR STOKES

The wet blanket has a very peculiar effect on waves. It exalts those of short length giving them increase of momentum and of energy, at the expense of the momentum and energy of those of greater length. This is obvious if you imagine the initial state of things to be two sets of waves, of length l and $\frac{1}{2}l$, superimposed. First, if there were rigourously just one set of rigourously constant waves: the wet-blanket, being massless, will instantly acquire translational velocity equal to the propagational velocity of the waves; and then, being not subjected to bending and unbending, it will consume no energy and things will go on forever uniformly. Hence with two sets of waves superimposed, the wet blanket will take a translational veloc. ⟨equ⟩ intermediate betw the propagational vel^ies of the two sets. It will consume energy on the whole, but will give momentum and energy to the slower waves which are the shorter.

But this result is a wet-blanket on my theory of the day before yesterday. It shows that the effect of a viscously flexible surface is to throw any possible given motion into confusion. It *cannot* alter the moment of momentum. It must cause ruffling to grow up, and must produce breaking waves, and a chaotic state, very difficult to follow, in which moment of momentum will spread down to the bottom, and the motion will tend ultimately [towards] uniform motion of the fluid en-masse from surface to bottom, which is the condition of least possible energy for given moment of momentum. Alas! I thought some clear and useful theorems of minimum energy were coming out quite clear! But the wet blanket itself is more wonderful in its effects than any such theorem could well be.

Sep. 23. A viscously elastic very stiff but not infinitely rigid bottom will do the same as the viscidly flexible sheet at ⟨surface⟩ surface supposing the bottom to be massless and therefore to take whatever horizontal motion is required to annul the horizontal component of forces on it.

This is finished in a carriage in motion (not in yacht) so excuse want of clearness. I must close now (Sep 23) but have more to write.

Yours
WT

405 KELVIN to STOKES, 24 September [1880][1]
      Stokes Collection, K364

Netherhall
Largs
Ayrshire
Sep 24

DEAR STOKES

Certainly I think you should include the Notes on Hydrodynamics.[2] I have also to write a word or two about Atmospheric Electricity.

I have more of maximum–minimum property in respect to Energy and momentum of waves coming out very nicely, but can no more for this post than the above about Notes on Hydrodynamics which I hope you will act on. The Note or two of mine[3] interspersed is of no consequence and yours are quite complete without them.

Yours
W THOMSON

1 The letter continues themes from letters 402 to 404 and provides a direct answer to Stokes's statement at the end of letter 403 concerning his 'Notes on Hydrodynamics'.
2 Stokes (16), (19), and (28), in *MPP*, II, 1–7, 36–50, and 221–42, respectively.
3 Kelvin (29.1), (29.2), and (40).

Lensfield Cottage, Cambridge, 4 October, 1880.

MY DEAR THOMSON,

Before I left Armagh I tried a numerical experiment as to how my method of getting the maximum wave would answer. I took for the trial curve a serrated outline, composed of straight lines of equal length inclined to the horizon at angles of 30°, alternately up and down. This form, egregiously wrong as regards the troughs, gave nevertheless for the first corrected form one which to judge by the appearance must have been very near the truth. It hardly differed from the other for a considerable distance from the crests, but the lower part was replaced by a gracefully flowing curve. If I were to use this, or any similar flowing curve as a guess-form, the tangents at the extremities being inclined at 30° to the horizon, I believe the first corrected curve would be sensibly exact.

It was for the case of deep water. The other extreme of very shallow water may be managed in nearly the same way. When the depth is neither very great nor very small, I meet a series that I cannot sum, and the calculation would have to be carried out in a different way which would probably be more laborious.

Yours sincerely,
G. G. STOKES

P.S. I followed your advice, and left the first of my notes on hydrodynamics[1] at the press today.[2]

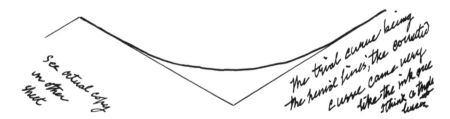

1 Stokes (16).
2 In Stokes's figure, the upper, smooth curve is the one in ink. The 'other sheet' that he mentioned is missing.

Oct 4/80[1]
Netherhall.
Largs.
Ayrshire.

DEAR STOKES (Wave motion)

With given momentum the energy is (easily proved to be) a minimax when the form of the surface is such as to remain unchanged when left to itself. The calculus of variations so far as I know has not generally, ⟨so f⟩ nor in any individual case by the regular methods of the calc of var^{ns}, been worked so as to distinguish thorough max^{m}, thorough min., and 'minimax' (do you like the word? It supplies a want long grievously felt; within Sir W Hamilton's 'stationary action').[2] In this case the Fourier analysis does the calc^s of variation's work well, and provides for distinguishing the variation for which there is min. from those for which there is max. Case of infinitely deep water, chosen for brevity.

Let
$$\eta = h_1 \cos(m\xi + \langle h_2 \rangle e_1) \\ + h_2 \cos(2m\xi + e_2) \\ + \&^c \qquad (1)$$

be the equation of the surface, subject to the sole condition of being periodic, with wave length $\dfrac{2\pi}{m}$, given. Let ⟨$x =$⟩ $\xi = x - Vt$ and let v be the component velocity at (x, y) parallel to y; and ϕ the velocity potential. We have

$$-v = \frac{d\eta}{d\xi}\left(\frac{dx}{dt}\right)_{\xi\,\text{const}} = V\frac{d\eta}{d\xi} \qquad (2)$$

Hence
$$v = mV(h_1 \sin\theta + 2h_2 \sin 2\theta + \&^c) \qquad (3)$$

where $\theta = m\xi + e_1$

Hence
$$\phi = -V\epsilon^{\langle -my\rangle}(h_1\,\epsilon^{-my}\sin\theta + h_2\,\epsilon^{-2my}\sin 2\theta + \&^c) \qquad (4)$$

This is the impulsive pressure required to get the *form* in motion with velocity V. Hence if M denote the momentum, per wave length

$$M = \int \phi_{y=0}\frac{d\eta}{d\xi}\,ds = \int_0^{\frac{2\pi}{m}} \phi\frac{d\eta}{d\xi}\,d\xi$$

(where ds denotes an element of length of the curve (1), which is infinitely nearly $= d\xi$.)

$\langle$ Hence $M = mV \int_0^{\frac{2\pi}{m}} d\xi (h_1 \sin \theta + h_2 \sin 2\theta + \&^c)^2 \rangle$

Hence $M = mV \int_0^{\frac{2\pi}{m}} d\xi (h_1 \sin \theta + h_2 \sin 2\theta + \&^c)(h_1 \sin \theta + 2h_2 \sin 2\theta + \&^c)$ (5)

$$= \pi V(h_1^2 + 2h_2^2 + \&^c);$$

and therefore if K be the kinetic energy

$$K = \tfrac{1}{2} VM = \tfrac{1}{2}\pi V^2 (h_1^2 + 2h_2^2 + \&^c) \tag{6}$$

Now if P be the pot^l energy we have

$$P = \int_0^{\frac{2\pi}{m}} g\eta \cdot \times [sic] \tfrac{1}{2}\eta \cdot d\xi = \tfrac{1}{2}g \int_0^{\frac{2\pi}{m}} \eta^2 \, d\xi = \frac{g\pi}{2m} (h_1^2 + h_2^2 + \&^c) \tag{7}$$

Hence if E be whole energy

$$E = \tfrac{1}{2}\pi \left\{ V^2 (h_1^2 + 2h_2^2 + \&^c) + \frac{g}{m} (h_1^2 + h_2^2 + \&^c) \right\} \tag{7 [sic]}$$

Consider $V, h_1, h_2, \&^c$ to be independent variables, and make E a minimax, subject to (5) with M given. To be as unanalytical and explicit as possible, eliminate V. Thus we have

$$E = \tfrac{1}{2}\pi \left\{ \frac{\pi^2 M^2}{h_1^2 + 2h_2^2 + \&^c} + \frac{g}{m} (h_1^2 + h_2^2 + \&^c) \right\} \tag{8};$$

and for minimax

$$\frac{dE}{dh_1} = 0, \quad \frac{dE}{dh_2} = 0, \quad \&^c \tag{9}$$

or

$$h_1 \left[\frac{g}{m} - \frac{\pi^2 M^2}{(h_1^2 + 2h_2^2 + \&^c)^2} \right] = 0$$

$$h_2 \left[\frac{g}{m} - \frac{2\pi^2 M^2}{(h_1^2 + 2h_2^2 + \&^c)^2} \right] = 0 \tag{$10)^3$}$$

$$\&^c$$

$$\&^c \, h_i \left[\frac{g}{m} - \frac{i\pi^2 M^2}{(h_1^2 + 2h_2^2 + \&^c)^2} \right.$$

The solutions are

$$h_2 = 0, \quad h_3 = 0, \quad .. \frac{g}{m} = \frac{\pi^2 M^2}{h_1^{\langle 2 \rangle 4}} \ldots \text{I.}$$

$$h_1 = 0, \quad h_3 = 0, \quad \ldots \frac{g}{m} = \left\langle \frac{x}{m} \right\rangle [?] \frac{\pi^2 M^2}{2 h_2^{\langle 2 \rangle 4}} \ldots \text{II.} \qquad (11)$$

$$\&^c \qquad \&^c$$

and so on, an infinite number of solutions, giving every simple harmonic infinitesimal wave for which the wave length is

$$\langle l \text{ or} \rangle \quad \frac{2\pi}{m} \quad \text{or} \quad \frac{1}{i}\frac{2\pi}{m}$$

Now to test the character of the minimax, suppose h_1, h_2, $\&^c$ to be each infinitesimal small except h_i; we have, by (8),

$$E = \tfrac{1}{2}\pi \left\{ \frac{\pi^2 M^2}{i h_i^2} \left(1 - \frac{h_1^2 + 2 h_2^2 + \&^c}{i h_i^2} \right) + \frac{g}{m} \, h_i^2 \left(1 + \frac{h_1^2 + h_2^2 + \&^c}{h_i^2} \right) \right\} \qquad (12)$$

Putting in the infinitesimal terms, $h_i^4 = \langle i \rangle \dfrac{\pi^2 M^2}{i \frac{g}{m}}$, we have

$$E = \tfrac{1}{2}\pi \left\{ \frac{\pi^2 M^2}{i h_i^2} + \frac{g}{m} h_i^2 + \frac{g}{m} \left[h_1^2 \left(1 - \frac{1}{i} \right) + h_2^2 \left(1 - \frac{2}{i} \right) + \&^c \right] \right\} \qquad (13)[4]$$

From this we see that E is a minimum in respect to different values of h_i, when

$$h_i = \sqrt[4]{\frac{\pi^2 M^2}{i \frac{g}{m}}} \, ;$$

and is a min^m in respect to h_1^2, h_2^2 ... h_{i-1}^2, for zero values of these; and is a max^m in respect to h_{i+1}^2, h_{i+2}^2 $\&^c$ ad inf. for zero values of these. This agrees with what I wrote you last. Excuse exceeding roughness because I have been interrupted several times and have not time to rewrite for this post. I hope however it will be clear enough. Please keep it as I *may* ask you to let me have it again, that I may rub it up a little for publication if you think it worth publication.

We are just off (5 $\langle$:20$\rangle$ pm) to sail for Rothesay and sleep in the Bay there to see the Craigmore $-\cdot-\cdot$[5] light & come back before breakfast tomorrow morning.

Yours

W THOMSON

1 Kelvin has written at the top of the letter, '$\langle$Write me if you have done anything on board

[illegible word] today.⟩ I think this minimax consideration may possibly help you in respect to the ⟨greatest⟩ highest possible wave?'

2 This is the principle of least action as employed by William Rowan Hamilton in his optical researches. (See Thomas L. Hankins's article on Hamilton in the *Dictionary of Scientific Biography*, VI, 87.)

3 The brackets in the equations are Kelvin's.

4 The brackets in the equations are Kelvin's.

5 Kelvin has written just below here, '(letter C, by eclipses, long short long short)'.

408   KELVIN to STOKES, [11 October 1880][1]
Stokes Collection, K251

$\dfrac{d\eta}{d\xi}$ is assumed infinitely small. Hence u & v are each infinitely small in comparⁿ with V. Hence $-v \fallingdotseq V\dfrac{d\eta}{d\xi}$:[2] understood that the fluid is given at rest and receives motion solely in virtue of motion given to the surface-form. Is this enough or is there anything else requiring explanation?

W.T.

Excuse the roughness in a carriage in motion.

1 This is a post card addressed to Stokes and post marked Glasgow–Carlisle Sorting Tender, 11 October 1880.

2 The symbol $\fallingdotseq$ means approximately equals.

409   STOKES to KELVIN, 15 October 1880
Kelvin Collection, S438

Lensfield Cottage, Cambridge, 15 October, 1880.

MY DEAR THOMSON,

I was looking today into a paper of mine 'On a Difficulty in the Theory of Sound' Phil. Mag. vol. 33, p. 349, year ⟨188⟩ 1848.[1] You pointed out to me that in the curious discontinuous motion I had speculated about, in which to take one instance, you might ? have air at rest in a tube, at a highish density, and passing off into rarer air in motion, like the combustible matter in a rocket, you pointed out to me I say that there was a violation of the principle of the conserbation [*sic*] of energy. Lord Rayleigh afterwards, and independently, pointed out the same.

I got two relations between three unknown quantities, namely the ratio of ro to ro', and the two differences between the three velocities w, w', and ou² ... For notation see p. 353. The conservation of energy gived [*sic*] another relation, which can be satisfied, so that it appears that such a motion is possible. Only the ratio of ro to ro' is determinate. I suppose the pressure to vary as the density, as supposed in the investigation. The ratio of the densities comes out as 5.033 to 1; to take the rocket case the velocity of the gas, i.e. the rare comes 80 per cent more than the velocity of sound, and the velocity of backward propagation of the surface of discontinuity about 45 per cent of the velocity of sound.

I have not yet worked it out numerically when account is taken of the development of heat. The result up to the moment when the change, whatever may be its precise nature, takes place is given in Earnshaw's paper in the Phil. Trans.[3]

I merely referred to the rocket as representing a possible case of motion, of a very peculiar character; it is not what would take place when the change came. The difference of density would not be near what the rocket requires.

When the ratio of densities is more nearly one of equality than 5.033 to 1, the energy, potential energy, of expansion more than suffices to generate the kinetic energy; when the difference is greater than 5.033 to 1, there is not potential energy enough in the ex[p]ansion.

The turn of this paper will come before long, and I am obliged to look a little ahead in order not to keep the book waiting.

Yours sincerely,
G. G. STOKES

1 Stokes (22), in *MPP*, II, 51–5. Stokes added a paragraph to the reprint (p. 55) relating to the topic of this letter.
2 In the original version of his (22), Stokes used the symbol ४ for the third velocity – the velocity of propagation of the surface of discontinuity.
3 S. Earnshaw, 'On the mathematical theory of sound', *Phil. Trans.* (1860), 133–48.

410 STOKES to KELVIN, 1 November 1880
Kelvin Collection, S439

Cambridge, 1 Nov. 1880.

MY DEAR THOMSON,

On further reflection I see that I was wrong, and that a surface of discontinuity in crossing which the density of the gas changes abruptly is impossible.[1]

As to what you said about the effect of reversing the motion, I did not see the solution at the moment, but it is very simple. In the original motion, the motion in certain parts of the wave becomes more and more abrupt, and in other parts more and more gentle. When the motion is reversed, the motion becomes more and more gentle in those parts in which in the forward motion it became more and more abrupt, and becomes more and more abrupt in those parts in which in the forward motion it became more and more gentle.

Yours sincerely,
G. G. STOKES

1 See Stokes (22), in *MPP*, II, 51–5.

411   STOKES to KELVIN, 3 November 1880
Kelvin Collection, S440

Lensfield Cottage, Cambridge, 3 Nov. 1880.

MY DEAR THOMSON,

I mentioned to you I think in a letter that I had found that my surface of discontinuity was bosh.[1] In fact, the equation of energy applied to a slice infinitely near the surface of discontinuity leads to

$$\int_{\varrho'}^{\varrho} \frac{p}{\varrho^2} \, d\varrho = \tfrac{1}{2}(w'^2 - w^2),$$

where ϱ, ϱ' are the densities, and w, w' the velocities on the two sides of the surface of discontinuity. But this equation is absurd, as violating the sencond [*sic*] law of motion. In this way the existence of a surface of discontinuity is *proved* to be *im*possible. If it be said, suppose the gas to be divided into two partitions by an infinitely thin solid partition, which is then annihilated, what will take place? I can only compare it with the problem of moving a perfectly flexible and inextensible heavy string by an impu[l]sive force acting at one end *not* in the direction of a tangent.

A paper 'Discussion of a Differential Equation Relating to the Breaking of Railway Bridges' is a little ahead.[2] I think I shall include it; but it is rather of practical than mathematical interest. It cost a good deal of numerical calculation, and did good service to a Royal Commission in its time, but it is not a paper of enduring interest.

Yours sincerely,
G. G. STOKES

1 See Stokes (22), in *MPP*, II, 51–5.
2 Stokes (32), in *MPP*, II, 178–220. See letter 57, note 2.

The University,
Glasgow.
9 Nov: 1880.

DEAR STOKES,

I use simply gun metal for the contact surfaces of the forks pressing on the surfaces of the iron globes in my finished tidal Harmonic Analyser. I have not given it a sufficiently rigorous test for accuracy yet, to allow me to form any independant [*sic*] opinion as to whether improvement in this respect is wanted. From what you told me, I presume you ⟨r⟩ have a reason for wanting something better than gun metal. I should think glass would answer exceedingly well, possibly as well as rock crystal, (considering that glass is harder than the gun metal globes) and it would be cheaper, and more easily ground true.

I am sorry to hear the rule of the Council is so rigid, about back numbers of the transactions [*sic*]. I think the ⟨y⟩ volumes should ordinarily be sent to the fellows' ordinary addresses, so that no fellow may be liable to fall into the snare into which I have fallen. If the ordinary address misleads the volume, so much the worse for the fellow, but then it would be distinctly his own fault; while it can scarcely be said to be his own fault that he forgets to ask for a volume before he finds that he wants it. It does seem to me that the Council's law of deprivation is very harsh, as the books must be there, and the property of the fellow who has not claimed them. A moderate fine for storage and for trouble to the Royal Society for announcement or correspondence, would it seems to me be a sufficient penalty for a fellow not asking for a volume which comes out at some time to him unknown and unforeseen. If ever the Council thinks it worthwhile to re-consider the subject I do think a rescinding of the old law, and the substitution of a milder and fairer one in its stead would commend itself to their judgment.

Yours very truly
WILLIAM THOMSON

413 KELVIN to STOKES, 28 November 1880
Stokes Collection, K249

> Nov 28/80
> The University,
> Glasgow.

DEAR STOKES

I am very sorry you are not Master of Pembroke.[1] I think it is very wrong that you are not, and I feel greatly disappointed. I felt sure that you would be elected and hoped much that you would consent to accept the office.

Did you receive a letter[2] from me (in my secretary's hand) about a fortnight ago answering your question about the contact surfaces of the forks in the harmonic analyser? I left London, (for full speed trials of H.M.S. 'Superb' at Sheerness) ⟨and⟩ suddenly and have never felt sure that the letter was posted. I meant to ask you also to tell me something of your observations on the work done by the machine in the meteorological office, and the amounts and characters of the errors you found. I did not do so by letter because I thought I should have seen you at Cambridge yesterday & this day week, as I had been summoned to London to give evidence respecting my affidavit about the telephone but the case was put off til[l] this week as I suppose you too know, and I am now under summons for next Wednesday possibly but more probably later.[3] I suppose I shall meet you at the trial, and perhaps we may have an opportunity of talking over the machine.

I am following your example about a reprint of papers, and the printing is now begun or about being begun.[4] Did you see in the last few weeks 'Natures' my short articles (from Brit. Ass. Swansea) about minim. energy in fluid motion. & elliptic whirls?[5]

My wife sends her kind regards to Mrs Stokes and bids me tell her she too is very sorry about the mastership.

> Yours very truly
> WILLIAM THOMSON

---

1 Charles Edward Searle (1828–1902), tenth wrangler in 1851, became master of Pembroke College in 1880 and, upon his death in 1902, was succeeded by Stokes. There are some forty letters from Searle to Stokes in the Stokes Collection.

2 The previous letter.

3 The telephone trial resulted in a judgement on 20 December 1880 that a telephone was a kind of telegraph, as *telegraph* was defined in the Telegraph Act of 1869, and, therefore, that it came under the monopoly of the Postmaster-General regarding telegraphs. Stokes and Kelvin were witnesses on behalf of private telephone companies against the government. (See F. G. C. Baldwin, *The History of the Telephone in the United Kingdom* (London, 1925), 42–7.)

4 The first volume of Kelvin's *MPP* was published in 1882.

5 Kelvin (242) and (244).

Lensfield Cottage, Cambridge, 2 December, 1880.

MY DEAR THOMSON,

I thought that I might possibly have seen you in London as I supposed you would be there for the great telephone trial[1] about the time I was there. I gather from what you said in your letter that you were at the R.S. on Thursday last week and were surprised not to see me. I have been incessantly at work at meetings of the Cambridge University Commission,[2] on account of which I gave up the meeting of the Royal Society last week. Today we were at it from 10 a.m. to 6-15 p.m., with an interval of 17 minutes for fresh air and luncheon, for those that wanted it or had time to get it.

As to the harmonic analyser, the test which it did not exactly satisfy was that on moving the bar to and fro a good number of times, the cylinders were not quite st[e]ady, as they should be. On examining the pushing screws or pushing disks . . . they are the flat ends of screws, the screw being to permit of exact adjustment . . . we found that they were slightly worn though the instrument has not yet had much use, and though the screws were of hard steel, and the balls were steel nickel plated. Glass might perhaps have been quite sufficient for capping the screws, but it is doubtful, and I thought it better not to economise the 15 shillings or so difference in the cost it might make, but to get rock crystal. They are not, I believe yet ready, but I hope will be in two or three days.

The instrument was found to work pretty well in following zig-zags, made up of vertical and horizontal lines. The chief errors found were such as were referable to errors of epoch. If these cannot be readily corrected, they can be allowed for in the final results.

On Saturday afternoon, we give over Commission work for a time. I gave you a wrong equation about the surface of discontinuity matter, but when the right one is substituted it shows that the thing is impossible.

I came across the figure for waves that I had mislaid, and send a pricked through copy of the figure[3] I got from the first approximation, starting from a serrated outline composed of straight lines inclined at angles of 30 degrees to the horizon. This is drawn faintly in red. For the first 4 sevenths or so of the half wave, measuring from the crest, there is hardly any change, then you get a nice rounded outline instead of the pointed trough. The reason why so little change is made for a long way is doubtless that the conditions would be satisfied exactly by the figure assumed for the crest were it not that as you go down the assumed figure changes into something else. The non-satisfaction of the conditions near a trough extends its influence some way up. Doubtless the next approximation would extend the curved part somewhat nearer the crest, and the trough would be a little higher, but I think not much. I tried the serrated outline to put the method to a rather severe test. If I had taken for the trial form an arc of a parabola bounded by tangents inclined at angles of 60 to the vertical diameter, the first approximation would I expect have been nearly exact. I have of course no time for work of this kind while these daily meetings of the Commission last.

Yours sincerely,
G. G. STOKES

P.S. I had not calculated the parabola numerically; it is a good deal too shallow. The trial curve need not however be any mathematical curve.

1 See the previous letter, note 3.
2 See letter 389, note 3.
3 The figure is no longer with the letter.

415   STOKES to KELVIN, 4 December 1880
Kelvin Collection, S442

Lensfield Cottage, Cambridge, 4 Dec. 1880.

MY DEAR THOMSON,

I have been closely engaged for the last fortnight nearly with meetings of the Commission.[1] We did not meet today, so that I have now a little breathing time.

I send you a proof of my last sheet but one. You need not trouble yourself to return it. Would you kindly glance at the introduced paragraph on p. 55?[2] I have cut out the part of the paper which related to the formation of a surface of discontinuity, but I was of course bound to say a few words to correct it.

The equation I sent you was wrong, as I had omitted the consideration of the work of the pressures at the two ends of the elementary portion, taking for granted without investigation that they would not come in, whereas I see they do. If w, w' be the velocities, ϱ, ϱ' the densities, p, p' the pressures at the two sides of the surface of discontinuity, and if we consider an element comprising that surface, we get from the principles of constancy of the mass and conservation of momentum, if I may so call it, $\forall$ being the velocity of propagation of the surface of discontinuity,[3]

$$\varrho(w - \forall)\,dt = \varrho'(w' - \forall')\,dt$$

$$(pw - p'w')\,dt = \varrho\,\overline{w - \forall}\,\,dt \cdot \overline{w' - w}$$

Whence
$$\varrho(w - \forall) = \varrho'(w' - \forall) = \frac{\varrho\varrho'(w' - w)}{\varrho - \varrho'}$$

and then from the eq^n of energy

$$pw - p'w' + \frac{\varrho\varrho'(w'-w)}{\varrho-\varrho'}\left\{\int_{\varrho'}^{\varrho}\frac{p}{\varrho^2}\,d\varrho - \tfrac{1}{2}\overline{w'^2 - w^2}\right\} = 0$$

and as
$$p - p' = \frac{\varrho\varrho'}{\varrho-\varrho'}\overline{w'-w}\;\overline{w'-w} = \frac{\varrho\varrho'}{\varrho-\varrho'}(w'-w)^2$$

we have
$$pw - p'w' + \frac{\varrho\varrho'(w'-w)}{\varrho-\varrho'}\int_{\varrho'}^{\varrho}\frac{p}{\varrho^2}\,d\varrho - \tfrac{1}{2}\overline{p-p'}\;\overline{w+w'} = 0$$

or reducing
$$\frac{2\varrho\varrho'(w'-w)}{\varrho-\varrho'}\int_{\varrho'}^{\varrho}\frac{p}{\varrho^2}\,d\varrho = \overline{p+p'}\;\overline{w'-w}$$

Whence dividing by $w' - w$ we have in the case of $p = k \cdot \varrho$ the equation written on the proof.[4]

Having occasion in the notes on hydrodynamics, (Demonstration of a Fundamental Theorem),[5] to use Cauchy's integrals, I thought it well to point out, what of course is obvious, how immediately two of Helmholtz's fundamental propositions respecting vortex motion flow from them when once the propositions have been suggested. I have used the expression 'vortex thread'. When we have the good Saxon monosyllabic word 'thread', I do not see why we need go to the trisyllabic word of Latin derivation 'filament'.

Yours sincerely,
G. G. STOKES

P.S. You need not trouble yourself to return the proof, but if you have any remarks to make please let me know without delay if it would affect anything that is shortly going to press.

1 See letter 389, note 3.
2 Stokes (22), in *MPP*, II, 51–5. Stokes's additional paragraph on page 55 of the reprint replaced most of the final four pages of the original article.
3 Larmor has made on the original letter several editorial changes in this sentence and the following ten lines:

change ꝏ to v throughout;
delete w and w' from the left side of the equation in line two;
substitute *From the former* for *whence* in line three;
substitute $-\dfrac{1}{\varrho}\dfrac{dp}{d\varrho}$ for $\dfrac{p}{\varrho^2}\,d\varrho$ in lines five, eight, and ten; and

insert *by the second equation* after *as* in line six.
4 Larmor has added the following footnote here: 'Namely $2\varrho\varrho' \log\dfrac{\varrho}{\varrho'} = \varrho^2 - \varrho'^2$, an equation which has only one real solution $\dfrac{\varrho}{\varrho'} = 1$, so that a surface of discontinuity is impossible'. This is the equation given by Stokes in his addition to (22), in *MPP*, II, 55.
5 Stokes (19).

416 KELVIN to STOKES, 13 December 1880[1]
Stokes Collection, K252

> The University,
> Glasgow.
> 13 Dec: 1880

DEAR STOKES,

I am much obliged to you for the Proof and your letter of the 4th, and am much interested in them.

Page 53, line 3; – Query, for 'Mathematical' substitute 'Analytical'?[2] I don't know if you are changing the wording at all of your old papers? I suppose you could write 'analytical' but perhaps you would prefer to leave 'mathematical' as it stood in the original.

I have now received up to page 63 in type of my reprint, and a great deal more copy is in the printer's hands. Shall we try a race, which will have a volume out soonest – your second or my first?[3]

> Believe me
> Yours very truly
> WILLIAM THOMSON

Professor Stokes

P.S. I am making no changes in my old wording: only making substantial changes when I find mistakes &[c].

1 LB.2.70 in the Kelvin Collection is a draft of this letter by Kelvin's secretary.
2 Stokes made the change in his (22), in *MPP*, II, 53.
3 The first volume of Kelvin's *MPP* appeared in 1882; the second of Stokes's in 1883.

417 KELVIN to STOKES, 11 January 1881
Royal Society of London, MC.12.139

> The University,
> Glasgow.
> 11 Jany 1881.

DEAR STOKES,

I enclose a paper[1] describing what I daresay you will agree with me in considering the best thing in the way of Seismographs yet out. It is impossible to get one for vertical component motion w[ch] would fully realize Ewing's principle; but I think a heavy mass hung on one end of the arm of an ordinary balance with its beam kept nearly horizontal by an exceedingly long and massive spiral spring, on the same principle as the hair-spring of a watch (a flat spiral) or of a chronometer, (a helical spiral) might serve, with other details like those of Ewing. What do you think? The object of course is to get a vertical mass supported by a spring in such a manner that if disturbed from it's [*sic*] position of equilibrium and left to itself, the period of oscillation shall be 5 or 10 or 20 seconds or more and yet the whole apparatus including both ends of the spring of moderate dimensions, within a few feet of space.

Yours truly

WILLIAM THOMSON

1 J. A. Ewing, 'On a new seismograph', *Proc. Roy. Soc.*, 31 (1881), 440–6.

418 KELVIN to STOKES, 28 January 1881
Stokes Collection, K253

The University,
Glasgow.
28th Jany '81

DEAR STOKES

I think the Proceedings would be more suitable than the Transactions for the paper⟨s⟩ which I return enclosed.[1] The subject has been pretty well beaten threadbare. I have been satisfied with what I read of it in Murphy's Electricity[2] 40 years ago, (except the last 2 lines of page 107 which have no meaning) and as I have read nothing that F. Neumann, C. Neumann,[3] Weber, Clausius, Helmholtz, Maxwell and Tait have written upon it, I am not very competent to give an opinion as to the relative or even absolute value of Watson & Burberry's [*sic*] paper. I can't say I feel quite confident that it should be printed for the Proceedings. I don't like the look of their 'Proposed law', page 17 but I may be wrong.

I don't think I am however when I look at the sentences marked with pencil on page 31. The whole affair seems to be a beating of the air. The paper seems longer than need be. If you look for instance at the marked passages on pages 18 and 43 you will see a repetition which is rather bewildering to the reader who expects he is going to learn something he did not know before when he reads the first line of page 43.

The authors don't quote Helmholtz. From what he told me in conversation I understand he discussed the question of what the formula would be supposing the mutual action to be not in the line joining them, and concluded if it is assumed in the line joining them it must be Ampère's. I think it might be well to ask the authors if they know Helmholtz' work.

Perhaps if they don't they might on learning it find their own unnecessary.

On the whole I think if the paper could be quietly stowed off, from occupying its space in the Proceedings there would be nothing lost.

Yours truly
WILLIAM THOMSON
per J[ohn] R[ennie][4]

Prof. G. G. Stokes

1 This refers to a paper by Henry William Watson (1827–1903) and Samuel Hawksley Burbury (1831–1911) which the Royal Society did not publish. Second wrangler in 1850, Watson was assistant master at Harrow from 1857 to 1865 and rector of Berkswell with Barston, Warwickshire, from 1865 to 1902. Fifteenth wrangler in 1854, Burbury was called to the bar in 1858 and practised at the Parliamentary Bar from 1860 to 1908. They co-authored *The Mathematical Theory of Electricity and Magnetism*, 2 vols. (Oxford, 1885–89). Their 'On the law of force between electric currents', *Phil. Mag.*, 11 (June 1881), 451–66, was probably based on the paper rejected by the Royal Society. It discusses research by many of the men mentioned in this letter.

2 R. Murphy, *Elementary Principles of the Theories of Electricity, Heat and Molecular Actions. Pt. 1. On Electricity* (Cambridge, 1833). Robert Murphy (1806–43) was third wrangler in 1829, became a fellow of the Royal Society in 1834, and was an examinar in mathematics and natural philosophy in London University in 1838.

3 Carl Gottfried Neumann (1832–1925), the son of Franz Ernst Neumann, was professor of mathematics at the University of Leipzig from 1868 to 1911.

4 John Rennie was Kelvin's assistant. There are numerous letters in the Kelvin Collection involving Rennie, especially LB4, a letter book consisting largely of press copies of letters written by Rennie for Kelvin in 1882 and 1883.

419   STOKES to KELVIN, 1 April 1881
Kelvin Collection, S443

Lensfield Cottage, Cambridge, 1 April, 1881.

MY DEAR THOMSON,

With reference to your question, it is to be remembered that Crookes took special precautions to prevent the entrance of vapour of mercury into the bulb of his apparatus. Of course it must have been present in the Macleod [*sic*] gauge;[1] and to the extent that its pressure was sensible it would vitiate the measures of the pressures at extreme exhaustions. It would of cous [*sic*] course, as far as it went, tend to exaggerate the exhaustions. For when the contents of the vessel in the gauge was compressed, the pressure of any rs [*sic*] residual vapour of mercury which remained uncondensed would go for nothing as agains[t] the increased pressure of the gas.

Yours sincerely,
G. G. STOKES

1 See W. Crookes, 'On the viscosity of gases at high exhaustions', *Phil. Trans.*, 172 (1881), 387–434, and Stokes (101). Crookes discussed the McLeod gauge on pages 393–5, while McLeod's own account is in H. McLeod, 'Apparatus for measurement of low pressures of gas', *Phil. Mag.*, 48 (1874), 110–13.

420   STOKES to KELVIN, 11 April 1881
Kelvin Collection, S444

Lensfield Cottage, Cambridge, 11 April, 1881.

MY DEAR THOMSON,

It seems to me that the practical detection of the partly-above-earth character of the cause that produces the magnetic disturbances would be almost too delicate a matter to be practiccally [*sic*] carried out if the theory that I advanced be true.[1] It is not as if the origin of the disturbance were outside the earth at a distance from the surface comparable with the radius.

The principle of the determination I presume to be this. Suppose we knew the horizontal components of the disturbance all over the earth. Then we should have the variation of the magnetic potential, and consequently the potential itself, save theoretically as to a constant, which would not signify. We could thence get the vertical component by calculation, get[t]ing one expression ⟨id⟩ if the disturbing cause were wholly inside, and a different expression if it were wholly outside; and if we like we may combine these expressions, which would be applicable to the case of a disturbing cause partly outside and partly inside. This is then to be compared with the observed vertical component of the disturbing force.

Of course we need not trouble ourselves with the whole earth. It would be sufficient to take a considerable tract of country sufficiently represented by observatories, and get the results from those.

The difficulty is this. The aerial currents I imagine to be at a height of not more than a very few miles from the surface. I am sceptical about the great heights which have been attributed to the aurora by some observers, or rather pairs of observers, who have endeavoured to measure it trigonometrically. That being the case, the magnetic effect of any aerial current at any station would be very nearly the same as if its path were immediately under the surface of the earth instead of in the air, except as regards the small portion of the whole aerial discharge which lies immediately overhead, or nearly so. And the question arises, is it likely that a considerable portion of the whole effect is due to aerial cur[r]ents within a few miles of the place of observation? In any case the currents would be, according to my view, half terrestrial, half aerial, and it is only on that small fraction of the latter which lies within a few miles of the place of observation that we can operate to detect its aerial character. The question is, does the local aerial current sufficiently make up by its proximity for its forming but a small fraction of the whole system of aerial currents?

In favour of the supposition that it does, may be mentioned the fact that there seems to be a general agreement, though not more than a general agreement, between the earth currents in the neighbourhood and earth currents which would be competent to produce the observed effect on the needle. And the aerial currents would be likely to be even more capricious in their character than the earth currents. For the aerial discharge is disruptive in its nature, and even when apparently steady would have a tendency to follow particular channels, whereas the terrestrial, being conductive, would be more regular in its distribution.

So on the whole it seems to me that though the thing ought certainly to be attempted, it is far from certain whether, with the data we should be able to obtain, we should arrive at a definite conclusion.

Yours sincerely,

G. G. STOKES

1 See Stokes (104).

421 KELVIN to STOKES, 4 July 1881
Stokes Collection, K254

The University,

Glasgow.

4th July '81

DEAR STOKES

The way to observe atmospheric electricity in a bal[l]oon is by an electrometer much less sensitive than my quadrant electrometer. My small portable electrometer would be perfectly suitable. The way to observe is by 2 water-droppers; one of them with its nozzle hanging ⟨20 feet⟩ down a little distance below the bal[l]oon, to get nearly clear of its inductive effect; say 20 feet below the car; and another 20 feet lower: one of them connected with the brass case of the instrument, which must be insulated from the bal[l]oon and from the observer's hand; and the other connected with the principle [*sic*] insulated electrode of the instrument. This would measure the difference of potential between 2 points, one 20 feet above the other. Suppose the difference of potential to be 38 Volts per foot, [see Reprint of Electrostatics and Magnetism; §295][1] the difference of potential to be measured, would be 760 Volts; which would be very suitable for measurement by the portable electrometer. The half mile you propose, would fill any electrometer hitherto made with [electrical][2] blazes. See 'Reprint' §§253 and 254–261[3] for explanation of the kind of information to be had by observations of atmospheric electricity from a bal[l]oon.

I am sorry to have been prevented by incessant occupation while in bed (hard work in the laboratory on Faure accumulators,[4] continually in progress and reported to me hour by hour almost every day &ᶜ &ᶜ) from writing to you in answer to your letters, in all of which I was much interested. The contact-electricity effects in electrolytes are terribly mixed up, and I am afraid it would be difficult to get measurements, although no doubt results are to be got by the method you propose. I have from time to time tried things of the kind but never very thoroughly. You will see a note of some attempts to it in the Report of the British Association Meeting at Belfast in 1852.[5]

As to your mathematical problem I quite saw the force of your second letter and have often thought of the problem proposed in your first on the subject and saw that it was very difficult.

I am still overwhelmed with work, Faure and dynamos, especially these 3 days, till I leave for London and Portsmouth (six compasses for the 'Inflexible') and Paris (Faure accumulators &c &c). I am now perfectly well.

Believe me
Yours very truly
for WILLIAM THOMSON
J Rennie

I have signed in Sir Williams [*sic*] Thomson's abscence [*sic*] so as to catch this mail.

J.R.[6]

1 Kelvin (111), in *PEM*, 227–9. The brackets in the letter are Kelvin's.
2 Kelvin's brackets.
3 Kelvin (121C), in *PEM*, 192–208.
4 The Frenchman Camille Faure is credited with inventing a storage battery around 1880. (See Percy Dunsheath, *A History of Electrical Engineering* (London, 1969, first published 1962), 155–6.)
5 Kelvin (54).
6 The letter is in Rennie's hand; hence, the spelling mistakes are his, not Kelvin's.

422 STOKES to KELVIN, 11 July 1881
Kelvin Collection, S444A

Meteorological Office,
116, Victoria Street, London S.W.
11 July 1881

MY DEAR THOMSON,

You kindly offered, I think, to lend us a portable electrometer, now I think at some instrument maker's.

Would you kindly write to Mr Scott[1] enclosing authority to the instrument maker to send us the instrument on loan in case we should ask for it. Our plans are not yet matured.

Yours sincerely,
G. G. STOKES

Sir Wm Thomson F.R.S.

1 Robert Henry Scott (1833–1916) was secretary to the Royal Society's Meteorological Committee and then to the Meteorological Council from 1867 to 1900. There is an extensive correspondence from Scott to Stokes in the Stokes Collection. See letter 345, note 3.

Yacht, Lalla Rookh.[1]
Portsmouth
July 20/81

DEAR STOKES

I am afraid I am in debt several letters.

[James] White has no portable electrometer ready at present. This is a most unfortunate time as the workshop is closed all this week (and has been so since Friday morning last) but I have written to have one finished for Mr Scott as soon as possible. I am to hear as soon as they can tell me when one will be finished and shall let you know. Meantime I have written for one of my own which I had altered for another purpose, and if I find when it comes here that it might serve for the balloon I shall be glad to send it. But whoever is to use it ought to have a lesson and some experience before trying it in a balloon. Could he come here if I find that the electrometer would do, and I should tell him all I could about it, and how to use it in the balloon? I am afraid instructions merely in writing might scarcely suffice, without more time for practice.

It ⟨would⟩ might [(] probably would be [)] be difficult or impossible to get *accurate* results with the quadrant electrometer by keeping a constant, small, differen⟨tials⟩ce of potentials between the quadrants, and measuring the difference betw the needle and one pair (which would be several thousand, or several hundred volts) by the deflection. ⟨The⟩ Want of perfect symmetry in the quadrants, ⟨ren⟩ and of perfect centring and perfect symmetry in the needle, renders it necessary to push out or in the quadrant to cause the zero when the jar is electrified and the pairs quadrants kept connected with one another and the outside coating, to agree with the mechanical zero (or zero when there is no electric force). Thus the *directive force* on the needle (⟨or,⟩ reckoned by the mechanical couple required to deflect it through a stated angle from the zero) depends on the electrification. Indeed this proposition is true even with perfect symmetry, because of the finiteness of the gaps between the quadrants. If the directive force were rigourously $= c + c'\, V^2$ accurate measurement might be made in the way proposed by Mr Scott; but the thing I fear would be rather complicated and precarious. A very slight change in the conditions of the instrument (levels &^{c}) might make troublesome irregularities. Still the thing is worth trying. Will you not give us a visit on board the L.R.? We shall be about here and the Solent till time for the British Ass^{n2} except a short sail across channel & to Paris. Do come & we shall to able to talk over things deliberately, besides going out to look for waves.

Yours very truly
WILLIAM THOMSON

1 Stokes has written at the top of the letter, 'ans^d & wrote to [Warren] De la Rue 22/7/81'. The extensive De la Rue correspondence in the Stokes Collection contains five letters dating from the summer of 1881, including D288 and D289, both from De la Rue, dated 24 and 27 July 1881, respectively.
2 In 1881 the British Association met in York, beginning August 31st.

424 KELVIN to STOKES, 13 November 1881
Stokes Collection, K256

Netherhall.[1]
Largs.
Ayrshire.
Nov 13, 1881

DEAR STOKES

Clairault's [*sic*] Theorem

Alas – I took your letter about it in my hand immediately after receiving it by post, (having just seen that it was about Clairault's theorem, but not read it) and carried it up to our drawing [room][2] with a number of papers' proofs &^c to be read in the evening. It has never been seen again! I missed it that evening but had no apprehension. Next day I looked for it, and we have had a general search in study and drawing room. I still felt sure it would turn up but day after day some little fresh search only tended to diminish the residue of hope, which is now all gone. I am afraid I must ask you to write it to me again and am very sorry to give you so much trouble. As to ⟨the⟩ your second letter, the case is clear. It is solely to moisture settling invisibly on glass or other insulating supports at temperatures above the dew point, that observers above that lowest depth of carelessness and want of judgment in which possible or visible bedewment could be ignored, have been led to imagine moist air more conductive or less resistant than dry air. It may be more or it may be less, but no observer has ever yet found any conduction at all through air dry or moist.

The invisible moisture on clean glass above the dew point is a fine subject for experimental investigation. The conductive effect on electricity is the only way I see for carrying it out. The electric test has splendid sensitivity; but it may be difficult to disentangle the results from effects of want of chemical cleanness of the glass.

Yours always
W THOMSON

We came down here from Friday to Monday. My wife begs to be kindly remembered to you and M^rs who we hope is better.

1 Kelvin has written at the top of the letter, 'Address University Glasgow'.
2 Larmor has inserted *room*.

Lensfield Cottage, Cambridge, 15 Nov. 1881.

MY DEAR THOMSON,

I am not sure whether I can recollect all my motives in writing the letter which has been mislaid, but I have a pretty good recollection of what I wrote about, and I think I can reproduce it. Moreover as I am blessed with the possession of a writ[i]ng machine I can write with facility what I have to say. You won't mind an occasional misprint in fast writing.

When I was writing about Clairaut's theorem, and had shown that there is no need to suppose that the internal distribution is in nearly ⟨spherical⟩ spheroidal shells, of equal density, while obviously at the same time it is not perfectly arbitrary, I was naturally led to think about possible internal distributions.[1] You may, as you know, have the attracting matter distributed over the surface, or you may have a distribution in which it is more centrally packed. I was able to prove that in the closest packing there was no matter distributed over space of 3 dimensions. For consider the mean potential. Even if all the matter were condensed into a point, this would be finite, and therefore for some distribution it must be a maximum. In the maximum, none ⟨cal⟩ can be distributed in space of 3 dimensions. For if possible let it be in 3 dimensions. Take a ⟨small⟩ sphere within this space, and consider so much of the matter within the sphere as corresponds to the smallest density within it. This matter might be collected into a point in the center without affecting the external potential, and this alteration of distribution would increase the mean potential, and therefore the supposed maximum-mean-potential distribution was not such, which is contrary to the supposition we started with. Hence for the maximum there can be no matter extending over 3 dimensions. Hence it can only be in surfaces, including, as degenerate cases of surfaces lines and points. Nor can one of these surfaces be a closed surface of finite curvature – or infinitely small, but not infinitely great, – with a finite density all over it. For place an electrical point within, and consider the electrical density induced by it over the surface, supposing the surface to be the inner surface of a conductor. The external potential due to the two would be nil, and therefore a superficial density of att[r]acting matter proportional to the induced electricity would produce the same external potential as if it were collected into a point in the place of the supposed internal electrical point, in which case it would have a greater mean potential; and by taking the quantity small enough we may effect this change without laying bare any portion of the surface, bare that is as to matter distributed on it; and therefore the distribution be [sic] started with is not that of ⟨mean potential⟩ maximum mean potential. A point however in a closed surface where the density is nil forbids further stripping. Such a point may however be regarded as an infinitely small hole, and in this way of looking at it the surface, though geometrically coincident with a closed surface, may be regarded as an open surface.

In the same manner a surface with a salient edge or conical point may be regarded as an open surface. At least a distribution with finite density over such a surface cannot have the matter more closely packed by the supposed electrical arrangement, and therefore will not form an exception to the statement that the distribution must be over o p e n surfaces provided we regard a surface, though closed, as an open surface when it has ⟨salient⟩ a salient ⟨edge⟩ wedge or conical point.

On the other hand there are cases, as the electrical consideration shows, where the matter distributed over a closed surface with a salient wedge or conical point where the density becomes infinite may yet admit of closer packing; and on the other hand there may be cases of closed surfaces with re-entrant wedges or conical points where the density vanishes, where nevertheless the vanishing line or point ought not to [be] regarded as a hole, and a closer distribution is possible. I did not go into the question of closed surfaces with infinite curvature about particular lines or points, nor do I think that they need be gone into, but may be treated as limiting cases of great but finite curvature.

Excluding then the case of closed surfaces with infinite curvature at any point, and leaving them to be treated when they arise as limiting cases, we may say that it is demonstrated that the distribution which gives a maximum mean potential can only be in open surfaces.

In writing to me you said that you had written a paper in the Cambridge Mathematical Journal as to the case of a sphere,[2] – was it? in which you concluded that when the series by which the external potential is expressed became divergent, on contracting the radius of the sphere, you had got to the limit of the inward encroachment on the larger sphere with which you started, which you could make without altering the external potential or coming across matter; that you saw the 'hole' through which you must have fallen; that it had not occurred to you that the surface might be still further contracted leaving a portion of the matter jutting out, or isolated in the external space. You said also that you supposed I assumed the matter to be positive, as otherwise there would be no limit to the mean potential. This I had seen. You also asked what led me to think of mean potential. In fact, I was not led to it by any physical consideration; I merely had recourse to it as affording a means of demonstration.

I mentally called the distribution I have referred to a 'fontal distribution'. I endeavoured to prove that a fontal distribution must be unique. It is easy to prove that there cannot be two different fontal distributions, u n l e s s p o s s i b l y two which together make up a closed surface with no portions jutting out. I suspected, but could not prove, that even this was impossible. It certainly is possible if you admit negative as well as positive matter. For take a closed curve, and imagine an electric current traversing it. The magnetic effect of the current may be replaced by that of a magnetic sheet capping the curve. Two such sheets therefore will produce the same attraction on a particle of the imaginary magnetic matter placed anywhere outside the space enclosed by the two sheets.

I never published anything about this investigation because I was unable to satisfy myself as to the uniqueness of a 'fontal distribution'.

As to the resistance of the air to electricity, the resistance I had in view was not ⟨that of a wire⟩ like that of a wire or electrolyte but resistance to a d i s r u p t i v e discharge. De La Rue, as you know, has shown that in an exhausted tube, be the discharge ever so steady, the laws of the resistance are those of the resistance to a series of sparks, and not at all Ohm's laws.[3]

Yours sincerely,

G. G. Stokes

1 See Stokes (27), (31), and (79).
2 I have not found this particular problem.
3 See W. De la Rue, 'The phenomena of the electric discharge with 14,400 chloride of silver cells', *Proc. Roy. Inst.*, **9** (21 January 1881), 461–92, especially 483–5.

426 Stokes to Kelvin, 31 December 1881
Kelvin Collection, S446

Lensfield Cottage, Cambridge, 31 Dec. 1881.

My dear Thomson,

On the whole I am disposed to think that Mr. Gray's paper[1] might be a candidate⟨d⟩ for the Transactions. The experiments have evidently been carefully made; the analyses of the glasses must have involved a great deal of labour, though the results pack into small compass, and the time variation which he has discovered in the electric resistance of glass is so far as I know quite new, and is very curious.

Would you write to him for an abstract? It may be quite brief; in fact, it had better be brief, merely stating the salient results of the investigation.

I return you your proof.[2] I think I shall win the race, for I have got to over 300 pages in my second volume. I have suggested in one place the omission of the word 'fine', as the woodcutter has not quite carried out your ideas, and it does not matter.

I recollected long ago when we were speaking about what I have called fontal distributions your saying that you saw the hole that you had fallen through, or some such expression, in referring to an oversight that you afterwards corrected.[3] I was not aware, I think, at the time that[4] you had already found in consequence of your electrical images work.

A happy New Year to you and Lady Thomson.

Yours sincerely,
G. G. STOKES

1 T. Gray, 'On the variation of the electric conductivity of glass with temperature, density, and chemical composition', *Proc. Roy. Soc.*, 33 (1882), 256–7, and 34 (1883), 199–208. Thomas Gray (1850–1908), educated at Glasgow, taught electrical engineering at the Imperial College of Engineering in Tokyo from 1879 to 1881, was Kelvin's assistant in electrical engineering work from 1881 to 1888, and finally became professor of engineering at Rose Polytechnic Institute in Terre Haute, Indiana.
2 Apparently for part of volume 1 of Kelvin's *MPP*, which appeared in 1882. Actually, Kelvin won the race, as Stokes's second volume appeared in 1883. See the last paragraph of letter 416.
3 See the previous letter, note 2.
4 This sentence would make more sense than it does if *that* were *what*. The letter is typewritten, so perhaps this is a typographical error by Stokes.

427 STOKES to KELVIN, 24 January 1882
Kelvin Collection, S447

Lensfield Cottage, Cambridge, 24 Jan. 1882.

MY DEAR THOMSON,

I have just seen that the demonstration of the uniqueness of a fontal distribution in the case which I could not satisfy myself about long ago is in reality absurdly simple.

Yours sincerely,
G. G. STOKES

428 KELVIN to STOKES, 27 January 1882
Stokes Collection, K257

The University,
Glasgow.
27th Jany 1882

DEAR STOKES

I am exceedingly glad you have made out the uniqueness of the fontal distribution satisfactorily. I hope you will immediately publish it to the Royal Society.[1] Do you care to have your last letter to me on the subject, either to work it into the paper or to use it for reference? Write simply on a post card, 'Send it', and I shall do so.

I think I at last see light on an old vexed and vexing question, referred to in

Thomson and Tait sec. 776.[2] An oblate spheroid of revolution is now, I see, certainly unstable, if its e⟨x⟩ccentricity exceeds a certain limit. Hence there is certainly a ring figure of equilibrium, but it is not certain that any ring figure is stable. It may be, and probably is, unstable, relative to thinning in some parts, and thickening in others. This is certainly the case for a very slender ring, and may be the case, for all I know, for any possible ring, however stout. A stable figure, when both ring, and oblate elliptic spheroid are unstable, is certainly two equal detached masses rotating round their common Centre of Inertia. When the moment of momentum is sufficiently great, there certainly are figures of equilibrium, consisting of separate rotating rings, like Saturn's rings, but it is probable that the equilibrium is unstable for all such cases. It is certain that the equilibrium is unstable for more than two detached portions rotating round their common Centre of Inertia.

Going back to a single continuous liquid mass; and referring to Thomson and Tait sec. 778; it is certain that with given moment of momentum, if sufficiently great, there are three ellipsoidal figures; one the ellipsoid of revolution, and two others falling under sec. 778.[3] This is obvious from the maximum–minimum form of the problem; which is – to make the sum of potential and kinetic energy a minimum ⟨of⟩ or a maximum, with given moment of momentum. If we reduce the energy to a function of a, and b, it is easily proved, that if there is, besides the figure of revolution ($a = b$), another solution, there must be two others; for one of which the energy is a minimum, and for the other a maximum. The energy is always a minimum for the figure of revolution,[4] *if we impose the condition that the surface is an ellipsoid of revolution*. But if the spheroid be very flat, it is clear that deviation from the ellipsoidal figure, but still keeping to ⟨the⟩ a figure of revolution, may diminish the energy. Thus if a considerable portion of a central part of the flat figure be thinned, and parts outside it, but not too near the rim be thickened by the liquid so removed from the central part, the whole energy can be diminished, the moment of momentum remaining constant. It is this consideration that proves the possibility of a ring figure.

With large moment of momentum, it is quite clear from sec. 778, that there is a figure of equilibrium, with c, excessively small, b larger than c by an infinitesimal, and a very large. This figure has minimum energy, if the condition that the surface be an ellipsoid be imposed; but without this condition, it is not a minimum, and the equilibrium is unstable. If the liquid have any viscosity it would tend to separate into two detached masses and settle into stable equilibrium by these rotating about their ⟨centre of⟩ common Centre of Inertia.

Believe me

Yours very truly
WILLIAM THOMSON

1 Stokes did not.
2 Kelvin and Tait, *TNP*. See Kelvin (259), read 3 April 1882.
3 Kelvin corrected this statement in letter 430.
4 Kelvin corrected this statement in letter 430.

429 KELVIN to STOKES, 21 March 1882
Royal Society of London, RR.9.88

The University, Glasgow
21st March '82

DEAR STOKES

My report on Thomson's paper[1] is that in my opinion it is suitable for publication in the Transactions. I think also the enclosed addition ought to be published along with it, and I enclose correspondence which if you care to glance at it will shew you how the addition originated. I also enclose a copy of my paper on Vortex Statics[2] referred to in the correspondence.

I should be glad to have the correspondence returned to me some time or other at your convenience.

Yours very truly
WILLIAM THOMSON

P.S. I am sorry to say I find I have no copy of the paper on 'Vortex Statics' mentioned above, but you could find in the Proc. R.S.E. Vol X page 443. I seem to have got no separate copies of it.

1 J. J. Thomson, 'On the vibrations of a vortex ring, and the action of two vortex rings upon each other', *Phil. Trans.*, **173** (1882), 493–521. Pages 517–21 contain a note added by Thomson on 21 March 1882 explaining what Kelvin had pointed out to him. See Kelvin to J. J. Thomson, 10 January 1882, Cambridge University Library, Thomson Papers, Add. MS 7654, K5, and J. J. Thomson to Kelvin, 25 January 1882, Kelvin Collection, T532. Joseph John Thomson (1856–1940) was second wrangler in 1880 and replaced Rayleigh as Cavendish professor at Cambridge in 1884, holding the position until 1918.
2 Kelvin (237).

430 KELVIN to STOKES, 15 April 1882
Royal Society of London, MM.16.32

The University,
Glasgow.
15th April '82

DEAR STOKES

I made a mistake in my letter to you of 27th Jan'y, in the middle of the third page.[1]

There are not three ellipsoidal figures but only two. The one of revolution is unstable, and the Jacobian figure[2] with three unequal axes is stable when the moment of momentum exceeds a certain limit.

There is also a correction wanted for the top of page 4.[3]

The energy is a minimum for the revolutional figure when the moment of momentum is less than a certain limit, and there is then no Jacobian figure: when it is greater than this limit the energy is a minimax for the revolutional figure, and a minimum for the Jacobian figure. The critical moment of momentum is that which makes $\frac{\sqrt{a^2 - c^2}}{c} = 1.39457$ for the revolutional figure. In this case the Jacobian figure coincides with the revolutional figure.

Yours very truly
WILLIAM THOMSON

1 See letter 428, note 3.
2 Carl Gustav Jacob Jacobi (1804–51) was professor of mathematics at the University of Königsberg. His research on the equilibrium of rotating fluid masses showed that a rotating ellipsoid was stable even when its three axes were unequal.
3 See letter 428, note 4.

431 KELVIN to STOKES, 23 April 1882
Royal Society of London, RR.9.86

The University, Glasgow[1]
April 23^d/82

DEAR STOKES,

Report on Lord Rayleigh's paper on 'Experiments to determine the Value of the B.A. Unit'.[2]

I received the paper yesterday morning and have read a considerable part of it with much interest and satisfaction. I saw some of the work in progress and heard many details regarding it from Lord Rayleigh from time to time. I believe it to be a most valuable work and that it will settle the value of the ohm with the very serious correction which Lord Rayleigh has made in it, amounting to 1.3 per cent of its value. The paper I believe to be suitable for publication in the Transactions.

WILLIAM THOMSON

1 Kelvin has written at the top of the letter, 'The paper goes by book packet registered to Secretaries &^c R.S. London'.
2 Rayleigh, 'Experiments to determine the value of the British Association unit of resistance in absolute measure', *Phil. Trans.*, **173** (1882), 661–97.

Lensfield Cottage, Cambridge, 24 May, 1882

MY DEAR THOMSON,

I thought I should have seen you at the R.S. this afternoon, but I heard that you were engaged in a most unpatriotic endeavour to oust the good old English inch.

May 25. I arrived late last night, and I did not get very far with my letter. When I showed you the formula

$$F(\phi) = \frac{1}{\pi} \sum \int_0^{2\pi} \frac{e^{nk} - e^{-nk}}{e^{nk} + e^{-nk}} \cos n\phi \sin n\phi' f(\phi') d\phi' \tag{1}$$

you suggested putting $\dfrac{e^{+[nk]} - e^{-[nk]}}{e^{+[nk]} + e^{-[nk]}}$ under the form $1 - \dfrac{2e^{-nk}}{e^{nk} + e^{-nk}}$, and then expanding as to the latter part. I did not at the time think that there was much in this, having in my head to sum the series if possible, to which the expansion did not help. Failing the summation, I did not think that it would be worth the trouble to attempt to make any use of the formula (1) and had not thought more about it.

But in seeking whether I could not find something in your remark, another idea occurred to me as to your meaning. I am disposed to think that it is not exactly what you meant, but is somewhat like it.

I am disposed to think that what you meant was to expand $\dfrac{2e^{-nk}}{e^{[+nk]} + e^{-[nk]}}$ and then sum the series $\sum \pm e^{\overline{2n + 2m}\,k} \sin(\phi' \pm \phi)$. We should then have to find a set of integrals of the type:–

$$\int \frac{\sin \overline{\phi' - \phi}}{e^{2mk} - 2\cos \overline{\phi' - \phi} + e^{-2mk}} f(\phi') d\phi'$$

and then sum a series which converges rapidly, in consequence of the e^{2mk} in the denominator.

This doubtless could be done, though the labour would be no light one. A better plan however, which perhaps is what you meant, would be the following:–

In the use of (1) we conceive the integration performed first, and then the summation. But for the limiting wave we encounter a very slowly convergent series; and it was to avoid this that I sought to sum first and then integrate.

But if we put (1) under the form

$$\frac{1}{\pi} \sum \int_0^{2\pi} \left\{ 1 - \frac{2e^{-nk}}{e^{nk} + e^{-nk}} \right\} \cos n\phi \sin n\phi' f(\phi') d\phi$$

we may treat the two parts differently; for the first we may sum and then integrate, while for the second we integrate first and then sum. The integral $\int_0^{2\pi} \sin n\phi' f(\phi') \, d\phi'$ will be nil when n is even, since $f(2\pi - \phi) = -f(\phi)$. As n increases it will get rapidly smaller at first, though very slowly in the end, converging ultimately at the same rate as $\Sigma n^{-\frac{1}{2}}$. But the factor $\dfrac{2e^{-nk}}{e^{nk} + e^{-nk}}$ will convert it into a rapidly converging series.

The convergence will be much the same by the two methods, but the integration is far simple[r] by the second.

Have I interpreted your meaning rightly?

Yours sincerely,
G. G. STOKES

---

433 KELVIN to STOKES, 16 September 1882
Stokes Collection, K258

Sep 16/82
Netherhall.
Largs.
Ayrshire.

DEAR STOKES

After writing to you, but too late to write & save you the trouble of answering as to Shida's paper,[1] I saw Shida and arranged that he would make a copy of the ⟨plates⟩ sheets of curves which we want most, for present use so that we may leave the whole paper in your hands as long as is necessary for references & reports *en regle*. After all the delay cannot be great, as no referee can keep a paper in any case for more than a month. (I hope no other referee has such sins on his conscience as I alas have on mine.)

I shall have the paper back from Shida in a few days and shall send it immediately on to you.

I hope your Vol II will soon come out.[2]

I hope you will get the high waves done.[3] Do try to throw off or postpone the other matter that stops the way. Could you not get *paid* assistance for the calculations. If paid work could serve you, the R.S. would be too delighted to vote the necessary funds, and no 'self denying ordinance' could stop it. Do think of this, but above all get the waves made.

Yours always truly
WILLIAM THOMSON

1 See letter 399, note 2.
2 The second volume of Stokes's *MPP* appeared in 1883.
3 See Stokes (106).

434 KELVIN to STOKES, 22 October 1882
Stokes Collection, K259

Hotel Chatham
Rue Daunou, Paris
Oct 22, 1882

DEAR STOKES

I am coming to Cambridge on Monday morning the 30th, for our College meeting. Could you give me a bed for the Monday night?

In any case I hope you will dine with us in Peterhouse hall.

I am here about Electric Units (Conférence Internationale des Unités Électriques.)[1] I shall tell you as much as you care to know of it. I think it probable that Lord Rayleigh's ⟨obser⟩ measurements of the British Ass[n] unit will be admitted to be the prob[ab]ly the most correct & ⟨w⟩ to be within 1/1000 of the true value.[2]

We remain here till Thursday morning, and after that we shall be at the

Grand Hotel
Trafalgar Square
London

till I go to Cambridge.

Yours very truly
WILLIAM THOMSON

1 For Kelvin's views on electrical units, see his (261), a lecture delivered at the Institution of Civil Engineers on 3 May 1883.
2 See letter 431, note 2.

435 KELVIN to STOKES, 17 December 1882
Stokes Collection, K260

Dec 17/82
The University,
Glasgow.

DEAR STOKES

I hear that you are to be one of the electors to the vacant Plumian Professorship and I write to say that George Darwin is ⟨a⟩ to be a candidate.[1] You will of course hear from himself that he is to be so but I wanted to early call your attention to his qualifications which seem [to] me very strong for such a post. You know how much connected with Astronomy his work has been for some years. He has very good capacity for exposition, as I have found by hearing him several times in Section A of the B.A. when what he has had to give has been *well given*, and quite in a way that would suit for a Cambridge lecture on Astronomy or experimental physics.

I enclose some sheets of the forthcoming last part of Thomson & Tait's Natural Philosophy[2] which contain some very important contributions given by Darwin at my request.

He is now going on in *very thorough* style with tidal analysis, which he agreed to undertake, as one of a committee of two (Adams & himself)[3] and I am sure he is going to do a great deal of good with it. He is capital in some of the spherical-trigonometry of 'equations of time' as it were, depending on the inclination & nodes of the moon's orbit, in all which I find him a first rate 'astronomer'. I don't believe you ⟨will⟩ could get a better man for the place and I am very confident that if he is appointed he will do much good in the University by the way he will work his professorship.

Believe me
Yours always truly
WILLIAM THOMSON

P.S. My spare time of which ⟨is⟩ there is very little just now, is all drawn to the subjects of your sound[4] & diffraction[5] papers, which I have been reading. Your last words on the direction of vibration ⟨of⟩ in polarized light, as proved by the polarization of the sky⟨e⟩ left the matter absolutely and irrefragably decided. Have you published this proof, otherwise than as implied in or deducible from your diffraction paper?[6] If you have not I think you ought. And *when* is the dynamical theory of phosphorescence to be published.[7]

1 The Plumian professor, James Challis, died on 3 December 1882, and G. H. Darwin was elected to replace him.
2 Kelvin and Tait, *TNP*.
3 See 'Report of a committee, consisting of Professors G. H. Darwin and J. C. Adams, for the harmonic analysis of tidal observations', *Brit. Assoc. Rep.* (1883), 49–117.
4 See Stokes (22), (33), (34), (46), and (62).
5 See Stokes (40), (63), and (66).
6 See the end of letter 438 where Stokes cites his (42).
7 See letter 395, note 2.

436 KELVIN to STOKES, 7 January 188[3]
Stokes Collection, K261

Jan 7/82[1]
The University,
Glasgow.

DEAR STOKES

Are there any rules as to the Smith's Prize papers – how much book-work, how much problems? *What subjects*? Has the Plumian Professor any special department or is each examiner a law to himself as to his choice? Do the examiners consult before hand about papers and marks, and do they show one another their papers before hand. I should be much obliged by any hints you can give as to what I should do.[2]

What is the thickness (in wave-length, supposing the refractive index of the oxide to be unknown) of the yellow or straw colour, which first appears, in tempering steel? What is the thickness of the blue, & what of the 'urine colour'? Is there any book or paper that tells of such matters. I know nothing except hear say, and by (rather dim) light of nature. I am to lecture at the Royal Institution on the Size of Atoms on Friday ev^g the 2nd of Feb.,[3] and I want all the knowledge I can get before hand on such matters.

Have you any knowledge or views as to the black (hole-like) spots which we see in soap bubbles & films before they break. They seem to me to prove that at thicknesses of a little less than a quarter wave length the law of film-tension changes to something analogous to the elasticity of a solid film. The hole does not seem to get larger and does seem bordered by a thickened rim. How do you account for the colours of thin plates not being seen on a piece of wet glass, at a certain stage of its drying? We do see the colours if we rub it, as if to dry it, by hand. Have you gone into the dynamics (Cauchy's[4] or your own) of *dispersion*? My little problems on vibrating strings of beads gives no sensible falling off of velocity of propagation till the wave length is only enough to contain a very small number of beads.

Are the particles that constitutue [sic] the blueness of sky (& of Tyndall's tubes[5] which I suppose are *very good*) – are those particles demonstrably a small fraction of λ, in their diameters? I well understand what you told me last on the polarization by reflection from them & appreciate it thoroughly. It seems absolutely conclusive ⟨as to⟩ that the vibration is perpendicular to the plane of polarization.

Yours always truly
WILLIAM THOMSON[6]

1 Kelvin has misdated the letter; the envelope is post marked 1883.
2 The Plumian professor was one of the examiners for the Smith's prizes, and Kelvin was apparently substituting for Challis, who had died a few weeks earlier. (See the previous letter, note 1.) However, letters 443 and 444 imply that Kelvin examined on behalf of the vice chancellor, James Porter, who also was listed as one of the official examiners. The three other examiners were the Lucasian professor (Stokes), the Lowndean professor (J. C. Adams), and the master of Trinity College, whose duties were delegated to A. Cayley, Sadlerian professor of mathematics. The year 1883 was the last in which the prizes were awarded for an examination and, also, the first in which they were given for an essay. That is, there were two sets of prizes in 1883.
3 Kelvin (262).
4 For an account of Cauchy's theory of dispersion, see E. Whittaker, *A History of the Theories*

of *Aether and Electricity*. Vol. 1: *The Classical Theories* (New York, 1960, reprint of 2nd edn of 1951), pp. 165–6. Kelvin discussed Cauchy's theory in his (262), in *PLA*, 1, 190–202, and (262A).

5 See J. Tyndall, 'On the blue colour of the sky, the polarization of skylight, and on the polarization of light by cloudy matter generally', *Proc. Roy. Soc.*, 17 (1869), 223–33. Kelvin used such a tube for demonstration experiments in his (262), in *PLA*, 1, 203–11.

6 Kelvin has written on the envelope, 'The necessity for *pressure* between two lenses or a lens & a pla⟨n⟩te, to produce the central black depends essentially on motes or shreds, preventing contact without strong pressure. I am confident. Don't you think so?' In his (262), in *PLA*, 1, 165–8, Kelvin argued that this phenomenon is caused by the presence of dust particles, not by a repulsion at a distance between two pieces of glass.

437 STOKES to KELVIN, 9 January 1883
Kelvin Collection, S449

Lensfield Cottage, Cambridge, 9 Jan. 1883.

MY DEAR THOMSON,

Just a few lines by this post to mention about the Smith's Prize. The examination is to begin on Monday the 29th twenty-ninth, [*sic*] and lasts 4 days; the first day we have a paper of essahys [*sic*] to which each examiner usually contributes one. If you would send in say two or three proposals, indicating the order of your choice, it would help us. We have been in the habit of setting 4 questions for essays. Tuesday your paper comes on. We used never to consult beforehand, and each had more or less a style of his own, so that the subjects were fairly represented among us. Latterly, only 3 or 4 yoers, [*sic*] we have looked at each other's papers beforehand, so as to make a better distribution of the subjects.

If you would permit us to see your paper before it is set, it might help us in distributing the subjects better than we might otherwise have done. I must post this now.

Yours sincerely,
G. G. STOKES

438 STOKES to KELVIN, 9 January 1883
Kelvin Collection, S450

Lensfield Cottage, Cambridge, 9 Jan. 1883.

MY DEAR THOMSON,

I wrote in a hurry to catch the post. There are some other questions which I have not yet answered.

As to the Smith's Prize papers, it is very much the case that each examiner is a law unto himself. We have however different branches, so as tolerably well to divide the ground between us.

I cannot answer your question about the colours of steel. The nearest approach I happen to know to anything of the kind is an attempt to determine the thicknesses of the films of iodide of silver giving Nobili's rings.[1] I forget who it was that did it. I don't know whether the chemists could tell us which of the oxides of ⟨silver⟩ iron it is that is formed in the process of tempering steel. This is one thing that would I presume want to be known.

I suppose the yellow comes when the thickness of the film becomes some moderate fraction of the length of a wave of blue light. Of course this rough estimate only goes to say in what order of magnitudes it probably lies.

As to the black spot in soap bubble films, my notion is that it depends on the heterogeneity of the soap mixture. I think it likely that this is partly a true solution, partly a glairy mixture not perfectly dissolved, but somewhat like very soft phlegm. The general appearance I think rather gives one that idea. I suppose the black spot is formed by a thin film of true solution. Anyhow the abrupt transition from the black – nearly black that is – spot to the part round it looks very like heterogeneity.

I was not aware of the disappearance of Newton's rings between two glasses with surface merely moist. One would ordinarily try to get the intermediate medium one thing or other either air or water. I must look for the thing, and then perhaps the cause of it may occur to me.

I have only just glanced, I may say, at Cauchy's theory of dispersion.[2] I have not much faith in that sort of thing. When the force exerted by the molecules upon the ether is not insensible at the distance of a wave length, then you get dispersion. The same would be the case of the ether itself if the same were true. Fresnel pointed this out.

I have sometimes thought that dispersion might perhaps depend rather on time than space. We can pass from the one to the other so far as units are concerned, as we have a velocity, that of propagation, essentially involved. But yet the physical ideas which group themselves around the notion of its depending on time may be very different from those which attend the notion of its depending upon space. I have not formed any particular theory as to a mode of accounting for it on the supposition that it depended upon time, but the possibility should I think be kept in view.

You asked what I had written about the polarization of the light of the sky, and the inference therefrom as to the direction of the plane of polarization. I have written nothing about the sky, but I have mentioned the pol[a]rization of the light scattered from very small particles in my paper On the Change of Refrangibility of Light in the Phil. Trans. for 1852. See art. 183, p. 530.[3]

I believe I have now answered all your questions.

Yours sincerely,
G. G. STOKES

1 Leopoldo Nobili (1784–1835) was professor of physics at Florence. See his 'Memoir on colours in general, and particularly on a new chromatic scale deduced from metallochromy for scientific and practical purposes', Taylor's *Scientific Memoirs*, 1 (1837), 94–121.
2 See letter 436, note 4.
3 Stokes (42). See the postscript to letter 435.

439 KELVIN to STOKES, 11 January 1883
Stokes Collection, K262

Jan 11/83
The University,
Glasgow.

DEAR STOKES

I am much obliged to you for your full answers to all my questions. I hope to learn a great deal more from you yet as to soap films. Yesterday morning in my bath (hot Loch Katrine water) I saw quite decidedly something that I did not expect: a very faint image of a candle from ⟨the⟩ a seemingly *black* hole in a soap film between my hands. I could distinguish no colour; but the seemingly unchanged tint of the candle flame itself. The image seemed as from a perfectly smooth surface. The film round the (seeming) hole was very streaky, quite answering your description.

Why do we notice thin films of pure water giving colours of thin plates? Should not a *small* bubble on the surface of water give brilliant colours before it breaks.

I want to speak of your explanation of phosphorescence in my R[oyal] I[nstitution] lecture,[1] if you have no objection. I have a model which will illustrate, or tend to illustrate, it; and a drawing which will help very much to illustrate it. I would of course say that I was taught it by you about four years ago.

I hope you will not object.

Yours always truly
WILLIAM THOMSON.

P.S. I *can* make my model show the thing perfectly. I have a simple harmonic vibrator at one end of the row. When the period of its vibration is less than the critical value no wave is produced, but harmonic vibrations with amplitude ϵ^{-mx}. When the period exceeds the critical value waves are produced travelling along the line, and absorbed in treacle or other viscous material at the far end. I shall not however have all this realized this time.

1 Kelvin (262). See letter 395, note 2.

440 KELVIN to STOKES, 21 January 1883
Stokes Collection, K263

Sunday Jan 21/83

DEAR STOKES

I mean without fail to send you for approval, my Smith's Prize Paper by tomorrow's post.

Will one of the following subjects do for Essay.

(1) On Capillary Attraction[1]
(2) On the direction of the Vibrations in plane polarized light[2]
(3) On Vortex Motion[3] in ⟨the⟩ an inviscid incompressible homogeneous liquid.
(4) On cyclic [or 'many-valued'][4] functions, as illustrated in vortex motion, and in the field of force of an electromagnet
(5) On the Dissipation of Energy from the Solar System.
(6) On reversibility in abstract dynamics, and in nature.

Yours truly
W THOMSON

Here is my 'dispersion'[5]-by-refraction, and phosphor[esc]ence, model[6]

I have at present 12 such pairs. One end of each pair of bars is marked with a circular disc of paper, to denote a molecule. They are strung at distances of 3 i[nches] consecutively along the piano forte wire which hangs vertically. A simple arrangement of two heavy pendulums allows me to give simple harmonic motion to the top particle in periods less than and greater than the critical value. When the period exceeds the critical valu⟨l⟩e, waves pass regularly down and give the energy to a bason of treacle. When the period is less than the critical value no waves pass down: infinitesimal energy only is given to the treacle: the pendulums left to themselves keep their energy a long time (laid-up light!). The bars Nos 2, &3, &4 vibrate in opposite directions (standing vibrations[)]

range of 2 (for example) 1/3 of range of 1
range of 3, 1/3 of range of 2
range of 4 insensible

I hope you won't object to my pronouncing the word phosphorescence in presence of this model at the Royal Institution on Friday week ev^g lecture.[7]

1 Stokes has written here, '1875'. This date and those in the next two notes refer to previous years when these essays were set for the Smith's prize examination.
2 Stokes has written here, 'n[ea]rly 1869'.
3 Stokes has written here, 'n[ea]rly 1881'.
4 Kelvin's brackets.
5 Kelvin has added a footnote reading, 'A frightful misnomer, this "dispersion"'.
6 In the left margin of the page beginning with Kelvin's figure and ending with the passage, *less than and greater than the critical value*, Kelvin has written, 'excuse great haste for sake of getting to church!'
7 Kelvin (262). See letter 395, note 2.

441 KELVIN to STOKES, 22 January 1883
Stokes Collection, K264

Jan 22/83[1]
The University,
Glasgow.

DEAR STOKES

I must send you the enclosed without having managed to read all through, or I shall miss the post. I think it is correct enough, for the printers and if it is approved I shall be obliged by your sending it to them with directions to send me *two* copies of a proof by ⟨Wed^y evening⟩ Wednesday's post so that I may receive ⟨it⟩ them here on Thursday.[2]

If they cannot let me have it by that time, it must be addressed Grand Hotel Trafalgar Square London. I shall be there on Saturday forenoon. I hope however I shall have the proofs here on Thursday morning, to give me proper time for verifying every thing besides correcting for press.

The phosphorescence & wave machine works splendidly.[3] When the period is less than the critical, the exciting pendulums lose but little energy in $1\frac{1}{2}$ minutes. When period greater than the the [*sic*] critical, nearly all their energy is taken from them in half a minute. The standing vibrations in the first case are manifest and show their law bea[u]tifully palpably.

The waves in the second case speak for themselves equally tellingly.

Yours always
W THOMSON

1 Kelvin has written at the top of the letter, 'N.B. There is nothing really but what is very easy (unprecedentedly so almost) in my paper, as I think you will see'.
2 This refers to Kelvin's questions for the Smith's prize examination. See the next two letters.
3 See Kelvin (262) and letter 395, note 2.

442   KELVIN to STOKES, 25 January 1883
Stokes Collection, K265

Thursd Jan 25/83
The University,
Glasgow.

DEAR STOKES

I enclose a proof with all the corrections I hitherto see to be needed, as it may save you trouble in case of your noticing any of them. I have another ⟨copy⟩ proof which I shall go through carefully and return to the Pitt Press, for press, probably from some place between this and London tomorrow. We leave for London tomorrow morning, and letters addressed Grand Hotel Trafalgar Square London will find me on Saturday fore noon.

Yours very truly
WILLIAM THOMSON

⟨P.S. Instead of 2⟩

443   KELVIN to STOKES, 26 January 1883
Stokes Collection, K266

Grand Hotel
Trafalgar Square
London WC
Jan 26/83

DEAR STOKES

I am sending off from here by same post as this, to the Vice Chancellor[1] (not to the Univ. Press) the proof of my Smith's Prize paper corrected for press.

I have made two corrections besides those on the proof I sent you: viz. in question 7[2] for $\qquad\qquad \sqrt{[\frac{1}{2}(\omega-\zeta)^2] + K[\frac{1}{2}(\omega+\zeta)^2]}\}$

substitute $\qquad\quad \sqrt{[\frac{1}{2}(\omega-\zeta)]^2 + K[\frac{1}{2}(\omega+\zeta)]^2\}}$

and in question 8, at end of first line insert

, viewed in any direction perpendicular to the sun's direction,

If you have found anything else requiring correction, will you give it to the Vice Chancellor or to Mr Clay?

Is what you found for fluorescence, *that it always consists of light of longer periods than any of the periods of the exciting light*, true of phosphorescence in general?

Fluorescence, as E. Becquerel showed by his phosphoroscope,[3] persists for 1/200 (?) of a second after the exciting light is stopped (I suppose I am right in attributing the ⟨discovery⟩ experimental demonstration to him. You indicated that it was a result to be looked for.

Are their [sic] intermediates of all grades, between the persistence for not more than 1/200 of a second, to persistence of a second or two, & up to minutes or hours?

Don't unless you are inclined be at the trouble of writing in answer to this (though I should be very glad to hear.) If I do not hear from you before I shall get the answers from you viva voce I hope at the R.S. on Thursday afternoon. Will you come before the R.S. meeting to the Royal Institution and see my mechanical models;[4] or immediately after the R.S. meeting, whichever is most convenient. Give me a line at least to answer this last question. Address Queen's Hotel, Southsea, Hants if you post tomorrow (Saturday.) If Sunday or Monday, address Grand Hotel &^{c}.

Yours always
W.T.

P.S. I have now a way of explaining refractive dispersion by rotating molecules in an infinitely fine-grained substance.

P.S. No 2. The 'gyrostatic' affairs of §345$^{\text{I.}}$ to 345^{XXVIII} of Thomson & Tait's Natural Philosophy[5] contain I believe not only the dynamical foundation of the explanation of Faraday's magneto-optic rotation[6] of the plane of polarization, but probably much more for the Undulatory Theory of Light. I have made out quite definitely, in the train from Glasgow today, the *same law as* the *approximate law of Cauchy's* for refractive dispersion[7]

$$\langle() \quad \text{viz} \quad V_\lambda = V_\infty \left(1 - \frac{C}{\lambda^2}\right)$$

where V_λ denotes the velocity for wave-length λ.

I make this out for an infinitely fine-grained substance, (elastic solid) with rapidly rotating infinitesimal fly wheels, pivotted [sic] in vesicles of the solid, with their axes in all directions; and I find

$$C = S/n$$

where n denotes an average angular velocity of the fly wheels, and S a constant depending on the elasticity of the solid, and ⟨geometri⟩ moment of inertia of fly wheel, and dimensions & shapes of cavities. Rotating liquid may be substituted for the solid flywheels.

I may perhaps manage to get a⟨n⟩ slight article ready for the R.S. meeting of Thursday.[8] Could it be taken if I do?

There is more & more behind it.[9] I want to do away with elasticity of solid entirely and with nothing but rotating liquid & perfectly rigid solid containing vessels & links, to get undulations proper for undulatory theory of light.

1 James Porter.
2 Kelvin's brackets.
3 With Becquerel's phosphoroscope, one could 'view substances in the dark only fractions of a second after they had been exposed to brilliant light . . . [and] measure the length of time that the substances continued to glow after exposure to light'. Becquerel used it to show that Stokes's fluorescence was phosphorescence of short duration. (*Dictionary of Scientific Biography*.)
4 See Kelvin (262).
5 Kelvin and Tait, *TNP*.
6 M. Faraday, 'On the magnetization of light and the illumination of magnetic lines of force', *Phil. Trans.* (1846), 1–20.
7 See letter 436, note 4.
8 He did not.
9 See Kelvin (263).

444 KELVIN to STOKES, 4 February 1883
Stokes Collection, K267

Feb 4, 1883
Druids' Cross,
Wavertree,
Liverpool.

Smith's Prize Examination.

DEAR STOKES

The marks which I have assigned for the answers to my paper are as follows.[1]

Welsh	310
Turner	230
Johnson	190
Carey	160

I don't remember the order in which the men stood either on the honours exam^n of last June, or in the recent class-exam^n.[2] I saw the results of this last in the Times a few weeks ago but I do not recollect it. So I am quite independent. I would like to hear how they stood before.

I am sending the Essays –

Four on Capillary Att^n
Thre[e on] Achromatism

to the Vice Chancellor,[3] to whom also (as I believe I am his delegate) I am sending my marks. I am telling him not to mind however as I am writing you also, in case he does not attend the meeting.

The Essays are *all* very poor, & could scarcely have weight to change the order but so far as I can judge they rather confirm it as above than otherwise.

Yours

W THOMSON

1 William Welsh (*c.* 1859–1925), who was senior wrangler in 1882 and first Smith's prizeman in 1883, remained at Jesus College as fellow and tutor until 1919. Herbert Hall Turner (1861–1930), who was second wrangler in 1882 and second Smith's prizeman in 1883, was Savilian professor of astronomy and director of the Oxford University Observatory from 1893 to 1930. Alfred Robert Johnson (1861–1937) was sixth wrangler in 1882 and eventually was rector of Marwood, Devon, from 1902 to 1917, and of Marston Morteyne, Bedfordshire, from 1917 to 1935. Frank Stanton Carey (1860–1928) was third wrangler in 1882 and professor of mathematics at Liverpool University from 1886 to 1923.

2 The examinations referred to by Kelvin were portions of the newly revised mathematical tripos. In 1882, the tripos was divided into three 'parts', parts I and II being taken at the end of the student's third year, part III in the middle of his fourth. Hence, the men cited in the previous note had taken parts I and II in the spring of 1882 and part III in December of 1882. By passing the spring examination, they took honours; their scores on the examination determined their positions as wranglers. Part III, which they had taken only a few weeks before the Smith's prize examination, was intended only for the best students and was what Kelvin meant by the 'class-exam^n'. On the basis of its results, students were not ranked individually, but were grouped into classes or 'divisions', with no ranking within a division being indicated. The four men in the previous note had placed in the first division for part III.

3 James Porter.

445 KELVIN to STOKES, 5 February 1883
Stokes Collection, K268

Feb 5/83
Druids' Cross,
Wavertree,
Liverpool.

DEAR STOKES

I sent the seven object glass & capillarity dissertations by book-post unregistered yesterday. Being Sunday I could not register them. I am sending one batch of the Tides by same post with this, letter post; the others I enclose.

I think Johnson's is on the whole the best, as his is the only dissertation that ⟨makes⟩ treats the subject in accordance with the prescribed title the '*Equilibrium* Theory of Tides'. It is however very poor and unclear, and does not point out that the moon & antimoon method is only an approximation (w^h leaves out the ter[1] diurnal comp^t &^{c}). This however is a minor matter, but a precise definition of what 'the equilibrium tide' rigorously is, is wanting. Some of the others perhaps give this, but very unclearly; and they make a sad hash of the diurnal, which comes out clearly enough in Johnson's. His mathematical work is however wo[e]fully untidy & unclear and the same may be said of most of the others. In fact the 'dissertations' would have been much better without any or almost any mathematical analysis. Altogether I think a *little* lift might be given to Johnson by the Tides if that could help him when the other work is put together. Welsh is perhaps a shade better than the two others but I think all three should get rather negative than positive credit for their Tides.

I am disappointed on the whole with the performances. I did not expect *very* much but the results are not so good as I expected.

Yours
W THOMSON

1 Kelvin apparently began writing the word *terms*, as in *diurnal terms*, but then changed his mind, neglecting to delete *ter*. See, for example, sections 804 to 811 in the 1912 edition of Kelvin and Tait, *TNP*.

446 STOKES to KELVIN, 20 May 1883
Kelvin Collection, S451

Lensfield Cottage, Cambridge, 20 May, 1883.

MY DEAR THOMSON,

Adams left here a few days ago a copy of his Smith's Prize paper, which contains a question he wished you to see.[1] I had forgotten to ask you where you were going to stay in London, and on asking my wife she told me she had got the address, but when she looked for it she could not find it. Today either she or Isabella mentioned that you were staying with Siemens. If I had known that before I could have sent you the paper at once.

As to what the analytical continuation of the highest wave may be, it seems to me not improbable that the solution, if the mathematical expression for it could be obtained, would be found to contain g in the form g^2, so that gravity down and gravity up are embraced in the same analytical expression, and accordingly a set of waves which would be the reflection of the actual waves in the horizontal line passing through the crests belong to the same analytical solution, so that the fluid we are dealing with extends infinitely both up and down except as to the portions of space, lenticular, in a general way, in outline, comprised between the wave outline and its image.[2]

Observe, you could not have the fluid extending all round the crest as a singular point, for the simple expression for phi or psi very close to the crest[3] gives something which does not recur when you go once round the singular point, but only when you go twice round it.

I forgot to say that I supposed that in the analytical expressions I imagined you would have to extract a radical, and one sign would belong to the portion of fluid below the line through the crests, and the other sign to the part above the crests. These portions of fluid do not join each other except in the singular points.

With kind regards to Lady Thomson, and also to the Siemens's [*sic*] I remain

Yours sincerely,

G. G. STOKES[4]

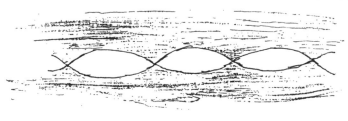

$$\star \quad c\, r^{\frac{3}{2}} \frac{\cos}{\sin} \left(\tfrac{3}{2}\theta \right) \quad [\text{W.T.}]$$

1 See letter 436, note 2.

2 See Stokes (106), read on 14 May 1883.

3 An *x* in purple pencil has been added after *crest*, thus indicating the position of the footnote mentioned in the next note.

4 The drawing and footnote following Stokes's signature are in purple pencil and may be by Stokes. He wrote letter 453 the next year in purple pencil. Larmor added the initials '[W.T.]' indicating that he thought the drawing and footnote were Kelvin's. Kelvin did use coloured pencils (though not a purple one) to mark on other letters from Stokes (see letters 456, 552, 583, 591, and 639).

447 KELVIN to STOKES, 14 August 1883
Royal Society of London, RR.9.189

Physical Laboratory
The University, Glasgow
Aug. 14, 1883

DEAR STOKES,

I return J. J. Thomson's paper[1] sent to me for report July 11. In my opinion it is suitable for publication in the Philosophical Transactions and if as I hope will be the case it is accepted it will I think form a very valuable contribution.

Yours truly
WILLIAM THOMSON

Professor G. G. Stokes Sec. R. S.

1 J. J. Thomson, 'On the determination of the number of electrostatic units in the electro-magnetic unit of electricity', *Phil. Trans.*, **174** (1883), 707–21.

448 STOKES to KELVIN, 22 January 1884
Kelvin Collection, S452

Lensfield Cottage, Cambridge, 22 Jan. 1884.[1]

MY DEAR THOMSON,

An application came in to the Government Grant Committee of the Royal Society from Messrs. A. Gray, T. Gray, and J. J. Dobbie for £100 for apparatus for certain experiments on the electrical conductivity of glass &c.[2]

The sum seems a somewhat large one as fas [sic] as one can guess what might be the nature of such an enquiry. You probably know all about it, and I should be glad of your opinion as to whether the experiments are likely to lead to a definite result, and to be of value.

Meanwhile the Committee have postponed the further consideration of the grant.

Yours sincerely,
G. G. STOKES

1 Kelvin's secretary has written in the upper left hand corner of the letter, 'Ans^d 25/1/84'.
2 See T. Gray, A. Gray, and J. J. Dobbie, 'On the relation between the electrical qualities and the chemical composition of glass and allied substances. Part 1', *Proc. Roy. Soc.*, **36** (1884), 488–98. James Johnston Dobbie (1852–1924), educated at Glasgow, Edinburgh, and Leipzig, was assistant to the professor chemistry at Glasgow from 1881 to 1884 and professor of chemistry at University College of North Wales, Bangor, from 1884 to 1903.

Jan 27/84[1]
Netherhall.
Largs.
Ayrshire.

DEAR STOKES

I was delighted to receive your vol II.[2] just before we left Glasgow on Friday and I thank you very much for it. It will be some time yet, (longer than I like to think.) before my Vol II. gets out.[3] When will the first instalment of your Aberdeen lectures be accessible?[4] They are to be all published I am glad to think, but I hope you will let the first instalment be *got* as soon as possible, and in fact the same for for [*sic*] each successive instalment.

Can you tell me if there is any marked difference in the law of relation of chromatic dispersion to ⟨wave length⟩ period (I mean law of velocity of propagation in relation to period) between the Faraday magneto-optic rotation & the helicoidal rotation? Also does either, or do both, follow nearly the same law as ordinary refractive dispersion? Also, how about dispersion of light ⟨in d⟩ according to direction of ray through doubly refracting chrystals [*sic*]? ⟨Do⟩ Are the differences of μ for different colours nearly proportional to the mean values of μ, for different directions of the ray?

How about the helicoidal (or helikoidal) rotation for rays in different directions through quartz? Is the proper helikoidal rotation null for a ray perpendicular to the axis? Or is the *rotation* the same for rays in all directions as in a ⟨solution of sugar⟩ liquid, and is the ordinary aeolotropic property of a chrystal [*sic*] merely superimposed on this. I suppose I ought to know this out of Airy's Tract.[5] If so I suppose I did once but I certainly don't now.

When will you publish your Dynamical Theory of Phosphorescence?[6]

Do you know Helmholtz's paper[7] of two or three years ago on abnormal refraction (or dispersion. I forget the title)? I think it refers to cases of maximum refracti⟨on⟩ve index for a certain colour & less for colours of longer and of shorter periods. Lady Thomson joins in kind regards to all & I remain

Yours truly
W THOMSON

1 Kelvin has written at the top of the letter, 'We return to Glasgow tomorrow'.
2 The second volume of Stokes's *MPP*.
3 The second volume of Kelvin's *MPP* was published in 1884.
4 Stokes delivered his three series of *Burnett Lectures* in Aberdeen in November, 1883, December, 1884, and November, 1885. Each series was published shortly after it was given, and the three were published together in 1887.
5 G. B. Airy, *Mathematical Tracts on the Lunar and Planetary Theories, the Figure of the*

Earth, Precession and Nutation, the Calculus of Variations, and the Undulatory Theory of Optics, 3rd edn (Cambridge, 1842).

6 See letter 395, note 2.

7 H. Helmholtz, 'Zur Theorie der anomalen Dispersion', *Annalen der Physik und Chemie*, **154** (1875), 582–96.

450 STOKES to KELVIN, 30 January 1884
Kelvin Collection, S453

Lensfield Cottage, Cambridge, 30 Jan. 1884.

MY DEAR THOMSON,

I will take your questions in order.

1. Some 2 or 3 weeks ago, [I] left the first 6 sheets of my lectures[1] for press, the whole of the MS. except the preface and title page and contents have been there some time before. I thought I should have got proofs of the conclusion almost immediately. But as they had not arrived I called at the press just before I received your letter to stir them up. I shall not need to keep the proofs when they do come. As the MS. was written with the machine,[2] I do not find that there is much correction to make. Very many pages vent [*sic*] back without a n y alteration.

2. I recollect Verdet's[3] mentioning that the magnetic rotation was compensated by a plate of quartz cut perpendicular to the axis, showing that the law of rotation as depending on wave-length or period must be sensibly the same in the two, and in quartz he had found the law to be sensibly the law of the squared reciprocal of the wave length. This law holds more or less approximately with fluids which rotate the plane of polarization; but it is not exact, and the tartrates show a considerable, at least a very sensible, departure from the law, analogous to the irrationality of dispersion.

3. In ordinary dispersion, the law of dispersion according to the inverse square of the wave length is only an approximation. Water and crown glass deviate from the law in opposite directions. The deviation in these cases is not great, but quite enough to show a marked irrationality when you acromatize a prism of the one by a prism of the other. With bisulphide of carbon and oil of cassia, the deviation is very large.

4. Kirch[h]off's measures of the angle between the optic axes of arragonite[4] compared with the angle calculated from Fresnel's construction with the numerical data given by Rudberg's measures of the principal indices,[5] shows that the difference at any rate cannot be great. The same results from Glazebrook's measurements made with the light of a soda flame,[6] which we may regard for the present purpose as light of a refrangibility taken at random. That being the case, you may find the dispersion in any direction by Fresnel's construction in the case of any crystal for which we know accurately the

principal indices for different colours. Rudberg has measured very accurately the principal indices of 4 crystals for the lines B, C, D, E, F, G, H. The four are calcite and quartz for uniaxal, arragonite and topaz for biaxal.

I have worked out the numbers for you for calcite, taking the inclination 45°. I write down also the principal indices. I have chosen the rays B and H.

Mu Extr. at 90°	Mu Extr. at 45°	Mu Extr. at 0°, or Ord.
1.49085	1.57203	1.66819
⟨0.03022⟩		
0.01389	0.02071	0.03022

The first line in the above gives the mean of the indices for B and H, the second the differences of the indices. The numbers for the extraordinary are quoted for 0° and 90°, and calculated for 45°. The extraordinary at 90° to the axis is of course the same thing as the ordinary. You will see that the delta mu's are very far indeed from being proportional to the mu's.

5. 5. [sic] We cannot speak properly of the rotation in quartz except in the direction of the axis. Inclined to the axis, the helocoidal [sic] property shows itself by so modifying the ordinary double refraction that the two waves which can be propagated independently in a given direction to the axis are elliptically polarized, of equal eccentricity, rectangular orientation, and opposite handedness. The effect which this produces on a beam of plane polarized light is more complicated than a simple rotation of the plane of polarization. I assume it was the influence of the helicoidal property that you meant to describe briefly and somewhat loosely as rotation.

According to the equation given my [sic] MacCullagh, which however is in a good measure empirical, the handedness of the ellipse remains of constant character throughout in quartz. The eccentricity does not become quite equal to 1 in a direction perpendicular to the axis. According to Airy the ellipticity of the ordinary or extraordinary is still sensible as far as 30° from the axis.

In magnetic rotation, the ordinary and extraordinary, as for distinction merely we may call them, are circularly polarized of opposite handedness, and the more refracted is of opposite handedness on opposite sides of the equator, or plane perpendicular to the line of magnetic force. Therefore the effect must vanish in the equator.

6. I have not done anything more as yet about phosphorescence. My hands are full of other matters at present.

7. I have just dipped into a paper or two, I forget by whom, as to anomalous dispersion. I took for granted the explanation offered would be by making mu imaginary.

Yours sincerely,
Yours sincerely [sic]
G. G. STOKES

1 See the previous letter, note 4.

2 *I.e.*, Stokes's typewriter.

3 For a discussion of the work by Verdet (as well as by MacCullagh and Airy, mentioned later in the letter) on the rotation of the plane of polarization in a magnetic field, see E. Whittaker, *A History of the Theories of Aether and Electricity*, vol. 1: *The Classical Theories* (New York, 1960 reprint of the 2nd edn of 1951), 191–3.

4 See Kirchhoff, 'Ueber die Winkel der optischen Axen des Arragonits für die verschiedenen Fraunhofer'schen Linien', Poggendorff's *Annalen der Physik und Chemie*, **108** (1859), 567–75.

5 See Rudberg, 'Untersuchungen über die Brechung des farbigen Lichtes im Bergcrystall und Kalkspath', Poggendorff's *Annalen der Physik und Chemie*, **14** (1828), 45–57, and 'Untersuchungen über die Brechung des farbigen Lichtes im Arragonit und im farblosen Topase', *ibid.*, **17** (1829), 1–28. Fredrik Rudberg (1800–39) was ordinary professor of physics in the University of Uppsala.

6 See R. T. Glazebrook, 'An experimental determination of the values of the velocities of normal propagation of plane waves in different directions in a biaxal crystal, and a comparison of the results with theory', *Phil. Trans.*, **170** (1879), 287–377, and 'Double refraction and dispersion in Iceland spar: an experimental investigation, with a comparison with Huyghen's construction for the extraordinary wave', *ibid.*, **171** (1880), 421–49. Glazebrook's first paper cites both of Rudberg's mentioned in the previous note.

451 KELVIN to STOKES, 17 February 1884
Stokes Collection, K270

Feb 17/84
The University,
Glasgow.

DEAR STOKES

⟨I have⟩ It is not exactly estimated the present 'rate of cooling' that can be estimated in terms of the thickness of the coat of ice that ⟨c⟩ would be melted by the heat that escapes per annum: because this, which is a perfectly definite quantity of heat, the amount of which is known with absolute certainty to a rough approximation, is taken in different proportions from different parts of a stratum of 20 or 30 or 40 kilometres thickness, *the* stratum through which the cooling has penetrated. The numerical parameters of the law of temperature in this stratum, and the thickness of the stratum from the outer surface, to a depth at which the rate of variation of temperature per metre for example is, for example, 1/100 of what it is ⟨at⟩ close to the upper surface, cannot be determined without knowledge of the date of solidification; but an inferior limit to the value of the parameter for instance defined above as the thickness, can be asserted with certainty from the knowledge we have for certain that the earth has been continuously inhabited for 6000 years; and a much larger limit can be asserted with almost certainty from ⟨the⟩ our almost certain knowledge that the earth has been continuously inhabited for more than 100 000 years.

The Appendix to Thomson & Tait Vol I. Part II.[1] on the Secular Cooling of the Earth, and my Glasgow 1876 Brit. Ass. Sec A. Presidential Address[2] contain between them all I have published and I think all I know of the subject. The former gives the principles & math[l] calculation; the latter some expansion and explanation of the grounds we have for definite estimates of limits.

You should look at Helmholtz on A[b]normale [*sic*] Dispersion near the beginning of the second volume of his collected papers.[3] He there anticipates most of what occurred to me in connection with my R. I. lecture,[4] on the dynamics of dispersion. Ordinary, non-'anomalous,' dispersion is in fact more difficult to explain than the 'anomalous' dispersion. One of the people quoted by Helmholtz virtually proposes an anomalous dispersion away beyond the ultra violet, to explain ordinary dispersion.

Yours always truly
WILLIAM THOMSON

1 Kelvin (141), reprinted in Kelvin and Tait, *TNP*.
2 Kelvin (217).
3 This is the article cited in letter 449, note 7, and reprinted in H. Helmholtz, *Wissenschaftliche Abhandlungen*, 3 vols. (Leipzig, 1882–95), II, 213–26.
4 Kelvin (262).

452 STOKES to KELVIN, 22 February 1884
Kelvin Collection, S454

Lensfield Cottage, Cambridge, 22 Feb. 1884.

MY DEAR THOMSON,

A paper[1] by Hicks on the vibrations of a vortex, which was referred to you, came on at a meeting of the Committee of Papers of the Royal Society on Thursday last. I felt nearly sure it was one on which you had favourably reported viva voce to me, and I said you need not trouble yourself to write a report. But on looking into the books I found that you had also had a paper[2] by J. J. Thomson on the number of electrostatic⟨s⟩ units in one electrodynamic, on which you also reported viva voce, and I did not feel absolutely sertain [*sic*] that that might not be the one I had in my head. Would you therefore be so goos [*sic*] as to send a line or post card to say if I am right in my supposition that you recommended the paper of Hicks for publication in the transactions?

I am sorry I gave you so muzh [*sic*] trouble about the cooling of the earth. What I meant to ask about was silply [*sic*] that that you regarded as so very simple, and so it is if you have the numerical data, the loss of heat from the earth across the surface. In the Phil. Trans. for 1873, p. 205, art. 178[3] Mallet quoted you as expressing the rate at which heat is lost across the surface of the earth by saying that it is what would suffice to melt a sheet of ice covering the whole surface, and having a thickness 0.0085 millimetre in one year. Must it not be 0.0085 metre? And where is the figure given?[4]

I have looked into your address,[5] and into Thomson and Tait[6] as you mentioned, and I don't see it there.

Yours Sincerely,

G. G. STOKES

1 W. M. Hicks, 'On the steady motion and small vibrations of a hollow vortex', *Phil. Trans.*, **175** (1884), 161–95. There is no report by Kelvin in the Royal Society for this paper, but he did write a report (RR.9.277, dated 8 October 1885) on Hicks's 'Researches on the theory of vortex rings. Part II', *Phil. Trans.*, **176**, (1885), 725–80.

2 See letter 447, note 1.

3 R. Mallet, 'Volcanic energy: an attempt to develop its true origin and cosmical relations', *Phil. Trans.*, **163** (1873), 147–227. Robert Mallet (1810–81), engineer and seismologist, based his career on the development of his father's plumbing and foundry businesses in Dublin and became a fellow of the Royal Society in 1854. There are over forty Mallet letters in the Stokes Collection.

4 Kelvin has written in this part of the letter:

$$7 \cdot 10^3$$

$$1° \text{ per 30 met[res]}$$

$$\frac{1}{200} \times \frac{1}{3000} \times \frac{1}{79} \cdot \frac{1}{92}$$

$$\times 31 \cdot 10^6 \cdot \frac{1}{200}$$

See Kelvin (141) and (151). The value of 1° Centigrade per 30 metres is Kelvin's figure for the rate of increase of the earth's temperature below the earth's surface. See also Joe D. Burchfield, *Lord Kelvin and the Age of the Earth* (New York, 1975).

5 Kelvin (217).

6 Kelvin (141), printed in Kelvin and Tait, *TNP*.

453 STOKES to KELVIN, 7 March 1884
Kelvin Collection, S455

London 7 March
1884
Athenaeum Club
Pall Mall

MY DEAR THOMSON,

Thanks for the pamphlets[1] which I now return. I hope I have not kept them too long.

Your figures give nearly the same result as I had worked out from measuring on some mass [?] of underground temperatures a little before I wrote, both results being comparable with but distinctly less than the figure given by Mallet[2] as from you. I wonder where he got his figures. His 0.007 millimetres should have clearly been 0.007 metre. He gives I think 0.0098 as your figure.

Got the paper you communicated on the stability of ships.[3]

Yours sincerely,
G. G. STOKES

1 Perhaps reprints of Kelvin (141) and (151). See the previous letter, note 4.
2 See the previous letter, note 3.
3 F. Elgar, 'The variation of stability with draught of water in ships', *Proc. Roy. Soc.*, 37 (1884), 205–29.

---

454   KELVIN to STOKES, 11 April 1884
Royal Society of London, RR.9.234

The University, Glasgow
11th April, 84

DEAR STOKES,

I return Poynting's paper enclosed.[1] I am of opinion it is suitable for publication in the Transactions. It is an interesting, and to some degree instructive, statement of important views connected with the theory of the energy of magnets and of distributions of electric currents. I have made two or three pencil jottings at Pages 1, 10, 12 and 16. That on page 16 is I think important, as the author's statement is not consistent with any definition ever given of potential that I know of.

Yours very truly,
WILLIAM THOMSON[2]

1 J. H. Poynting, 'On the transfer of energy in the electromagnetic field', *Phil. Trans.*, 175 (1884), 343–61. This is the paper which develops 'the Poynting theorem'. John Henry Poynting (1852–1914) was third wrangler in 1876 and was professor of physics at Birmingham University from 1880 to 1914.
2 Stokes has written on the reverse, '1884. Poynting by Thomson'.

---

455   STOKES to KELVIN, 19 April 1884
Kelvin Collection, S456

Lensfield Cottage, Cambridge, 19 April, 1884.

MY DEAR THOMSON,

When you asked me last night how the rotating journal[1] was supported, though I knew that – according to theory – it was by friction, I did not on the spur of the moment recollect how it was that the friction acted. And my mind I believe⟨d⟩ reverted to some ideas which crossed it when the thing was still in a very immature state with me. It is by the indirect, not the direct, effect of the fluid friction or viscosity. By the indirect effect, I mean the augmentation of the pressure due to viscosity. The pressure incre[a]ses from the mouth, where it is nil, omitting the atmospheric pressure, to a point a little before the place where the surfaces are most nearly in contact, where it is a maximum. It is this increase of pressure which supports the loaded 'brass.' This indirect effect of the friction or viscosity is of the order L by T as compared with the direct effect, where L is the length of the arc of the brass that covers the journal, and T the thickness, or a length comparable with the thickness, of the film of oil between the brass and the journal.

Possibly the friction might have been measured with greater delicacy than was done by Tower by using some different method. But I see no reason for questioning the general correctness of his numbers.

I left by the 10 o'clock train, and got to the station here at about 9-30, having had about an hour and a half in York for seeing the Minster etc.

Yours sincerely,
G. G. STOKES

1 This refers to research done by Beauchamp Tower and reported in 'First report on friction experiments', *Proceedings of the Institution of Mechanical Engineers* (1883), 632–52, and 'Second report on friction experiments', *ibid.* (1885), 58–63. Tower (1845–1904) began his engineering career in Newcastle-on-Tyne and along the way worked with William Froude and Lord Rayleigh, becoming a member of the Institution of Mechanical Engineers in 1883. His work on journal friction was his best-known research and was conducted at the request of the Institution's Committee on Friction Experiments.

456 STOKES to KELVIN, 23 April 1884
Kelvin Collection, S457

Lensfield Cottage, Cambridge, 23 April, 1884.

MY DEAR THOMSON,

The mere supposition of incompressibility introduced into the equations for the motion of a homogeneous elastic solid will leave them more general than if we first suppose, as Green did,[1] that of the three possible rectangular directions of vibration for a given direction of the plane wave two are strictly transversal, and the third therefore strictly normal, and *then* introduce the supposition of incompressibility. In the former case there will be two possible directions of vibration, which will be rectangular and strictly transversal, but the ⟨trn⟩ transversal vibrations will in general call into play a pressure perpendicular to the plane of the wave. In the latter case there is no such pressure.

I have no faith in the equations of motion of an elastic solid as giving the true explanation of the propagation of light in crystallized media, though they may guide to the correct mathematical laws of double refraction, just as we are led to the same fundamental cubic equation in investigating the principal axes of a surface of the second order, or the principal axes ⟨of⟩ through the centre of gravity of a rigid body, or a variety of other investigations. But the fundamental supposition of one homogeneous medium is so utterly different from what must be the true state of things in a crystal, where we have the vibrating medium existing in the interstices between the molecules of the ponderable matter, that as I say I have no faith in a priori conclusions d[e]rived from the results applicable to a homogeneous elastic medium.[2]

I made some investigations once in this direction which seemed to lead to a more likely state of things than that in either of Green's two theories, and left the vibrations perpendicular to the plane of polarization, as I believe they are. I mentioned the thing one time to Maxwell at Glenlair, but I never published it, because Maxwell seemed to get out the results from his electromagnetic theory. There is not however I think necessarily opposition between the two; it may be two apparently very different modes of viewing the same thing, but which we might be able to see came to the same thing if we knew more about the real state of things.

I have not yet referred to your paper that you mentioned to me but my own lucubrations some time ago led me to a similar conclusion as to the greater generality of the equations when you make no supposition beyond that of incompressibility.

Yours sincerely,
G. G. STOKES

1 For a standard discussion of the optical research involving Green, Cauchy, MacCullagh, Kelvin, and Stokes, see Edmund Whittaker, 'The aether as an elastic solid', chapter v in his *A History of the Theories of Aether and Electricity*, 2 vols. (New York, 1960 reprint of the 2nd edn of 1951), I, 128–70. See also Stokes (72) and Kenneth F. Schaffner, 'The elastic solid aether', chapter IV in his *Nineteenth-Century Aether Theories* (Oxford, 1972). This research is discussed in many of the next several letters.
2 There are two vertical lines at the left side of the text (extending from *conclusions* to *medium*) and at this point is written: 'Nor have I. W.T. nor I. H. Helmholtz'. *H. Helmholtz* is written in blue pencil and appears to be Helmholtz's signature. The rest is in orange pencil and is in Kelvin's hand. The vertical lines are in blue pencil.

457 KELVIN to STOKES, [9 May 1884][1]
Stokes Collection, K271

the[2] ratios of the sides that I forgot [yes]terday. Thus if a, b, c denote the [l]engths of edges parallel to OX, OY, OZ, we have the following parameters

$a/b, a/c$ --	2
stiffnesses of edge springs -------------------------	3
[stiffnesses of] face-diagonal [springs] -----------------	6
[stiffnesses of] body-[diagonal springs] ----------------	4

longitudinal modulususes [*sic*] of the parts of $\Big\}$
the edge-cord parallel to OX, OY, OZ $\dfrac{3}{18}$
and transformation to any other

axes -- 3

In all, available for independ^t moduluses   21/!!

1 This is a post card in Kelvin's hand, addressed to Stokes and post marked London, 9 May 1884.

2 The upper, left-hand corner of the post card is torn away, removing at least one word before *the* and the first parts of *yesterday* and *lengths*.

458   KELVIN to STOKES, 17 May 1884
Stokes Collection, K272

May 17/84
12, Grosvenor Gardens.
S.W.

DEAR STOKES

An application has been made by my nephew James Bottomley for a grant of £75 out of the Gov^t Fund, for investigating thermal emissivities in the most perfect vacuum attainable (rates of loss of heat in less perfect vacuums would almost necessarily be included.) He has already got some important ⟨preliminary⟩ results by a preliminary investigation on which he has been at work for 6 months, and he is anxious to continue the investigation, up to higher temperatures and with variations of condition as to quality of surface and shape of radiating body and higher temperatures. This he cannot do without somewhat large expenditure, and I hope the R.S. committee may see its way to let him have the £75.[1]

I was very sorry not to be able to come and see you last Thursday at the R.S. Next Thursday I shall keep myself free. What would be my best time for a good talk with you, not so much over the hopeless (?) luminiferous either [i.e., ether], as experimental results and observations bearing on the difficult questions regarding which I wish to extract from you as much knowledge as I can. Mean time, as a little instalment, can you tell me if observations have been made as to the angle of maximum polarization of the different visible rays ⟨at⟩ reflected from diamond, or glass, or water, or sulphuret of carbon. It seems to me that the differences of angle for the different rays must be less than the formula $\tan^{-1} \mu$ would give, else there would be more appearance of colour than the almost absolute blackness shown by water & glass with a black ground behind, when a Nicol's prism,[2] or a second reflection, is used to show polarization. But I have never looked at either diamond or sulphuret of carbon this way!

I want also to know what is really known definitely from Jamin[3] or others as to intensities of light at different angles.

I have been putting down the equations for refraction & reflection at the separating surface between two homogeneous elastic solids, for vibrations in the plane of incidence. The thing is not very formidable – 8 simple equations for 8 unknown quantities. I don't think it should be at all difficult to bring out a formula for intensity & phase of both refracted and reflected ray, with any ratios of densities & rigidities (for simplicity the condition of incompressibility being imposed; though it is really almost as simple without this condition). The other 4 quantities are the intensity and phase of the $\epsilon^{\pm my}[A\cos(mx - \omega t) + B\sin(mx - \omega t)]$[4] motion in the two mediums.

Yours always truly

W Thomson

⟨P.S. W⟩

1 See J. T. Bottomley, 'On loss of heat by radiation and convection as affected by the dimensions of the cooling body, and on cooling in vacuum', *Brit. Assoc. Rep.* (1884), 623–5.

2 William Nicol (1768–1851), who lectured on natural philosophy at Edinburgh early in his career, invented the prism named after him in 1828 as a means of separating the extraordinary and ordinary rays in double refraction from one another so they could be viewed individually. (*Dictionary of Scientific Biography*.)

3 Between 1847 and 1851, Jamin published several articles on the reflection of light in *Comptes Rendus* and *Annales de Chimie et de Physique*.

4 Kelvin's brackets.

459   Stokes to Kelvin, 20 May 1884
Kelvin Collection, S458

Denver Rectory

Downham 20 May 1884

My dear Thomson,

Thursday next being Ascension Day there is no RS meeting and if there were it is doubtful whether I would go. My only surviving brother[1] the Rector of Denver who is in his 83^d year is dying. I went to Cambridge yesterday morning for my lecture and returned after it. I telegraphed this morning to Isabella, with whom I had left instructions, to give notice that I don't lecture today. Tomorrow I had 2 committee meetings in London but I shall probably cut them.

I always supposed that the problem of reflection on the common boundary of two homogeneous elastic solids, even though crystalline, would be a straightforward one though long. I never attacked it far – cui bono? Its chief interest is in connexion with light, but I have little faith in the representability of the ether within a crystal by a *single* homogeneous medium.

As you speak of vibration in and $\perp$ to the pl[ane] of incidence you seem to have in mind chiefly isotropic media. Green has virtually done this case; for the accessory hypotheses w^h he introduced as to relations between the constants don't affect the difficulty and but little the length of the work. Green's work might be much shortened by adopting Cauchy's artifice of representing vibrations by imaginary exponentials instead of circular functions.

Yours sincerely,
G. G. Stokes

The artifice reduces the 8 arb^y constants det^d by 8 eq^{ns} to the arbitrary const[ant]s det^d by 4 equations. Each a. c. is a mixed imaginary.

1 W. H. Stokes.

460   KELVIN to STOKES, 11 November 1884
Stokes Collection, K273

The University,
Glasgow.
11th Novr. 1884.

DEAR STOKES

I am afraid I did not make quite clear enough the exact question I wished to ask. It was not with reference to total internal reflection, but to ordinary reflection in air. Since writing to you I have seen that almost certainly Glazebrook is wrong in the place referred to, [end of Chap. XII, top of page 370 of edition 1883]:[1] but small blame to him (unless he was working at the subject himself) as he has taken Jamin's actual words ⟨'compos-⟩ 'vibration polarisee . . . . la composante normale' (Annales de Chimie et de Physique, Vol. 31, 1851, Page 167, lines 13–12 from bottom).[2] It seems almost certain that these words are to be interpreted in a non-natural sense; not line of vibration perpendicular to the plane of incidence, but plane of polarisation perpendicular to the plane of incidence. Glazebrooke [*sic*] states the case as if Jamin had meant, line of vibrations perpendicular to &c. On the other hand Quincke,[3] who worked at the subject himself, found out somehow or other what Jamin meant, and his statement is exactly the opposite ⟨of⟩ to what Glazebrooke's becomes, when in Glazebrooke's you substitute *plane perpendicular to plane of polarisation* for 'plane of vibration'. There can be no doubt but Quincke's reading is correct. The case is an exquisite instance, not only of French logic, which generally strikes me as peculiar, but also of the accursed confusivity of nomenclature of plane of polarisation &c. This confusivity does not ⟨confuse⟩ excuse Jamin, but rather the other way, as all the world knows it to exist, and therefore he ought to have been specially careful to make his language unambiguous.

Thanks for what you say as to a wave surface in a magnetic medium. I see that you assume that the magnetic influence does not produce besides the special magnetic effect, anything of the properties of a uniaxal crystal. This supposition is no doubt the right one, when the magnetic effect is so infinitesimal as it is in transparent bodies. If it produced a molecular influence on the effective rigidity or density of the material considered in the luminifer-ous vibrations, compared with that which in iron or nickel it produced on thermoelectric conductivity, then no doubt we should have the rotatory property superimposed upon the ordinary double refraction of a uniaxal crystal. The questions you raise as to the trans⟨mitting⟩itional conditions on either side of the equator are very interesting.

The question I asked just before I sailed for America,[4] was about the transmission of light through, and reflection from, thin plates. I wanted to know if this had been worked out on the homogeneous elastic solid theory. I have worked it out myself for the case of vibrations perpendicular to the plane of the three rays, for which it is very easy; and in which it gives, as it obviously ought to do, the well known result – the one ordinarily obtained by summation of the effects of repeated reflections. But for the case of vibrations in the plane of the three rays, it is equally obvious that the ordinary result obtained by the summational method cannot be true, because it neglects the interfacial wave. I have not yet worked it out, either by the summational method with this correction, or by the direct analytical method of expressing the proper surface conditions for stress and displacement at each surface. I suppose nobody has done anything of this kind yet. There is not much difficulty in it, but it is somewhat long and I have not had time to do it yet. Don't you think it is worth doing, because it seems certain that the interfacial wave will give, when the thickness of the plate is comparable with the wave length, a law of intensities for reflected and transmitted light, sensibly different from the ordinary result calculated summationally.

I have a good deal more to say but must defer it, because of introductory lecture of the 1ˢᵗ John Elder Prof. of Naval Archit[e]cture (Elgar)[5] and degree examination which keeps me all this evening off Wave Theory (except certain remarkable statements which I find I have rather to remark upon than to mark positively).

Yours always truly
W THOMSON[6]

1 Kelvin's brackets. R. T. Glazebrook, *Physical Optics* (London, 1883). Richard Tetley Glazebrook (1854–1935) was fifth wrangler in 1876 and was at the Cavendish Laboratory from 1880 to 1899 as demonstrator and later as assistant director. In 1883 he was also appointed to a Cambridge lectureship in mathematics, and in 1899 he became the first director of the National Physical Laboratory, a position he held until 1919.

2 J. Jamin, 'Mémoire sur la réflexion de la lumière à la surface des liquides', *Annales de Chimie et de Physique*, 31 (1851), 165–87. Jules Célestin Jamin (1818–86) was professor of physics at the Sorbonne from 1863 until his death.

3 Georg Hermann Quincke (1834–1924) was appointed extraordinary professor at the University of Berlin in 1865 and later held professorships at Würzburg and Heidelberg. Among his many papers are sixteen 'Optische Experimental-Untersuchungen' published between 1865 and 1873 in Poggendorff's *Annalen der Physik und Chemie*.

4 Kelvin attended the 1884 British Association meeting in Montreal in August and September and, afterwards, delivered his Baltimore lectures at Johns Hopkins.

5 Francis Elgar (1845–1909) held the professorship from 1883 to 1886.

6 See letter 470.

461   STOKES to KELVIN, 13 November 1884
Kelvin Collection, S459

Lensfield Cottage, Cambridge, 13 Nov. 1884.

MY DEAR THOMSON,

Sir John Conroy's[1] address is. Sir John Conroy, Bart. Arborfield Grange, Reading.

I notice you say that all who had investigated the subject made the 'virtual' rigidity the same in the two media. I am not quite sure what you m[ea]n by 'virtual' rigidity. All seem to throw overboard the direct action of the ponderable molec[u]les. And to tr[e]at the media as two homogeneous media. But the adherents of the view that in polarized light the plane of polarization contains the direction of vibration have to suppose that it is the density that is the same in the two media, and that it is the difference of elasticities, or rigidities, that produces the difference in the velocity of propagation.

If in your model[2] you make mu a p u r e imaginary, I don't see how you afterwards make it a mixed imaginary. Perhaps however the constants you speak of afterwards introducing come to the same thing as making it a mixed imaginary. Mu a pure imaginary would not probably be very far out for silver, but it would for steel. To coin words, in silver the metallicity almost swallows up the vitreosity; in steel the vitreosity is very strong.

Yours sincerely,
G. G. STOKES

P.S. Of course you know of Green's investigation as to the great diminution of right [i.e., light] reflected near the polarized angle when the incident light is polarized perpendicularly to the plane of incidence entailed by the supposition that the transition from medium to medium is not quite abrupt.

1 John Conroy (1845–1900) graduated from Oxford and was fellow and Bedford lecturer at Balliol College. There is a large correspondence from him to Stokes in the Stokes Collection. There are a few letters from Stokes to Conroy at Balliol. There is also one from Kelvin to Conroy at Balliol, dated 12 November 1884, in which Kelvin wrote:

A large divergence from the $\left(\dfrac{\mu-1}{\mu+1}\right)^2$ law of intensity for direct reflected light would be necessary to allow any sufficient divergence from the generally assumed equality of the virtual rigidity of the luminiferous ether in the different transparent mediums to be assumed, in order to account for the prodigious difference which experiment shews between Green's result and observations in respect to the polarization of light by reflection at the surface of a transparent body.

2 In developing his theories of light during the 1880s, Kelvin proposed various mechanical models with properties analogous to those of light. See, for example, Kelvin (265), (302), and (315). Unfortunately, the letter is missing which contained a drawing of the model referred to here. (See letter 464.)

462 STOKES to KELVIN, 15 November 1884
Kelvin Collection, S460

Lensfield Cottage, Cambridge, 15 Nov. 1884.

MY DEAR THOMSON,

I had not thought of the objection you raise to Green's explanation of the nearly complete absence of light at the polarizing angle when the reflected light is analysed. I do not however think it is by any means fatal. Without entering into some actual investigations, one could not say what the amount of coloration ought to be, but I think one c a n say it would be very small. If the transition were sufficiently slow there would be no light, and therefore no colour. On receding from the polarizing angle a cause of light begins to operate which is independent of the colour. If on the other hand the transition were abrupt, there would be light without colour, but too much light. I think it more probable than not that when the transition is almost enough to prevent any light, the coloration, though theoretically it would be there, would be extremely feeble.

The central spot of Newton's rings, when viewed by reflection [b]eyond the critical angle, the light of course veing [*sic*] incident internally, is theoretically larger from the red than the blue. Yet the amount of coloration towards the edge of the black spot is so small that you would probably not notice it if you were not warned to look for it. Assuming Fresnel's formulae to be true, there would theoretically be a coloration depending on the chromatic variation of the polarizing angle. Yet under ordinary circumstances you don't perceive it.

I recollect some years ago scrutanising [*sic*] the light reflected from glass about the polarizing angle, using sunlight, and quenching it as nearly as might be by a Nicol. I was struck by the difference of coloration between crown and flint glass. I could distinguish the two kinds of glass in this way, and in flint the coloration was not such as could be explained by a chromatic variation of the polarizing angle.

Yours sincerely,
G. G. STOKES

463 STOKES to KELVIN, 17 November 1884
Kelvin Collection, S461

Lensfield Cottage, Cambridge, 17 Nov. 1884.

MY DEAR THOMSON,

Your former post card, which was completed by Bottomley, was quite inyelligible. [*sic*]

I have just got your two P.C.'s from Netherhall. I shall address to Glasgow, as I suppose you only went for the Sunday, or rather Saturday and Sunday.

In your two formulae you assume I take for granted that the two isotropic elastic solids are incompressible.

I am no advocate of Green's conjecture, but I don't think it is by any means so easily disposed of on the ground of the absence of colour. In the early part of the first bright Newton's ring – reflected system – the coloration is but slight. And there is reason a priori to think that the coloration due to finiteness of transition would be very much less than in the case of thin plates. For in thin plates, with strictly homogeneous light, on increasing the thickness the intensity does not approach a limit, but merely goes on fluctuating with increasing rapidity – in the case of the rings formed in the usual way – but between the same limits all along; and the reason why with white light the intensity and colour so soon approach a limit is merely that the ring-systems of the different colours overlap. But in the other case the intensity rapidly approaches a limit which is the same for all the colours. Hence we cannot say that the objection is fatal till we have worked the thing out, at least in one or two cases, and then ascertained from the formula whether the coloration would be sensible. I feel pretty certain it would not be vivid. As I told you I think I worked out the problem of reflection with continuous change, according to one particular law of change which gives the result in finite terms,[1] assuming as known the intensity for a single reflection. For light, this would really apply only to light polarized in the plane of incidence, or I should rather say to vibrations perpendicular to the plane of incidence, as in the other case the disturbance corresponding to the ghosts of the normal vibrations, which would be reflected or refracted an [*sic*] angle whose sine in [i.e., is] infinity, would come in. I have not the result by me, and don't know where it is. If imaginary expressions for the vibration are used, in the manner of Cauchy, the problem, analytically considered, becomes identical with that of

565

which I gave the solution in a paper in the Proceedings of the R.S. On the Intensity of the Light Reflected from or Transmitted by a Pile of Plates.[2] I recollect the general character of the result, but not the details.

As to examining the degree of regularity of vibrations from different sources of light, I have often thought of the thing, and have thought of trying to work out experimentally an idea about interference. Fizeau and Foucault, as you doubtless know, obtained interference with a retardation of many thousand undulations.[3] They did not, so far as I know, try different sources of light, and it is possible that even with this some might break down. But when the retardation is so great the bands in the spectrum become so fine and numerous that the observation becomes difficult, and you are pretty well confined to very britht [sic] sou[r]ces, like the sun, that will admit of your using high dispersion and a very narrow slit.

Now my idea was to compensate a retardation T in air by a retardation T' in say water, equivalent to $\mu' T'$ in air, in such a manner that

$$\frac{d}{d\lambda} \frac{\mu' T' - T}{\lambda} = 0$$

for some part of the visible spectrum. Thus supposing as an approximation that

$$\mu' = A + \frac{B}{\lambda^2}$$

we should have

$$\frac{T - AT'}{\lambda^2} - \frac{3BT'}{\lambda^4} = 0$$

giving the condition

$$T = AT' + \frac{3BT'}{\lambda^2} \qquad \left\langle B = \frac{\lambda^2}{3} \left(T - \frac{AT'}{} \right) \right\rangle \qquad \text{for } \lambda = \text{say } \lambda_\circ$$

and leaving the outstanding difference of retardation

$$T' \left(\mu' - A - \frac{3B}{\lambda_\circ^2} \right) \div \lambda \quad \text{wave lengths}$$

Now as the difference of the retardation, expressed in the number of wave lengths, would be a maximum of [sic] minimum within the spectrum, the absolute difference of retardation might be very considerable, and yet near the place of maximum the bands would not be narrow, though on receding from the place of maximum the width would decrease as the square of the distance, and the band would be too fine to be seen. But that does not signify, as a slight change in T or T' would make the place of maximum change from one part of the spectrum to another, the use of a liquid would allow of a small alteration of the length T'. With bisulphide of carbon a smaller thickness would suffice; but the larger thickness with water would I think be more manageable that [*sic*] the smaller with bisulphide of carbon.

It is possible that in some cases the refusal to show bands of interference beyond a certain retardation might show itself even with such retardations as could be managed without compensation.[4] But I think that with a compensated retardation one could go a long way further. The idea of this experiment has for a long time been in my mind, but there would be considerable experimenatal [*sic*] difficulty in carrying it out.

I should not imagine that any great regularity is required for exciting fluorescence. The experiment would be much easier to try with fluorescence, but I expect the result would be negative and one would be left in doubt whether the vibrations were really so very regular, or the method failed to detect irregularity. The method of compensated retardation would allow one to say either the vibrations from such a source are not sufficiently regular to show good interference beyong [*sic*] such a number, or, even up to such a number they are sensibly regular, and I don't know how much further.[5]

Yours sincerely,
G. G. STOKES

P.S. I don't myself attach much weight to conclusions as to the direction of vibration in polarized light derived from such calculations as you refer to, because I think that the supposition that the ponderable molecules have done all their work when they have modified the ether, and you may then throw them overboard and suppose you have got two uninterrupted homogeneous isotropic media to deal with, is most likely wide of the actual truth.

1 Larmor has added a footnote here reading, 'Cf. Lorenz'. This is perhaps a reference to the paper by the Danish physicist Ludwig Valentin Lorenz (1829–91), 'On the reflexion of light at the boundary of two isotropic transparent media', *Phil. Mag.*, **21** (1861), 481–91, in which Lorenz speaks of a gradual, not sharp, transition from one medium to the other.
2 Stokes (71).
3 See Fizeau and Foucault, 'Sur le phénomène des interférences entre deux rayons de lumière dans le cas de grandes différences de marche', *Comptes Rendus*, **21** (1845), 1155–8, and 'Mémoire sur le phénomène des interférences entre deux rayons de lumière dans le cas de grandes différences de marche, et sur la polarisation chromatique produite par les lames épaisses cristallisées', *Annales de Chimie*, **30** (1850), 146–59.
4 Larmor has added a footnote reading, 'But see Rayleigh'.
5 Larmor has added a footnote reading, 'If irregular the light can be spread out into a spectrum of sensible breadth by a prism or grating, and a narrow portion of this spectrum will show greater regularity (cf. Rayleigh)'. Rayleigh published a number of papers on diffraction gratings in the 1870s and early 1880s.

Lensfield Cottage, Cambridge, 17 Nov. 1884.

MY DEAR THOMSON,

You must have thought it odd that I did not refer in my letter tonight to your letter of the 14th with the drawing of the model.[1] The fact is on returning from the post I found the letter on my table unopened. It lay with recent letters, and I suppose some other letter engaged my attention, and I forgot that I had not opened all.

I quite understood that you had a real model, and in calling mu a pure imaginary, I meant the same thing as mu square being a real negative quantity.

I don't see anything w r o n g in Green's second theory, that is to say, the premises are dynamically conceivable, and the equations follow from them, though I have always regarded the failure to explain the velocity of propagation's being the same when the direction of vibration is the same, failure in the sense that there is nothing in the theory to point it out, though the equations may be made to square with it by two arbitrarily assumed relations between three constants, as a weak point of the theory as a physical, as didtinguished [*sic*] from a merely mathematical, theory. Nor did I like the idea of the tensions different in different directions in the undisturbed state.

Yours sincerely,
G. G. STOKES

1 See letter 461.

Lensfield Cottage, Cambridge, 21 Nov. 1884.

MY DEAR THOMSON,

Green is quite right. You have not written down the terms of the first order in the displacements, and have consequently neglected the terms of the second order in the rotations which spring out of those of the first order in the displacements, and which in the case you mention cancel those of the second order that you have written down.

Take the expression you refer to at p. 299.[1] As the three constants A, B, C are independent, and the terms they multiply are derived from one another by symmetry, it will suffice to consider one ⟨te⟩ set. Take then

$$A\left\{2\frac{du}{dx}+\left(\frac{du}{dn}\right)^2+\left(\frac{dv}{dn}\right)^2+\left(\frac{dw}{dn}\right)^2\right\} \tag{1}$$

Take the most general small displacement by pure rotation of an element.

The most general displacement will be a rotation ϱ round a line passing through a fixed point O, which we may take for origin, the direction-cosines of the axis of rotation being say l, m, n. Let P be a point whose coordinates are x, y, z; draw PM perpendicular to the axis of rotation, PN perpendicular to the plane OPM. Let $PM = p$, $O\langle P \rangle M = q$.

The displacement of $\langle P \rangle$ the particle P will be in a circular arc of radius p and angle ϱ. Project this along $P\langle M \rangle N$, $P\langle N \rangle M$. The projections, as far as the order ϱ^2, will be ϱp, $\tfrac{1}{2}\varrho^2 p$. As to the first, the projections along the axes will be the same in expression as if we were dealing with infinitely small displacements, and for these we shall accordingly have

$$u = \varrho(mz - ny)$$
$$v = \varrho(nx - lz)$$
$$w = \varrho(ly - mx)$$

As to the displacements along PM, the coordinates of M being lq, mq, nq, where $q = lx + my + nz$, we shall have for the projections of PM on the axes

$$l(lx + my + nz) - x$$
$$m(lx + my + nz) - y$$
$$n(\langle m \rangle lx + my + nz) - z$$

and consequently we shall have for the complete expressions of the displacements, taken to the second order in ϱ,

$$u = \varrho(mz - ny) + \tfrac{1}{2}\varrho^2(lq - x)$$
$$v = \varrho(nx - lz) + \tfrac{1}{2}\varrho^2(mq - y)$$
$$w = \varrho(ly - mx) + \tfrac{1}{2}\varrho^2(nq - z)$$

substituting now in (1) the values of u, v, w, and retaining terms to the order ϱ^2 we have

$$A\left\{ 2 \times \frac{\varrho^2}{2}(l^2 - 1) + \varrho^2(n^2 + m^2) \right\}$$

$$= \varrho^2 A^{\langle 2 \rangle}(l^2 + m^2 + n^2 - 1) = 0$$

Yours sincerely,
G. G. STOKES[2]

$$\theta = \bar{E}^{-kr}$$

$$-y\theta = u, \quad +x\theta = v \qquad\qquad \frac{du}{dt} + \frac{dv}{dy} = 0$$

$$\frac{du}{dt} = -y\frac{d\theta}{dt} + k\frac{xy}{r}E^{-kr} \qquad\qquad \frac{dv}{dt} = E^{-kr}\left(1 - k\frac{x^2}{r}\right)$$

$$k\frac{xy}{r}\left(2 + k\frac{xy}{r}E^{-kr}\right)E^{-kr} +$$

Try θ const, $\frac{du}{dt} = 0$, $\frac{dv}{dt} = 0$, energy $\qquad\qquad T =$ couple per unit

$$\delta\theta \qquad\qquad \frac{\delta\theta \cdot r}{\delta r} \qquad u\left(\frac{r\,d\theta}{dr}\right), 2\tau r^2 = T.$$

$$d\theta = \frac{T}{2\omega r}\cdot\frac{dr}{r}$$

$$r = Ae^{\frac{2\tau n\theta}{T}} \qquad\qquad \frac{dr}{d\theta} = \frac{T}{2\omega r}\frac{dv}{\delta y}$$

$$\phi = Ae^{(\pm)\theta}$$

1 G. Green, 'On the propagation of light in crystallized media', in N. M. Ferrers, ed., *Mathematical Papers of the Late George Green* (London, 1871), 293–311.

2 The calculations below Stokes's signature are in pencil, apparently by Kelvin.

466 STOKES to KELVIN, 24 November 1884
Kelvin Collection, S464

Lensfield Cottage, Cambridge, 24 Nov. 1884.

MY DEAR THOMSON,

I got your card this morning. I am perfectly aware of all you mention, but that does not alter my opinion. I still maintain the correctness of Green's theory, in the sense that the conclusions are rightly deduced from the premises, which is what I understood you to call in question. I never was satisfied with it as the theory of nature; but that is quite a different thing.

As I told you I think many years ago I made a slight modification of the theory which led to the same differential equations but seemed more conformable to what was likely to be true in nature.[1] In this I discarded Green's axiom that the force-function is independent of rotation, which I don't think likely to be true in a crystal, and in lieu of Green's axiom that the force-function is independent of a rotation, I adopted another consideration, and ultimately came to this:– that what takes the place of a rotation in not introducing a phi is of this kind. Imagine a medium magnified or diminished differently in each of three rectangular directions, and call the former medium the isotropic image of the latter. The latter being supposed to answer to the ether in a crystal, the displacement which involves no external work is such that yhe [sic] isotropic image simply revolves as a solid. When the inequality of magnification vanishes, the medium which before was crystallized becomes isotropic, and Green's axiom now holds. Whereas in MacCullagh's theory a simple rotation, even in vacuo, involves work.

Yours sincerely,
G. G. STOKES

1 See section 11 of Stokes (40).

467 STOKES to KELVIN, 25 November 1884
Kelvin Collection, S465

Lensfield Cottage, Cambridge, 25 Nov. 1884.

MY DEAR THOMSON,

I am glad you see that Green's expression is right, and hope you may be in time to correct what you said in your lecture.[1] I return you the copy of your letter to Mr. Calthamay [i.e., Hathaway], as you may not have another.[2]

Your reference to my report pointed out to me another argument which I might have used. At p. 282 of my report Brit. Ass. Rep. 1862,[3] I have given the part of the force-function for Cauchy's formulae which involves the six constants of the arbitrary stress in equilibrium. This is e x a c t l y t h e s a m e as in Green's theory; the terms wherein they differ, and Green's is more general than Cauchy's, are all among those which are independent of any stress in equilibrium. This part contains in Green's theory 21 arbitrary constants, which in Cauchy's are reduced to 15; the additional 6 which come in when there is stress in equilibrium raise Green's to 27 and Cauchy's to 21.

It is the additional part of the function, which I have written on p. 282, and which is common to the theories of Green and Cauchy, that alone has the property of not vanishing for a simple rotation w h e n y o u t h r o w a w a y the terms of the first order in the displacements. This part does vanish for a pure rotation when you retain the terms of the first order, and consequently those of the second order in the rotation which arise from those of the first order in the displacements. But of this by the way; I have mentioned it already. The new argument is:– the additional part that you objected to in Green's is exactly the same in Cauchy's. But Cauchy's is derived from a system of attracting and repelling particles, regarded as points, the mutual force between any two being supposed to be some function of the

571

distance, and not of the direction of the joining line. In such a system it is obvious that a mere rotation will not store up any work in an element.

Different functions phi may lead to the same equations of motion, as I have noticed in my report, but the same function phi leads to the same conclusions in all respects.

Yours sincerely,
G. G. STOKES

1 Kelvin's *Baltimore Lectures* (1884).
2 Arthur Stafford Hathaway (1855–1934) was the stenographer for Kelvin's *Baltimore Lectures*. He received his B.S. from Cornell University in 1879, was at Johns Hopkins from 1880 to 1885, and, afterwards, taught mathematics at Cornell and Rose Polytechnic Institute in Terre Haute, Indiana. The copy of the letter has not survived.
3 Stokes (72).

468 KELVIN to STOKES, 30 November 1884
Stokes Collection, K274

Nov 30/84
8 Belgrave Crescent
Edinburgh

DEAR STOKES

Porter sent me your letter to him of the 25th.[1] I have not written sooner to you on the subject because I thought you would be turning it over in your mind and judging whether your feeling *against* making the change must or must not have decisive effect.

I do *not* think you need be at all deterred by 'electricity and magnetism'. The lecturing on heat and light, or even on 'light' without the name 'heat' would, it seems to me, be in all respects a proper fulfilment of the 40-lecture part of the duty. Some of the assistants would partly in lecturing and partly in the Laboratory carry out the special requirements in respect to Electricity and Magnetism. And the laboratory work in which I am sure you would take tremendous interest, would always be carrying out largely the primary object of 'teaching and illustrating the laws of Heat Electricity and Magnetism', and not these only but optics &c &c as at present, together with optics and investigations in optics, more than as at present very probably.

But what occurred to me in respect to yourself, was that I think it might allow you to give more of your time to the more congenial pursuits of scientific work, ⟨and⟩ (whether experimental investigation or theoretical) and less to such work as you have at present for the R.S. I suppose the income of the Exp¹ Physics chair is decidedly more than you have in the Lucasian and I thought possibly the difference might amount to even a money compensation for giving up the R.S. work. Thus I thought of the thing rather as freeing you from fatiguing or possibly irksome work (and work that ⟨gives⟩ leaves you less time for what you like best than you would have without it) than as entailing a new and laborious departure.

In fact, I think that if you would accept the Exp¹ Physics, you might find yourself less harassed by numerous irksome calls, and more free for doing what you like best, than you are at present.

Yours always truly
WILLIAM THOMSON

P. S. I ⟨retu⟩ am to read three papers (I wish they were written) at the R.S.E. (on the subjects named in the enclosed billet) on Monday evening.[2] We return to Glasgow on Tuesday morning.

Do you believe in 'Boltzmann's Theorem'? (set forth by Maxwell Camb. Phil. Soc. about 1873,[3] & in Watson's Kinetic Theory of Gases)[4]

1 Stokes's letter to James Porter has not survived. However there are five letters between Porter and Kelvin dating from November and December 1884 in the Kelvin Collection.
    This letter concerns the Cavendish professorship of experimental physics, resigned by Rayleigh in 1884. Despite Kelvin's urging, Stokes did not stand (see the next letter), and J. J. Thomson was selected for the position.
2 Kelvin (267B), (267C), and (267D).
3 Kelvin has written a ? above *1873*. J. C. Maxwell, 'On Boltzmann's theorem on the average distribution of energy in a system of material points', *Trans. Camb. Phil. Soc.*, **12** (1879), 547–70.
4 H. W. Watson, *A Treatise on the Kinetic Theory of Gases* (Oxford, 1866).

469 STOKES to KELVIN, 6 December 1884
    Kelvin Collection, S466

49 Don Street, Old Aberdeen, 6 Dec. 1884.

MY DEAR THOMSON,

I have been pretty busy since I came here completing the preparations for my lectures[1] or I would have written to you before.

I had intended to make no final absolute decision till the lectures here were over. I have lectures on Monday and Wednesday, and immediately after my lecture on Wednesday I must rush off to the train, as I have to be in London on Thursday for the Royal Society. I hope to return to Cambridge on Thursday night.

I feel that I am too old to take up a completely new set of subjects, as to its giving me more leisure, I fell [*sic*] decidedly that it would givw [*sic*] me less. Besides I feel that those who would be under me would be knowing more about the subjects than I do myself. Also it is hardly fair to block the way of promotion to younger men who might reasonably be expected to rise in their profession. Also I have just heard of the intention of a strong man to come forward.

Yours sincerely,
G. G. STOKES

1 Stokes's *Burnett Lectures*.

470   STOKES to KELVIN, 8 December 1884
     Kelvin Collection, S467

49 Don Street, Old Aberdeen, 8 Dec. 1884.

MY DEAR THOMSON,

I yesterday got your letter of Nov. 11, which my wife had found on the floor of my study unopened. How it came to escape being opened I don't know. I can only conjecture that a lot of letters came together, and one of them was pressing, and engaged my attention, and so the other was forgotten. If that be the true account, it is an indication that I am getting to be, or rather have got to be, an old man, and an old man does not do well to make a complete change in his work. Besides there are strong men coming forward. I have had letters from Osborne Reynolds[1] and Fitzgerald of Dublin.[2] I suppose Glazebrook will be a candidate, but I have not heard at present that he has sent in his name.

I thought I would look at the Cambridge postmark of your letter which remained unopened, and strange to say there was none. It had the Glasgow postmark of Nov. 11, but no Cambridge postmark of the date of reception. So perhaps I may throw the fault on some irregularities of the post office.

I must look at the passages you refer to when I get access again to my books. There is no confusion as to the meaning of the term 'plane of polarization', but I am always careful if I have occasion to speak of the direction of vibration in connexion with observation to let it appear which theory is supposed as to the relation between the two. Or rather, I would be careful if I ever employed the term in reference to observation; for as a rule I have avoided it, and I don't know that I ever used ⟨in⟩ it in describing observations.

By the interfacial wave in thin plates in the case of vibrations in the plane of incidence, I suppose you mean the representatives of the refracted and reflected normal vibrations, for which the angle of refraction would be that whose sine is infi[ni]ty if the ether be supposed incompressible. The name 'interfacial wave' would hardly imply this, for there are interfacial waves – according to the derivation of the term – in the case of vibrations perpendicular to the plane of incidence, and the quasi-normal disturbance does not represent the whole of the 'interfacial' disturbance in the case of vibrations in the plane of incidence; but the interfacial disturbance, except the quasi-normal part, i s taken into account in the usual investigation.

I am to leave for London immediately after the delivery of my lecture on Wednesday. I return to Cambridge on Thursday night.

Yours sincerely,
G. G. STOKES

1 The letter has not survived.
2 G. F. Fitzgerald to Stokes, 4 December 1884, Stokes Collection, F190. George Francis Fitzgerald (1851–1901) took his B.A. at Trinity College, Dublin, in 1871 and was Erasmus Smith professor of natural and experimental philosophy there from 1881 until his death.

471   KELVIN to STOKES, 9 December 1884
Stokes Collection, K275

The University,
Glasgow.
9th Decr 1884

DEAR STOKES

By 'interfacial wave' I mean a wave which runs along the interface, and of which the amplitude diminishes logarithmically according to distance from the interface in each or either medium. The interfacial wave I meant in my previous letter to you, was the irrotational wave, with exactly the same Kinematics as the deep sea wave of water, which is called into play by ordinary reflection at the interface between two transparent mediums.

The problem of working out the reflection of light from and transmission through a thin plate, according to Green's theory for vibrations in the plane of the three rays, (but without the supposition of equal rigidities in the two mediums), is I see not at all difficult, when once the single reflection is worked out fully for the same case. The ordinary formulas for a thin plate hold, with simply a letter to denote the ratio of amplitude of reflected to amplitude of ⟨reflected⟩ incident wave for a single reflection. It is only this formula, which gives the ratio in terms of the angle of incidence, that has the complication of the general problem of vibrations in the plane of the three rays. It is easy of course to write down the proper formula for the double interfacial wave in the circumstances now supposed.

Yours
W THOMSON

8 Jany 1885
Athenaeum Club
Pall Mall

MY DEAR THOMSON,

Would you kindly look at the enclosed and say if you think it would be suitable for the R. S. Proceedings?[1] You will see that though printed it is not at present published. Unfortunately I am not well acquainted with these things. He writes like a man who knows, practically at least, and more or less theoretically, what he is about. You would be able to see in a moment whether the thing is good or not.

Pardon the trouble but I don't think it will be much trouble to you.

Yours sincerely,
G. G. STOKES

Prof. Sir Wm Thomson

---

1 The 'enclosed' was a paper by Sir David Lionel Salomons, which Kelvin apparently judged as not suitable for the *Proceedings* (see the next letter) and which did not appear there. Salomons (1851–1925) was vice-president and treasurer of the Institution of Electrical Engineers and director of the South-Eastern Railway; in *Who's Who* he listed scientific research as his recreation.

Lensfield Cottage, Cambridge, 13 Jan. 1885.

MY DEAR THOMSON,

I am extremelt [*sic*] obliged to you for your kind advice as to Sir David Salomon's [*sic*] paper.[1] From the style in which it was written I supposed that he had extensive practical acquaintance with the subject. I must apologise for all the trouble I have given you.

I have to thank you also for the second volume of your collected papers.[2] You have beaten me altogether. My vol. 3 has remained in statu quo for [a] long time.[3] I wanted to re-reduce Baily's experiments, taking the correction for the residual air in accordance with Maxwell's law that the viscosity is independent of the density, but my han[d]s were generally full of other matters.[4]

I have been extremely interested by that remarkable discovery of Herbert Tomlinson's which I mentioned to you.[5] I am satisfied from the account that it is a real phenomenon, and not merely an error arising from cogglesome [*sic*] support. It brings us face to face in a very remarkable manner with the ultimate constitution of matter.

Yours sincerely,
G. G. STOKES

1 See the previous letter, note 1.
2 Kelvin's *MPP*.
3 Volume three of Stokes's *MPP* was not published until 1901.
4 For Stokes's additions to his (47) which discuss Baily, Maxwell, and Tomlinson, see his *MPP*, III, 76–7n, and 137–41. Francis Baily (1774–1844) was a London businessman who helped found the Royal Astronomical Society and who became a fellow of the Royal Society in 1821. Tomlinson's article cited by Stokes is his 'The coefficient of viscosity of air', *Phil. Trans.*, 177 (1886), 767–85, 795–9. The paper was received on 6 January 1886, nearly one year after the date of this letter. Herbert Tomlinson (1845–1931) graduated from Oxford and was demonstrator and lecturer in natural philosophy at King's College, London, from 1870 to 1894.
5 See Tomlinson, 'The influence of stress and strain on the physical properties of matter. Part I. Moduli of Elasticity – continued. The viscosity of metals', *Proc. Roy. Soc.*, 38 (1884–85), 42–5. The paper was received on 9 December 1884 and read 18 December 1884.

474 KELVIN to STOKES, 22 January 1885[1]
Royal Society of London, RR.9.309

The University,
Glasgow.
22nd Jany. '85

DEAR STOKES

I think Hele Shaw's paper on 'Continuous Calculating Machines & Mechanism &c', which I return (paper and atlas of drawings) by parcel post, addressed ⟨by⟩ to Mr White, is suitable for publication in the Transactions. It has been impossible for me to go through his work in detail, but it seems very carefully done and I cannot doubt but that it is all right.

Many thanks for the proof of

1. Stokes apparently separated this, the first part of the letter, from the rest, which does not survive. He typed at the top of the letter: 'Report on Mr. Hele Shaw's paper "The theory of continuous calculating machines, and of a mechanism on a new principle for this and other pur[p]oses["]. [*Proc. Roy. Soc.*, 37 (1884), 189–91.] By Sir William Thomson. N.B. The rest of the letter relates to another matter'. Henry Selby Hele-Shaw (1854–1941) was professor of engineering at University College, Bristol, and later at University College, Liverpool. His full paper was published in *Phil. Trans.*, 176 (1885), 367–402.

475 STOKES to KELVIN, 23 January 1885
Kelvin Collection, S470

Lensfield Cottage, Cambridge, 23 Jan. 1885.

MY DEAR THOMSON,

I thought you would be greatly interested with Tomlinson's paper.[1] I got him to modify the title, which as sent in implied that he had discovered molecular vibrations having a period of some seconds. I think his experiments do prove that the effect is related to a time defined by molecular conditions; but I do not believe that that time is in the strict sense of the words a time of vibration. I am rather disposed to think that it has reference to a rate of change of a kinetic state. In phosphorescence, we are brought in contact with molecular vibrations which have hundreds of millions of millions of vibrations to the second, while as regards the fading we are brought in contact with times comparable with several seconds or more. At the same time I don't profess to have made out the equations of motion in Tomlinson's experiment. At first sight the phenomenon looks so like the sympathy of pendulums, or of the two scales of a balance, that I am not surprised that Tomlinson imagined that he had detected molecular vibrations with a period of some seconds; though how he imagined that sufficient inertia could be got up I do not see.

He has worked hitherto at his house, but he is going to set up an apparatus at King's College, and I am engaged to see the experiments on Wednesday next if the apparatus is ready by then.

Yours sincerely,
G. G. STOKES

P. S. In case you should think of repeating his experiment, I may as well warn you, as a result of my correspondence with him, that it will be necessary to take great care that the torsional strain is sufficiently small.

1 See letter 473, note 5.

476 STOKES to KELVIN, 31 January 1885
Kelvin Collection, S471

Lensfield Cottage, Cambridge, 31 Jan. 1885.

MY DEAR THOMSON,

I heard from Tomlinson this morning. His discovery[1] seems to be a mare's nest.[2] I assumed that he had taken sufficient precautions against want of stability; but the cylinders of the vibrator were hung by wires which were too fine, and permitted of a rotation round their own axes in a time comparable with what was supposed to be the time of molecular vibration.

The thing looked so like the sympathy of pendulums that it was only on the assumption that the observer was fully alive to this source of error and had sufficiently guarded against it that one could accept the result.

Yours sincerely,
G. G. STOKES[3]

1 See letter 473, note 5.
2 Kelvin has underlined *be a mare's nest* and written the following note to P. G. Tait, to whom he obviously sent Stokes's letter: 'Did not you O T' think it would be so?'
3 Kelvin has written at the end of the letter, 'Return to T (Glasgow). T Bangor Feb 1/85'.

477 STOKES to KELVIN, 31 February 1885
Kelvin Collection, S472

Lensfield Cottage, Cambridge, 31 [*sic*] Feb. 1885.

MY DEAR THOMSON,

I told you I was to have seen Tomlinson's apparatus[1] on Wednesday. I did not do so, as he wrote to me to say he was not ready. The thing from the first had looked so like the 'sympathy of pendulums' that one would be prepared from the first to attribute it to that if there were a loophole. The account in the abstract seemed to guarantee the stability of the support. I did not know how the cylinders used as weights to regulate the moment of inertia were hing [*sic*] on to the vibrator. I thought possibly there might have been a ring, permitting of some motion of the vibrators about their own axes independently of the vibrator. I questioned him by letter about this, but it seemed secured. It now appears that the weights were suspended from the bar by fine wires; so fine that when they were set purposely rotating round their own axes they did so in a time that was approximately that of the 'molar' vibrations. So the whole thing now appears to be cleared up, and the paper must be withdrawn.

Yours sincerely,
G. G. STOKES

1 See letter 473, note 5.

478 KELVIN to STOKES, 3 April 1885
Royal Society of London, RR.9.315

The University, Glasgow
3rd April, 1885

DEAR STOKES,

I return J. J. Thomson's paper on 'Some applications of Dynamical principles to Physical Phenomena'.[1] It is in my opinion suitable for publication in the Transactions. I have made several pencil marks upon it to which the author's attention might perhaps be called.

Yours very truly,
WILLIAM THOMSON

1 J. J. Thomson, 'On some applications of dynamical principles to physical phenomena', *Phil. Trans.*, **176** (1885), 307–42.

479 KELVIN to STOKES, 4 May 1885
Stokes Collection, K276

The University,
Glasgow.
4th May, 85

DEAR STOKES

I enclose this paper by J.T. Bottomley.[1] I am going up to London tomorrow to be at *12 Grosvenor Gardens* for 3 weeks or so. I shall be present at the R. S. on Thursday & could take charge of Mr Bottomley's paper if you desire it.

Yours very truly
WILLIAM THOMSON

P. S. This new alloy platinoid promises to be very useful. It can take a high polish; is but little affected by oxidation; and seems better than German-silver for resistance coils to have a minimu[m] alteration of resistance w[it]h temperature. I shall have specimens with me.

I also enclose a paper by L. Casella,[2] communicated by me.

1 J. T. Bottomley, 'On the electric resistance of a new alloy named platinoid', *Proc. Roy. Soc.*, **38** (1885), 340–4.
2 Louis Pascal Casella (1809–97) was born and educated in Edinburgh and became a scientific instrument maker in London. The paper cited here was not published and is not in the Royal Society archives. The only item I find there relating to Casella is a letter (MC.11.148) from him, dated 10 January 1878, soliciting (unsuccessfully) election to the society.

480 STOKES to KELVIN, 1 June 1885
Kelvin Collection, S473

Lensfield Cottage, Cambridge, 1 June, 1885.

MY DEAR THOMSON,

On Saturday evening I worked out the problem of oscillatory waves of finite height so far as to see that there was so [*sic*] no difficulty at all in the principle. And it merely required a little patience to work out. When I say 'a little', that entirely depends on the order of approximation to which you go. In the simplest case – that of an infinite depth – it would not be ⟨very⟩ long to go to the third order, which would give the lowest term of the correction of the period depending on the height.

The method I gave at the end of my ⟨second vovulme [sic]⟩ first volume[1] would be of no use here, as we don't know a priori the form of any of the stream-line trajectories except for the bottom.

As to the highest possible wave of this kind, I think it is a series which at the moment of greatest height presents a succession of cusped curves like the cycloid, but probably a narrower curve than the cycloid.

As to the determination of the motion by approximation, there is not much difficulty in going as far say as to the third order, and no difficulty of principle, but I don't think the result is of very much interest.

I think the possibility of a finite pulse running along a stretched inextensible string without change of form is, so to speak, an accident, depending on the conditions which belong to this particular problem. In waves on water, the transmission without change of form demands a particular shape. In the linear propagation of sound it cannot be at all, be the shape of the disturbance, so to speak, i.e. the form of the function expressing the disturbance, what it may.

Yours sincerely,
G. G. STOKES

1 Stokes (99A), in *MPP*, 1, 314–26.

481   STOKES to KELVIN, 28 July 1885
   Kelvin Collection, S474

Lensfield Cottage, Cambridge, 28 July, 1885.

MY DEAR THOMSON,

I got your telegram today. Isabella is away in Norfolk, and does not return till tomorrow, and she is to start for the Continent on the 7th of Aug. with the Michael Fosters.

Your kind invitation is very tempting. But I fear I must decline it, as we are to go to Ireland on the 7th of August, and I have more to do between that and now than I fear I can get through.

This morning's post brought me a short but interesting paper by Wro-[b]lewski[1] from the Vienna Citzunssberichte [sic]. He has determined the electric resistance of copper down to the boiling point of nitrogen, about −201 Cent. He finds the resistance decreases much faster than the absolute temperature. At this low temperature it is only about one-tenth of what it is at the freezing point of water. It appears therefore that a wire with a resistance nil is roughly realisable in actual experiment.

Yours sincerely,
G. G. STOKES

1 Z. F. von Wróblewski, 'Ueber den elektrischen Widerstand des Kupfers bei den niedrigsten Kältegraden', *Sitzungsberichte der kaiserlichen Akademie der Wissenschaften. Mathematisch-Naturwissenschaftliche Classe*, **92** (1886), Abth. 2, 639–51. Zygmunt Florenty von Wróblewski (1845–88) was professor of physics at Jagiellonian University in Cracow from 1882 until his death.

482   KELVIN to STOKES, 28 December 1885[1]
Stokes Collection, K277

Dec 28/85

How thin can you split mica, to get pieces of an inch or two broad or long? Can I get such pieces, as thin as 1/100 of a millimetre? Can I split them for myself or are there professional mica splitters who will supply them cheaper?

A happy new year to all at Lensfield.

W. T. & F. A. T.[2]
c.o. A H Brown M.P.[3]
Druid's Cross Wavertree
Liverpool

1 This is a post card addressed to Stokes.
2 I.e., Kelvin's wife, the initials being in her hand.
3 Alexander Hargreaves Brown (1844–1922) was the husband of Kelvin's second wife's sister.

483   STOKES to KELVIN, 29 December 1885
Kelvin Collection, S475

Lensfield Cottage, Cambridge, 29 Dec. 1885.

MY DEAR THOMSON,

There are no professional mica splitters that I know of, unless it be those who split it for making lanterns, for which of course it is not to be required very thin. You want the pieces it seems about the 100th. of a millimetre thick, which translated into intelligible English means 4 thousandths of an inch. You do not say whether you want them so strictly uniform in thickness as to give a perfectly uniform field in polarised light. If you do, there might I should think be some difficulty about it. If you do not, and do not care that the thickness should be exactly so and so, but only thereabouts, I should not think there would be any difficulty. And I think you might do it quite well yourself. You would probably get pieces cheap if you come across a lantern maker who uses it, and then you could try your hand.

A Happy New Year to you and Lady Thomson.

Yours sincerely,
G. G. STOKES

484 STOKES to KELVIN, 30 October 1886
Kelvin Collection, S476

Lensfield Cottage, Cambridge, 30 October, 1886.

MY DEAR THOMSON,

I have found the question in the Smith's prize paper which I had in my mind. It was suggested as I mentioned by the form of the integrals whereby Cauchy and Poisson express the wave disturbance in terms of the initial disturbance. The question in full is as follows:– (year 1876.)[1]

'11. Find the expression for the velocity of propagation of a series of simple periodic waves in water of uniform depth, the motion being small and in two dimensions.

If two such series, of equal amplitude and nearly equal wave length, travel in the same direction, so as to form alternate lulls and roughnesses, prove that in deep water these are propagated with half the velocity of the waves; and that as the ratio of the depth to the wave-length decreases from ∞ to o, the ratio of the two velocities of propagation increases from $\frac{1}{2}$ to 1.'

Yours sincerely,
G. G. STOKES

1 The question is printed in Stokes's *MPP*, v, 362, along with Larmor's footnote that 'this [i.e., question 11] is usually quoted as the source of the now well-known theory of wave-groups'.

485 KELVIN to STOKES, 8 November 1886
Stokes Collection, K278

The University,
Glasgow.
Nov 8/86

DEAR STOKES

My nephew J.T. Bottomley is a candidate for the vacant professorship⟨s⟩ of physics in the Normal College of Science, South Kensington and I would like you just to know something, more than can have come under your notice hitherto, of his qualifications for such a place. I enclose a copy of printed testimonials which he received in 1870 to support a candidature for Owens College, in which he was successful. He was appointed to be professor of mechanics and mathematical physics, at the same time that Balfour Stewart was taken for experimental physics. But the separation of experimental physics (according to an arrangement made after the candidates had offered themselves) made the post less eligible and he preferred to remain in King's College London. Soon after, the position he now has in Glasgow was offered to him and he accepted it and has been here ever since. He gives more than half of the public lectures (I ⟨taking⟩ giving the other half) his subjects at present being experimental physics (⟨thre⟩ two hours weekly); elementary dynamics with experimental illustrations (two hours weekly) and higher mathematical dynamics (two hours weekly). In all these lectures he acts quite independently of me. He assists me in managing the laboratory and in teaching the students in it; and he has been most useful to me in respect of designing new electric instruments. His strongest inclination is for experimenting, and he has always instinctively devoted his spare time to it. A chief inducement to him to apply for the post in South Kensington is the prospect of having more time for original work than he has here. You may see by the printed testimonials that he began in a good school under Dr Andrews in Belfast and had farther advantages under W. A. Miller[1] in London. Particularly from Andrews he learned perseverance and acquired skill in making and putting together apparatus required for research, and he has now both qualities, quite remarkably, and most usefully for work. His glass-blowing has allowed him to do things in Sprengel-pump[2] arrangements that without such skill, he simply could not do by aid of the instrument maker. His good knowledge of chemistry and practical skill in chemical manipulation is a great advantage in a physical laboratory, and I do not believe any of the other candidates is likely to have such a combination of good practical qualities with mathematical knowledge, and experience in lecturing and in laboratory work. I feel confident that if elected he will be most successful with the teachers who come from all parts of the country to the S. Kensington school, in teaching them how to work with their own hands, and put apparatus together for themselves, besides giving them good theoretical instruction.

I enclose a printed list of papers which shows good work and promises more. The six articles which I have marked × are instalments of results and methods and instrumental appliances in a very serious investigation on which he has been at work in most of his spare time for the last two years – the determination of thermal radiation in absolute measure. He is now getting together results, and reducing them (which involves rather long numerical work) for ⟨the⟩ a paper which I hope will soon be sent to you for the Royal Society.[3]

I am afraid I have taxed your patience with a very long letter. I do not know if you will take any part in advising the Gov^t as to the choice to be made, but in any case you will understand my wishing you to know of my nephew's qualifications.

Yours always truly
WILLIAM THOMSON

P. S. I have been getting out some very curious things about waves (water.) among them complete confirmation of Scott Russel[l]'s doctrine of sudden diminution of force, in towing a *boat* in a canal, when the velocity is got to exceed $\sqrt{9D}$. I find (which is now quite obvious) that if water ⟨being⟩ were inviscid, zero force would suffice to keep a boat moving at any constant speed $> \sqrt{9D}$, whether in a canal or in open water.

1 William Allen Miller (1817–70), who became a fellow of the Royal Society in 1845, was professor of chemistry at King's College, London.
2 Hermann Johann Philipp Sprengel (1834–1906) was educated in Hanover, coming to England in 1859 and residing in London from 1862. He developed his vacuum pump in the 1860s.
3 Kelvin communicated two papers by Bottomley to the Royal Society in the spring of 1887: 'On thermal radiation in absolute measure', *Phil. Trans.*, ser. A (1887), 429–50, and 'On radiation from dull and bright surfaces', *Proc. Roy. Soc.*, **42** (1887), 433–7.

486 STOKES to KELVIN, 9 November 1886
Kelvin Collection, S477

Lensfield Cottage, Cambridge, 9 Nov. 1886.

MY DEAR THOMSON,

I have just got your letter, you had told me – but it had gone out of my head – that Bottomley was going to be a candidate. I consulted [G. C.] Foster as to whether I should keep myself open in case the minister wished to consult me confidentially,[1] and he did not think I need. ⟨I⟩ So I wrote a testimonial yeaterday [*sic*] for Glazebrook, who had asked me. I know I think of three very good candidates, Bottomley being one. The other two I refer to are Glazebrook and Rücker.[2] Clifton[3] goes in strongly for Rücker.

I see what you mean by the non-resistance of a canal boat pulled in a perfect fluid with a velocity greater than that that you mention.

Here is a very simple case of possible steady motion in two dimensions in a perfect fluid, the motion being rotational, of continuously varying rotationality ψ being the stream-line function we have for steady motion

$$\frac{d^2\psi}{dx^2} + \frac{d^2\psi}{dy^2} = f(\psi)$$

and the particular simple case I refer to is

$$\psi = C \sin\frac{\pi x}{a} \sin\frac{\pi y}{b}$$

$$\psi = \int (u\,dy - v\,dx)$$

[w]hich gives for the lines of motion infinitely near the middle a set of similar and concentric ellipses, passing on to a rectangle at the boundary. I should

have said that I suppose the fluid to be bounded by the sides of the rectangle whose edges are *a* and *b*.

Your[s] sincerely,
G. G. STOKES

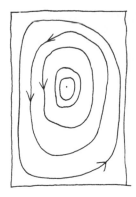

The rotation

$$\left(= \tfrac{1}{2}\overline{\frac{dv}{dx} - \frac{du}{dy}} = -\tfrac{1}{2}\overline{\frac{d^2\psi}{dx^2} + \frac{d^2\psi}{dy^2}} = \frac{\pi^2 C}{2}\overline{\frac{1}{a^2} + \frac{1}{b^2}}\sin\frac{\pi x}{a}\sin\frac{\pi y}{b} \right)$$

vanishes at the perimeter.

1 At this time, Stokes was president of the Royal Society, and it was no doubt in that capacity that he thought he might be consulted. Presumably, it was not Michael Foster, but the physicist, George Carey Foster, who was involved in appointing the professor of physics.
2 Arthur Rücker (1848–1915) studied at Oxford and was professor at the Yorkshire College of Science from 1874 to 1885, before becoming professor of physics at the Normal School of Science and Royal School of Mines in 1886. From 1901 to 1908 he was principal of the University of London.
3 Robert Bellamy Clifton (1836–1921) was sixth wrangler in 1859 and was professor of experimental philosophy at Oxford from 1865 to 1915, where he taught Rücker.

487 STOKES to KELVIN, 4 February 1887
Kelvin Collection, S478

Lensfield Cottage, Cambridge, 4 Feb. 1887.

MY DEAR THOMSON,

It is a pity you were not at the R.S. yesterday to do battle. You say:– it is impossible in our ideal inviscid incompressible fluid . . . to form a vortex sheet . . . by any natural action.

It seems to me perfectly certain that it i s possible. I hold that a surface of discontinuity if [*sic*] actually formed whenever a fluid gores itself – whenever a portion projects like a cow's horn and strikes another part of the free surface, or to take a particular case, in a curling wave. You even go so far as to assert the continuity in the case of a raindrop striking a mass of fluid at rest. I mean of course a mass of water, supposed like the drop itself to be composed of ideal inviscid fluid.

When the fluid is contained in a closed ⟨f⟩ vessel of any form, which it completely fills, the bounding surface of the fluid is prevented from impinging on itself, which makes a profound difference.

The onus probandi clearly lies on the person who asserts that in the case supposed there is no discontinuity. I really do not know by what reasoning you were led to the conclusion that there is no discontinuity.

I have asked Lord Rayleigh to keep back the paper[1] from publication, if the exegencies [sic] of getting on permit it, till he has had time to hear from you. He is staying now, and is to stay for a couple of months or so, at 4 Carlton Gardens, S.W.

Yours sincerely,
G. G. Stokes

Take this figure in two dimensions.[2]

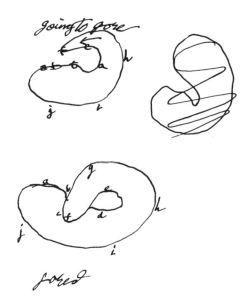

1 Both Kelvin (282) and (283) were read to the Royal Society on 3 February 1887. Rayleigh had replaced Stokes as secretary of the Royal Society.
2 Kelvin has written near Stokes's figures, 'Keep with care till returned T'.

8 Belgrave Crescent.
Edinburgh.
Feb 6/87

DEAR STOKES

If while the goring is in process the horn and dog become both in an instant inviscid liquid, a vortex sheet is certainly formed: not otherwise. If this is a natural action I withdraw my statement.

As to rain-drops falling into flowing water, the reign of continuity is infinitesimally and instantaneously interfered with at the instant of each contact at a point; but at no time or place is there any vortex sheet formed, or any rotation imparted to any part of the fluid.

Lord Rayleigh also wrote to me expostulat⟨ed⟩ing.[1] He supposed two parallel plane surfaces bounding two portions of liquid moving with relative motion parallel to the planes, to come into contact. But Whitworth[2] was not there to make the true planes, and to set them exactly parallel: and if his work had been inexact to 10^{-21} of an inch, there still would be no vortex sheet. I am writing him to this effect.

We are here from Sat. to Tuesday morning for a R.S.E. meeting.

Yours very truly
WILLIAM THOMSON

P. S. An old illustration which I gave in the R.S.E. was a globe moving through an inviscid liquid and suddenly liquified.[3] This illustrated the translation of a portion of liquid in connection with a vortex ring. I did not then know how to deal with the peculiar vortex sheet so formed. It is clear now. There is virtual annulment of energy of a very curious and interesting kind.

1 Rayleigh's letter is in neither the Kelvin Collection nor the Kelvin Papers at Glasgow.
2 Sir Joseph Whitworth (1803–87), renowned for developing a method of constructing truly plane surfaces and for his work with parallel plane surfaces.
3 See Kelvin (190).

7 Feb. 1887[1]
Athenaeum Club
Pall Mall S.W.

MY DEAR THOMSON,

Lord Rayleigh is in the Club, and we have both been speaking about your paradox which neither of us admit.

As to the hour and day I am not an artist and I did not propose to draw the actual forms. But if you have the liquid (I suppose it perfect, = inviscid) all alone first like this

and then like this[2]

there *must*[3] be a surface of separation (drawn in red) such that the matter at one side of it previously belonged to the horn (a curling wave) and that on the other side previously belonged to the 'dog'. There will of course be continuity *of matter* in crossing the surface and also of *normal* vel[y]. But it seems to me[4] that there must be *in general* discontinuity of tangential velocity. Only in some very particular case can you avoid this. If you traced continuously along the surface in the two cases you get[5]

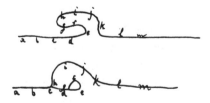

If the motion in the case drawn were in two dimensions the space occupied by the fluid would have become doubly connected from having been singly connected unless you regard the red as part of the original surface which appears as surface in two capacities, and which you cannot press without a violation of continuity.

Yours sincerely
G. G. STOKES

Tomorrow morning I understand you to say you return to Glasgow and as it is now $11\frac{1}{2}$ p. m. I address there.

1 Kelvin has written at the top of the letter, 'Answ^d Feb 9'.
2 In the figure in the text here, Stokes has drawn in red the short, horizontal line which connects the inner oval with the long, curved line.
3 Kelvin has placed an asterisk here and written in the margin, '*No* K[elvin] Oct 24 1905'.
4 Stokes has deleted four or five words here, which are not now legible.
5 As in the figure mentioned in note 2, the short, horizontal line (from *c* to *d*) in the lower figure here is in red.

490   KELVIN to STOKES, 9 February 1887
Stokes Collection, K280

Glasgow University
Feb 9/87

DEAR STOKES

The horn first touches the dog at just one point. Instantly after that there is the double continuity *abcdlm*, – – – and *efghijkd'ef* – –

There is no one instant at which, or time during which, there can be finite slip over a finite area: or any excuse for the inviscid liquid taking the liberty of exacting more work from its surface than ⟨that whi corresponds⟩ the very least with which it can move consistently with the actual motion of the surface. The thing does not admit of argument; but I wish you would write and say so, or let Lord Rayleigh write so,[1] for you as well as himself.

The drop falling directly on water presents a very nice problem, not quite do-able, even in two dimensions, but quite readily imaginable. The arrow-heads represent absolute velocities of the water a very short time after geometrical contact: heaviest representing the previous undisturbed velocity of the drop, and lighter & lighter arrows representing smaller and smaller velocities. N.B. I am not supposing capillary attraction to have any effect. It is

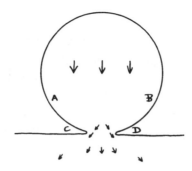

quite possible or probable that the drop may curl down at A and B and make a second contact; this time in a horizontal circle. It is impossible that there can be any sliding contact at C & D.

The collapse of a symmetrical spherical shell of water enclosing vacuum, and subjected to a given constant pressure P at its outer boundary is a very nice and easy dynamical problem. I am happy to present to you and Lord Rayleigh the loss of energy with which it ends.

Yours
W. T.

1 There is no such letter from Rayleigh in either the Kelvin Collection or the Kelvin Papers at Glasgow.

491 Stokes to Kelvin, 8 November 1887
Kelvin Collection, S480

Lensfield Cottage, Cambridge, 8 Nov. 1887.

My dear Thomson,

I have had a letter from Sharpe,[1] in which he quoted the sum of the series in one of the forms which I had sent him; so I may as well copy it for you. I have not looked since for my work, nor worked it out afresh, though it is not long. I was led to put it into the enclosed form[2] in order to exhibit more clearly the singular, or critical, nature of the points B, B' as well as O.

If we travel from an outer point P to an interior point Q by a lot of paths, some going right and some left of B, there is no ambiguous function, which has different values according as we go by the one set of routes or the other, except ϑ – I suppose that no two of the routes include B' or O – the difference of ϑ by the two sets of routes is 2π. Hence for the motion which is the difference of the two motions according as we travel, keeping the motion continuous with the motion outside leaving B to the left or to the right

$$\psi + i\psi = \pi \left\{ i \left(2 - \overline{\varrho + \frac{1}{\varrho}} \sin \theta \right) - \left(\varrho - \frac{1}{\varrho} \right) \cos \theta \right\}.$$

To make the motion unique inside we must draw a barrier from B to B' which we are not to cross. In crossing the barrier, the velocity potential and the flux function would both in general change discontinuously. If however we wish the barrier to be representable by a line of sources there must be no discontinuity of the velocity potentaial [sic], but only of its diff. co. with respect to a normal variation. We must have therefore for the motion which is the difference of the two

$$\left(\varrho - \frac{1}{\varrho}\right)\cos\,\theta = 0,$$

and therefore we must take for barrier either the semi-circle BAB', or the opposite semi-circle, or the line BB'. In the last case however the density at a point Q in the line OB becomes infinite as Q approaches O. The best way I think of considering it is to regard as the boundary a small circle drawn with O for centre and the portion of the diameter which lies outside that small circle; and in the end we may take the radius of the small circle as small as we please. The flux will take the form infinity minus infinity, having a finite limit for the difference.

I have not at present worked out a case for 3 dimensions; but it is easy to see from analogy that there will be a curve of double curvature – there may actually be two or more – which is a critical curve which must remain unchanged, but which may be capped in more ways than one by a surface of sources. It might be capped by an arbitrary surface if we merely wanted a barrier, and did not care that that barrier should be representable by a surface of sources.

Yours sincerely
G. G. STOKES[3]

Found the knife was Isabella's.

1 See H. J. Sharpe to Stokes, 17 October 1887, Stokes Collection, S499. Henry Josiah Sharpe (1838–1917) was sixth wrangler in 1861 and was vicar of Marham, Norfolk, from 1868 to 1906. There is an extensive correspondence from him to Stokes in the Stokes Collection.
2 The enclosure has not survived.
3 Kelvin has jotted in the margin, '30 grammes', '.86×', '.77', '$\frac{55}{60} = \frac{11}{12}$', and '.77'.

Nov 23/87
Glasgow University

DEAR STOKES

I should have written sooner to thank you for your letter about the gravitational skeleton, which is most interesting,[1] but that I have been under great pressure to get the minimal tetrakaidecahedron paper[2] (rough proof enclosed) launched, besides my university work which has been getting *into* *swing*. I have also been drawn to the Green 'extraneous pressure' explanation of waves of light in a crystal, with some results of an almost satisfactory character. I find a perfectly clear and definite solution for the velocity of laminar waves in an incompressible isotropic homogeneous medium, stretched in the ratios

> 1 to α in direction OX
> 1 to β [in direction] OY
> 1 to γ [in direction] OZ,

($\alpha\beta\gamma = 1$ because of incompressibility). I find for the velocities of waves in the principal direction as follows.

⟨Wave-front is perpendicular to⟩

(1) direction of normal to wave-front
(2) direction of vibration
(3) velocity of propagation

(1)	x		y		z	
(2)	y	z	z	x	x	y
(3)	$\alpha\dfrac{P-R}{\beta-\gamma}$;	$\alpha\dfrac{R-Q}{\alpha-\beta}$ ⟩	⟨β^{P}⟩			
(3)	$\alpha\dfrac{Q-P}{\beta-\alpha}$;	$\alpha\dfrac{R-P}{\gamma-\alpha}$	$\beta\dfrac{R-Q}{\gamma-\beta}$;	$\beta\dfrac{P-Q}{\alpha-\beta}$	$\gamma\dfrac{P-R}{\alpha-\gamma}$;	$\gamma\dfrac{Q-R}{\beta-\gamma}$

Hence if

$$\frac{1}{\alpha}\frac{R-Q}{\gamma-\beta} = \frac{1}{\beta}\frac{P-R}{\alpha-\gamma} = \frac{1}{\gamma}\frac{Q-P}{\beta-\alpha}$$

the velocities of the principal waves are the same for the same directions of vibration, and we have Fresnel's wave surface, on Fresnel's supposition as to direction of vibration. The assumption to bring out this result is, you will see, much less strained than Green's, on which you comment in your B.A. Report on Physical Optics;[3] and it is satisfactory that this view reduces the whole theory to stress in an isotropic solid; instead of, as in Green's '2nd Theory', taking an aeolotropic solid with 18 ⟨coeff^{ts}⟩ moduluses, reduced to 3, and *modifying* it by stress. But besides, Green's is not very intelligible, if intelligible at all; and his formula gives virtual rigidity to a fluid pressed equally (or drawn equally with negative pressure) in all directions. Still I feel that Green really discovered the truth, if this is the truth, that unequal stress in different directions explains the otherwise intractable part of the theory of double refraction.[4]

We were *very much* displeased with that article in Nature.[5] I think on the contrary, your agreeing to be member was most patriotic and public-spirited. Personally, and for the sake of science I can't help feeling sorry that it will take up so much of your time. I hope after all that you will really like it yourself, and feel happy in it. Lady Thomson thanks Isabel for the letter she had the other day & sends love to her and Mrs Stokes and sympathy & best wishes to you. She hopes that you will keep your & my countrymen in order.

Yours always truly
WILLIAM THOMSON

1 Kelvin has added a footnote here reading, 'I hope you will find time to publish the whole theory, even if quite shortly'. Stokes did not publish it.
2 Kelvin (283A).
3 Stokes (72).
4 See letter 456, note 1, for secondary works on this material.
5 T. H. Huxley had published an anonymous article in *Nature* arguing that, as president of the Royal Society, Stokes should not also be a Member of Parliament. See Stokes's *Memoir*, I, 177–9.

493   KELVIN to STOKES, 14 December 1887
Stokes Collection, K282

Physical Laboratory,[1]
The University,
Glasgow.
Dec ⟨15⟩ 14/87

DEAR STOKES

Do you admit Glazebrook's conclusion (Trans R.S. June 1878)[2] that 'Fresnel's theory[3] is only true ⟨to⟩ as a first approximation'.

Does Glazebrook's work prove any deviation from Fresnel? I think I understood from himself that he was not satisfied with his old work (the 1878 I suppose) and that he was going to repeat it, with some causes of error eliminated. Meantime is *anything known* inconsistent with the absolute accuracy of Fresnel's wave surface, whether in Iceland spar, or in biaxal crystals. Your 12 lines in the 1872 Proceedings[4] demonstrate an accuracy for Iceland spar ⟨far⟩ much within the errors indicated for Arrogonite by Glazebrook. Has Glazebrook added to the accuracy with which you have proved Huyghen's construction (i.e. Fresnel's wave surface) for Iceland spar? I cannot quite make out what his conclusion at the foot of p 618 of Phil Trans. 1882 Part II. is.[5]

I should be greatly obliged by one line or two lines in answer by return of post as I have a proof coming from Ed° [i.e., Edinburgh] tomorrow morning in which I wish to insert a reference.[6] Lady Thomson joins in kind regards to you all & I remain

Yours truly
W THOMSON

1 Stokes has written at the top of the letter, 'ansd 15–12–87'.
2 R. T. Glazebrook, 'An experimental determination of the values of the velocities of normal propagation of plane waves in different directions in a biaxal crystal, and a comparison of the results with theory', *Phil. Trans.* (1879), 287–377. The paper was read 20 June 1878.
3 Kelvin has written above the line, 'p 375'.
4 Stokes (87).
5 R. T. Glazebrook, 'On the refraction of plane polarized light at the surface of a uniaxal crystal', *Phil. Trans.* (1882), 595–620.
6 In his (294), Kelvin cited Stokes (72) but not Glazebrook's papers.

494 KELVIN to STOKES, 2 March 1888
Stokes Collection, K283

Glasgow University
March 2/88

DEAR STOKES

If you chance to be at the Athenaeum on Monday afternoon between 4 & 6 will you vote for Ingleby. He is son of an old member of the Athenaeum who died last September, and a still older Cambridge friend of mine, C. M. Ingleby of Trinity.[1]

I hope you have been enjoying Parliament. It must be very satisfactory, and pleasant, to see all going so well. We were greatly pleased with Doncaster and Deptford. Everything seems to promise well for a long and useful tenure of the present ministry, and I am now feeling very hopeful that I may myself live to see the last of government by party.

Do you still care for viscosity? I am greatly exercised with it at present – to work out a little hydrokinetic analogy for electromagnetic induction. By the bye – I remember you asked me what I thought of viscosity in a compressible fluid. I don't know if I saw the question effectively then, but now I have no doubt: there must be two independent coefficients of viscosity: distortional and compressional.

Yours always
W THOMSON

Lady Thomson sends her love to Mrs Stokes & Isabel.

1 Clement Mansfield Ingelby (1823–86) took his B.A. at Cambridge in 1847 and became a Shakespearean scholar. His son, Arthur (1852–1929), took his B.A. at Cambridge in 1875.

495 STOKES to KELVIN, 10 and 11 March 1888
Kelvin Collection, S481

Lensfield Cottage, Cambridge, 10 March, 1888.

MY DEAR THOMSON,

I would have answered your letter before only that between 3 lectures a week in Cambridge, one Royal Society in London, and a good deal of attendance in the House of Commons, besides some correspondence, I had not much spare time.

I always I think felt that there was doubt about the evanescence of the coefficient of viscosity in a motion of compression or extension alike in all directions. I think however that there is good reason to think that thought [sic] perhaps it may not be absolutely nil, it is but small compared with that belonging to a motion of distortion. The original idea I had was that of agitations produced by a rearrangement of the molecules.[1] Suppose you had an Indian rubber bag, in tension, filled with smooth marbles, or at least marbles which were very nearly smooth. Then it [sic] you were to give it a motion of distorsion, [sic] every now and then a marble would start into a new position among its fellows, and the change would be accompanied by a sudden disturbance among the whole set, though strongest in the neighbourhood of the marble that started. Now suppose you had molecules at distance apart. A similar motion of distortion in the assemblage as a whole would produce something of the same kind. But suppose that instead of a distortion the walls of the space in which the molecules were confined expanded alike in all directions. One cannot of course say, not knowing the law of force, that the molecules would be in equilibrium if there was a uniform expansion of the assemblage as a whole; but it seems likely that that would at any rate be very approximately the case. And I showed that the same result followed from Poisson's hypotheses, though he himself left his equations with the two coefficients. And then again Maxwell obtained from his suppositions as to the molecular constitution of gases, and the actions which went on in them, the same equations, with one coefficient only, that I had given.[2] And then K [*sic*] think the argument I used with you one day leads to the same conclusion: viz. that the second coefficient, if not wholly nil, is at any rate very small compared with the other.

Suppose the containing boundary to be absolutely impervious to heat, and to contract, and then expand to its primitive volume with indefinite slowness. The temperature would rise in contraction, remain so while contracted, and after expansion resume its original value. In the cy[c]le, no work would be done. But now suppose the change to take place rapidly. If there were any difference, one would naturally suppose that it would be in the direction of producing greater molecular agitation in contracting. But if that greater agitation at any step were sensibly the same as it would be if the expansion were permanently to stop there, the temperature would be higher than it would be if the change were to take place with infinite slowness, the contraction, I mean, of volume.

11 March. I had intended to go on, but I withdraw the last. I think that all that you can say for certain is that so and so are the equations, with their two unknown constants. But there are I think strong reasons for suspecting that one of the constants is, if not absolutely nil, at any rate very small compared with the other.

Yours sincerely,
G. G. STOKES

1 See Stokes (11).
2 Stokes has drawn a line through the rest of this paragraph and all of the following one.

496 KELVIN to STOKES, 4 January 1889[1]
Stokes Collection, K284

Glasgow Jan 4/89

Thanks for your letter and enclosure. The latter has not suffered any serious damage through its 8 weeks residence in the sleeve of your gown. Possibly it may even have gained in effectiveness through age. Give our kind regards and best wishes for a happy new year to Mrs Stokes & Isabel, and the boys[2] if still with you. We hope Mrs Stokes is keeping better.

W. T.

1 This is a post card addressed to Stokes.
2 Stokes's sons, Arthur and William George Gabriel (1863–93). The latter took his B.A. at Cambridge in classics in 1884 and was a practising physician when he died, possibly by suicide.

497 KELVIN to STOKES, 23 January 1889
Stokes Collection, K285

The University,
Glasgow.
23^{d} Jany '89

DEAR STOKES

I have today sent you by parcels post Mr Wel[l]don's[1] draft Report for the Teaching University for London Commission. After you have read it and made your remarks upon it will you return it to him. It seems to me very good and nothing has occurred to me to add in the way of suggestion. I have made two or three remarks which I have pencilled upon it.

Yours very truly
WILLIAM THOMSON

1 James Edward Cowell Welldon (1854–1937) received his B.A. from Cambridge in 1877 as senior classic and was headmaster of Harrow from 1885 to 1898. Shortly after the date of this letter, he wrote Stokes about the commission's report, commenting: 'How the present University of London is to work if it be so constituted as a University, partly examining and partly Teaching, partly Imperial and partly local, partly dissociated from existing institutions and partly dependent on them I have never seen, nor do I see now'. (Welldon to Stokes, 12 March 1889, Stokes Collection, W286.)

498 KELVIN to STOKES, 11 August 1889
Stokes Collection, K286

Aug 11/89
Netherhall.
Largs.
Ayrshire.

DEAR STOKES

I should be glad if I could, to take part in anything along with you and Lord Rayleigh.

If the Lighthouse investigation[1] could be held at any time between the 24th of October and the 5th of November, in Cambridge or London, I should be glad to join you in it. I am afraid I could scarcely undertake it at any other time, but I hope from what you say that that time may be convenient.

Yours always truly
WILLIAM THOMSON

1 The investigation, which Kelvin, Stokes, and Rayleigh did undertake, concerned the inventions of an intensity burner and a giant lens by John Richardson Wigham (1829–1906). For drafts of the report and correspondence on the matter (mainly between Wigham and Stokes), see Stokes Collection, TH1 to TH58.

Athenaeum Club
Pall Mall
Jan 13/90

Dear Stokes

I have seen Hopkinson just now and he tells me that in the S. Foreland experiments the electric light was arranged to throw light through a range of altitude greater than that corresponding to perfect focussing with so large a lense[*sic*]-arrangement as that used. I said was this done by throwing the source slightly out of focus, & [he] said no, but by an arrangement of prisms giving the desired result better than ⟨throwing⟩ placing the source out of focus. This I presume is the prism-arrangement which was referred to several times in our recent meetings; but we understood that this arrangement was *not* in action. Hopkinson is quite sure it *was*. The report should make this clear, as I suppose it does.

Hopkinson says *he* does not think the special arrangement necessary, as the source is large enough to give illumination over all the useful range, even if placed perfectly in focus for a lense of 70 cm focal distance. The two carbons are 3 mm or 4 mm distant from one another. The current, being 'alternate' makes each pole conical, and probably the bright part of each may be another 3 mm or so. This would make the whole vertical depth of the source about 10 ⟨cm⟩ mm, and at 70 cm distance would subtend an angle of 1/70. A light house 300 feet high subtends an angle of 1/60 at a distance of a nautical mile; so I think probably Hopkinson is right in this matter, and that the electric light *in* the focus of a 70 cm focal distance ⟨compoun⟩ lense, would illuminate the sea from the horizon to within a mile of the light house; which I think is practically all that is wanted. This would cut away the part of Wigham's objections of which ⟨we⟩ you and I were last talking. Hopkinson is very warm (almost hot) in saying that the report is thoroughly fair in respect to gas. He thinks it overestimates the expensiveness of the electric light.

I return to Glasgow tonight.

Yours very truly
William Thomson

500 KELVIN to STOKES, 13 January [1890][1]
Stokes Collection, K288

Euston for Gl[asgow]
Jan 13.

In my today's letter we had 6000/300=60; In reality it =20.

We must however find the true dimensions of the source in the light house electric light. Do you think you could ask Sir James Douglas[s].[2]

To lose the light at 3 nautical miles from a light house 300 feet high, adapted to throw *upper edge* of cone on the horizon would not nearly suffice.

WT

1 This is a post card addressed to Stokes and post marked London, 13 January 1890.
2 James Nicholas Douglass (1826–98) was an expert on lighthouses and in 1862 became chief engineer to the corporation of Trinity House. During the 1870s and 1880s he carried out studies of lighthouse illumination.

501 KELVIN to STOKES, 16 January 1890
Stokes Collection, TH29

The University
Glasgow
16 Jany '90

DEAR STOKES

I am much obliged to you for your letter *re* Lighthouse Illuminants. I highly approve of your suggestion that an interview between some representative of the Trinity Board and yourself and Lord Rayleigh should be asked for.

Yours truly
WILLIAM THOMSON

502 KELVIN to STOKES, 18 January 1890
Stokes Collection, K289

The University,
Glasgow.
18 Jany '90

DEAR STOKES

Your letter of yesterday makes it even more desirable than before that you and Lord Rayleigh should have the meeting with Sir Jas. Douglass or some one else representing the Trinity Board. I cannot think the Committee was consciously unfair, but it seems as if it was somewhat incautious at least in respect to the real merits of oil and the other illuminants, even although the conclusions may be practically correct.

Yours truly
WILLIAM THOMSON

Lensfield Cottage, Cambridge, 30 August, 1890.

MY DEAR THOMSON,

As there was some sun yesterday, I went to my lecture room to repeat better an experiment I tried before.

The reflected sunlight was passed through a lens, which had its focus on the glass front of a trough with glass also at the back. The trough was 6 or 8 inches a[c]ross. water [sic] was put into the trough, and then milk added by small quantities at a time, and a [sic] looked from behind, with the eye either close to or only a little way fron [sic] the glass at the back. Pretty soon the direct image of the sun was lost, but there was a bright glare for some distance round the place of the image, then becoming less bright, and extending considerably further. Even after putting a comparatively large quantity of milk into the water, the directed glare was still perceptible. By 'directed' I mean that though the glare extended over a wider and wider angle as more milk was put in, and was less and less bright, it was by no means alike in all directions, but a person in it could have told approximately, though less and less definitely as the turbidity increased, where the centre of the glare lay. On moving the eye right or left, which represents the effect of the revolution of the beam condensed by an annular lens, the eye being fixed, there was a marked change of intensity. In an advanced stage of turbidity, when the light was weakened by a coloured glass the glare became insensible, but if it were seen at all the middle of the glare was still identifiable, though with increasing vagueness.

I think any useful glare is produced, not by reflec[t]ion or refraction, but by diffraction, and not only by diffraction once but by re-diffraction, in part by diffraction several times repeated.

I think the reporters have been deceived by adopting an overhasty generalisation of what was seen in the long gallery – Lord Rayleigh and I saw it – when it was filled with condensed steam. They say that if the observer is in the fog he may be conscious of light, but will not be able to tell from what quarter is [sic] comes. This would be true in the limit, but that likit [sic] lies altogether outside the conditions of lighthouse illumination. If a ship were at the smallest distance from a lighthouse at which warning would do any good, and we suppose the density of fog, supposed uniform, to be continually increased, long before the condition of quaquaversus illumination was reached the glare, even for the most powerful source employed in actual practice, would be too feeble to be sensible. I asked Professor William Adams[1] about this and he said that if they saw light at all, they never had any difficulty in telling from what direction it came.

As regards direct vision, any light that is diffracted is done for, but not so as regards the production of glare. Light may be diffracted a few time[s] in succession without becoming useless for contributing to a directed glare. And as bound up with this it may be noticed that glare does not suffer such rapid obstruction by fog as direct light. A simple consideration shows that that of the light obstructed by the fog-globules from continuing its course, half is reflected or refracted, and half diffracted. The former half is so dispersed in direction as to be useless, but the latter retains an approximation to its previous direction, and still therefore remains more or less available for glare.

If you meet Lord Rayleigh at Leeds[2] I should be glad if you would show him this. I do not know whether he is in the United Kingdom. It is probable that I may be going to Ireland about the middle of next week.

Yours sincerely,
G. G. STOKES

1 William Grylls Adams (1836–1915), brother of John Couch Adams, was twelfth wrangler in 1859 and was professor of natural philosophy and astronomy at King's College, London, from 1865 to 1905.
2 The British Association for the Advancement of Science met in Leeds in September 1890.

504   STOKES to KELVIN, 2 September 1890
       Kelvin Collection, S483

Lensfield Cottage, Cambridge, 2 Sept. 1890.

MY DEAR THOMSON,

The following extremely rude calculation may illustrate what I wrote in my last about the penetration of diffracted light.

Let I be the residual intensity of direct light, coming suppose from a lighthouse, after passing over a distance r, D the total quantity of diffracted light at the distance r; I make abstraction for simplicity of the effect of divergence, as weakening by divergence is common to both. In passing over the distance dr, let I be weakened by $2qI\,dr$ in consequence of fog. Then $qI\,dr$ is reflected and refracted, and practically lost, and $qI\,dr$ passes into diffracted light. Of the already diffracted light, $qD\,dr$ is practically lost, and $qD\,dr$ is re-diffracted. Hence

$$dI = -2qI\,dr \quad (1) \qquad dD = -qD\,dr + qI\,dr \quad (2)$$

$$\therefore\; I = Ae^{-2qr} \qquad d \cdot e^{-qr}D = qe^{qr}I\,dr = qAe^{-qr}\,dr$$

$$D = e^{-qr}(B - Ae^{-qr})$$

and if we start from $D = 0$ when $r = 0$

$$D = A(e^{-qr} - e^{-2qr})$$

The first exponential in D may remain sensible long after the second has become insensibly small, so that a glare may be seen well after the direct light can be seen no longer. The direct light as seen is however concentrated in what appears almost a point, whereas the diffracted light is spread over a more or less considerable angular space. As the diffractions are multiplied, the glare continually widens. Thus for example if we take only two diffractions, a ray coming from the first diffraction in the direction of a line L making an angle a with the primitive direction suffers a second diffraction, and gives birth to diffracted light making angles comparable with a in all directions fron [sic] the line L, some portions therefore being brought more nearly back to the original direction, and some portions being made to deviate from it further than did the once-diffracted rays. The graduaal [sic] angular extension of the glare which results from this can readily be understood without entering into calculation.

The light must be powerful, and not too far off, in order that the glare may be of importance.

I mean to go to Ireland tomorrow afternoon. My address for about 12 days will be 4 Windsor Terrace, Malahide.

Yours sincerely,
G. G. STOKES

505   STOKES to KELVIN, 3 September 1890
      Kelvin Collection, S484

Lensfield Cottage, Cambridge, 3 Sept. 1890.

MY DEAR THOMSON,

I had a post card this morning from Lord Rayleigh,[1] who I find is going to Leeds. Please remember that I have no copy of the draft except the two that are in your and Lord Rayleigh's hands, or more properly speaking you have the original and Lord Rayleigh has the copy.[2]

In one place I wrote something like this:– Two of us have had the advantage of seeing on one occasion the experiments at the South Foreland. This was written under the impression that you had not been there; but if you too have seen them, please alter the sentance [sic] to make it right.

I leave for Ireland in about 4 hours. My address will be 4 Windsor Terrace, Malahide, Ireland.

Yours sincerely,
G. G. STOKES

1 The post card is not in the Stokes Collection.
2 Drafts of the report are in the Stokes Collection, TH55 to TH58.

506 KELVIN to STOKES, 11 September 1890
Stokes Collection, K290

> Claremont
> Leeds
> Sep ⟨13⟩ 11/90

DEAR STOKES

I showed all your letters to Lord Rayleigh and we had a good deal of conversation on the subject of them and the Report. We both think the Report will do very well as it is; and as yet have not suggested any modification. He wishes to go over the Report again with the documents which he left at Terling, and promises to write to me or you very soon. So I think we may consider the thing as well on to settlement.

I hope you and Lady Stokes are both well and enjoying your holiday. Lady Thomson joins in kind regards.

> Yours very truly
> WILLIAM THOMSON

507 KELVIN to STOKES, 25 September 1890[1]
Stokes Collection, K291

> Netherhall
> Largs Ayrshire
> Sep 25/90

Your letter of 19th and post card of 22nd recd. I approve of the omission which you propose. I have just arrived home after 3 weeks' absence and moving about. I suppose you will like to have your d[ra]ft report back, and I shall send it to you by registered ⟨lette⟩ packet on Saturday (if not tomorrow). I want to read it all through again carefully.

> W. THOMSON

1 This is a post card addressed to Stokes.

Sep 26/90[1]
Netherhall.
Largs.
Ayrshire.

DEAR STOKES

I return your draft with a few pencilled suggestions of my own, and with your alterations of Sep 18 & 19 made in ink and pencil in pp 13 and 14. All the other pencillings are mine.

What I have written in, and deleted, in p 4 seems to me of considerable practical importance.

As to p 11 also, I think we had better not give weight, so far as our noticing it in that way would give weight, to the idea of changing from a fixed to a revolving light unless absolutely necessary to get the distance-penetration required. The revolving light is much less valuable for practical navigation than the fixed light with occultational distinction when the fixed light can be seen at all. I believe the lands-men engineers and optical advisers of light house works have exaggerated ideas of the practical value of the superiority in distance-penetration of the revolving light and have in some respects done harm in consequence. I wish they had more experience of the 'picking up' of lights in dirty & variable-showery weather at sea than they have ⟨experience of⟩: I believe it would favourably modify some of their designs and works.

Yours always truly
WILLIAM THOMSON

1 Kelvin has written at the top of the letter, 'Address henceforth The University Glasgow. We leave this on Monday and shall be much on the move all October, but letters will be forwarded every day'.

Sept 30th
Lochinch,
Castle Kennedy,
Wigtonshire.

DEAR STOKES

I have received your letter of 27th Sept[r] and I agree to every thing you propose regarding our report. I have heard nothing from Lord Rayleigh on the subject since I saw him in Leeds. The time integral of a flash of light of very short duration, and the resulting perceptivity, make a very interesting subject for investigation. I scarcely think however that the shortest lighthouse flash hitherto used is short enough to lose perceptivity on this account. But there certainly is a difficulty both in 'picking up' a revolving light, and in holding on to it when picked up, as compared with a fixed light of intensity equal to the maximum of the revolving light; because of the eye wandering during the times of obscuration. I believe a fixed light will be more easily descried and used to advantage, in practical navigation, than a revolving light whose maximum intensity is even somewhat greater, or considerably greater, than the steady intensity of the fixed light.

Yours very truly
WILLIAM THOMSON[2]

1 The date is determined by the content of the letter which fits with that of the letters before and after.
2 Except for Kelvin's signature, the letter is in Lady Kelvin's hand, and she has written at the bottom of the letter, 'I hope Lady Stokes is well. Has she been with you in Ireland? My best love to her. F. A. T.'

510   KELVIN to STOKES, 4 October 1890
      Stokes Collection, K294

Oct 4/90
Loch Luichart,
Ross-Shire, N.B.

DEAR STOKES

I am sending off today to Sir M. ⟨H. P.⟩ E. Hicks Beach our report.[1]

I have altered a 'by' into be, competative into competitive; and for clearness I have inserted two commas and deleted one; and in line 4 from foot of p 5 I have changed 'a given' into 'the same': so that it now stands . . . 'that even for the same quantity of light produced, decidedly more heat would be given out . . .'.

'the same' expresses the idea more logically than 'a given' and will I think be clearer to persons unaccustomed to mathematically [*sic*] phraseology. I assume that you and Lord Rayleigh would approve and prefer not to be troubled by a request to say if you approve!

We leave this place for Glasgow on Monday and from Tuesday, for a week, shall be at Roxburghe Hotel Edinburgh, on acc^t of Universities Commission.[2]

Yours very truly
WILLIAM THOMSON

1 Michael Edward Hicks Beach, later the first Earl of St Aldwyn, (1837–1916) was president of the Board of Trade from 1888 to 1892.
2 For a recent, brief summary of the influence of this commission, see Michael Sanderson, *The Universities and British Industry, 1850–1970* (London, 1972), 156.

511   KELVIN to STOKES, 20 October [1890][1]
Stokes Collection, K365

Octr 20th
Netherhall
Largs
Ayrshire

DEAR STOKES

I received the same letter as yours from the Board of Trade with only the requisite change of names.[2] I am much obliged to you for your copy of it. I could not have saved you the trouble of sending it, as you kindly did it so promptly, even if I had telegraphed on receipt – of mine! – it was delayed a day on account of my absence from home.

I feel that the Commissioners owe much gratitude to you for having earned for them such appreciative thanks from Sir Michael Hicks Beach.

I am sorry to say we are not to be at Cambridge this autumn as I am tremendously taken up with the Universities Commission and the Master,[3] in consequence, excuses my attendance at the College meeting of the 29th Oct^r.

Yours always truly
WILLIAM THOMSON[4]

---

1 The date is determined by the content of the letter which fits with the previous several letters.
2 See Board of Trade to Stokes, 13 October 1890, Stokes Collection, TH37A. The letter was written by Henry George Calcraft on behalf of M. E. Hicks Beach.
3 James Porter.
4 Except for Kelvin's closing and signature, the letter is in Lady Kelvin's hand, and she has written at the bottom of the letter, 'I hope Lady Stokes and Isabel are well. My love to them please. F. A. T.'

512   KELVIN to STOKES, 16 November 1890
Stokes Collection, K295

⟨Dec⟩ Nov 16/90
The University,
Glasgow.

DEAR STOKES

I should be greatly obliged if you would tell me what will be required of me on the 1st of Dec, both at R.S. meeting, and dinner. I suppose I have *no* speaking at the meeting?[1]

At the dinner does the in-coming President make any speech regarding the Royal Society, or does he merely act as chairman in proposing toasts &c? I feel rather appalled at the thought of even the least that may be required.

Is there any occasion for me to be up *before* Monday Dec 1?

I hope Lady Stokes and Isabel are both well. Lady Thomson joins in kind regards and love to Lady Stokes.

Yours always truly
WILLIAM THOMSON

<hr>

1 Kelvin became president of the Royal Society on 30 November 1890.

513 KELVIN to STOKES, 17 December 1890
Stokes Collection, K296

Dec 17/90
The University,
Glasgow.

DEAR STOKES

The enclosed letters, and the accompanying book (which I send you by book-post) are your property, as you were P.R.S. when they were despatched, and when it could not be known in India that I might be your successor when they arrived. I might however have kept them, as possibly my legal right, unless you wished to claim them as your right; had not I already received the book (or papers akin to it) from Col Leslie (about a year ago I think) and acknowledged them with thanks.[1] I am afraid I was not so encouraging as Spottiswoode was eight years ago. I certainly mingled an ample supply of cold water with my thanks; but the present despatch proves it to have been unavailing. I suspect Spottiswoode's good nature has not been beneficial to Col Leslie; and if he had been rougher, some of the⟨se⟩ labours of these years might have been spared, to the great benefit both of Col. Leslie himself and of people who have tried to read his papers.

I am sorry to trouble you with this, but I think if you would write quite a short line of thanks, accompanied with a little of as cold water as your good nature allows you to administer, Col. Leslie would be pleased and benefitted.

Yours always truly
WILLIAM THOMSON

<hr>

1 I have been unable to identify Col. Leslie.

514 STOKES to KELVIN, 2 January 1892
Kelvin Collection, Pr385

Lensfield Cottage, Cambridge, 2 Jan. 1892.[1]

MY DEAR LORD (What?),

I write to congratulate you on the great honour Her Majesty has bestowed on you, and through you on science, by creating you a Peer. At the same time I may add my congratulations to those of of [sic] my wife to The Lady Thomson, or whatever she is to be called. I was speculating whether you would be Lord Thomson, or Lord Netherhall, or Lord Largs, or what. Time will tell. Meanwhile I must make a shot at it, or better perhaps address you as I would have done on Dec. 31. Or better I will enclose my letter in my wife's to Lady Thomson, and if we are wrong about her title the error will be less glaring, as a modification of her former title may pass muster in either of two ways.

I wonder whether you will now come to live in London, so as to be ready for Parliament as well as the royal society [sic].

Giving again my most hearty congratulations to you both, I remain

Yours sincerely,
G. G. STOKES

P. S. I find my wife's letter closed, so I must make a shot.

1 Kelvin has written at the top of the letter, 'answ^d through F., to Lady Stokes about Jan 5'.

515 STOKES to KELVIN, 26 January 1893
Cambridge University Library, Stewart Papers, V.G16

Lensfield Cottage
Cambridge
26 Jan. 1893

DEAR LORD KELVIN,

When I called at Cayley's this afternoon the maid said that he was pronounced to be convalescent, and had been able to be on a sofa in Mrs. Cayley's room. Mrs. Cayley's limb was examined yesterday, and the doctor said the progress was quite as good as he could expect. The broken bone was uniting.

Yours sincerely,
G. G. STOKES

516 KELVIN to STOKES, 15 May [1893][1]
Stokes Collection, K296A

> In train to Oxford
> May 15

DEAR STOKES

I had not a moment's time before leaving London to thank you for your two letters, which were most welcome and have been very useful. I am sorry I was not in when you came to see me on Thursday. I had found that [W. H.] Miller was absolutely right. When we met at the Imperial Institute I was wrongly under the impression that his rule for intercepts of possible faces did not include certain planes which I knew to be faces; but I soon found it was wholly equivalent to what I had been using, and which is founded on Bravais' doctrine of homogeneous assemblages.[2] It is that the plane of *any* three points of a homogeneous assemblage is a possible face. Now it is clear that every row of points cut by a plane through any three points is cut between two points of the row in commensurable parts. Hence Miller's rule holds for *any* three rows selected as axes: and conversely if Miller's rule is fulfilled by any particular plane, this plane is parallel to the plane of three points of the assemblage.[3]

On ⟨Thurs⟩ Wed^y evening when we spoke for a moment at the soirée I was under ⟨the⟩ a misapprehension that Miller's definition of a 'form' gave 48 faces even when the axes chosen are not rectangular, and with equal parameters. Re-reading showed me that he limited it correctly to symmetries, and correctly gave only *two* faces for the 'form', in the doubly oblique class. So even before receiving your first letter I had seen that Miller is all right. But I was glad to see your way of considering tetrahedrons, right angles, symmetries &^c. And I was particularly glad to see in your second letter a more general definition of twinning than that usually given. No more because retardation is just being annulled (annulled this ins^t.) at Oxford.

> Yours
> KELVIN

---

1 On 16 May 1893 Kelvin delivered the Robert Boyle Lecture to the Oxford University Junior Scientific Club. Entitled 'On the molecular tactics of a crystal', it was printed as appendix H in his *Baltimore Lectures* (1904).

2 A. Bravais, 'Sur les systèmes formés par des points distribués régulièrment sur un plan ou dans l'espace', *Journal de l'École Polytechnique*, 19 (1850), cahier 33, 1–128, cited in Kelvin (337).

3 W. H. Miller, *A Treatise on Crystallography* (Cambridge, 1863), cited in Kelvin's paper mentioned in note 1.

517 STOKES to KELVIN, 27 May 1893
Kelvin Collection, S485

Lensfield Cottage, Cambridge, 27 May, 1893.[1]

DEAR LORD KELVIN,

I have nothing particular to remark on the paper[2] you sent me, further than to refer to Marbach's work, from which I leaned [*sic*] the facts that I mentioned to you. I have not worked at the subject myself, further than just to prepare a little of Chlorate of Soda, and verify the statement that the crystals do act on poralised [*sic*] light as mentioned by Marbach. I have no credit in the matter beyond calling your attention to Marbach's work.

We have a general College Meeting on June 1, and I shall not go to the R. S. election of Fellows, which after all is Practically [*sic*] only a formality. We may expect to meet at Greenwich on June 3.

Yours sincerely,
G. G. STOKES

1 Stokes has written at the top of the letter:

(I), p. 3. The discovery was made by Marbach. Several papers by him are referred to in the Royal Society's Catalogue. The first brief notice mentioned is given:– Breslau, Schless. Gesell. Uebersicht, 1854, pp. 17–18. Shortly after is a paper in Pogg. Ann. 91 (1854) p. 482–487, or Ann. de Chimie, 43 (55) pp. 252–255.

Christian August Hermann Marbach (1817–73) was professor extraordinary at the University of Breslau from 1861 to 1873. His papers cited by Stokes are: 'Ueber die Circularpolarisation des Lichtes durch chlorsaures Natron und über die Krystallisation dieses Salzes', *Jahresbericht der Schlesischen Gesellschaft für vaterländische Cultur* (1854), 17–18, and 'Die circulare Polarisation des Lichtes durch chlorsaures Natron', Poggendorff's *Annalen der Physik und Chemie*, 91 (1854), 482–7, and *Annales de Chimie*, 43 (1855), 252–5.

2 Kelvin (337), which cites the second of Marbach's papers mentioned in the previous note.

518 STOKES to KELVIN, 13 June 1893[1]
Kelvin Collection, S487

Lensfield Cottage, Cambridge, 13 June, 1893.

DEAR LORD KELVIN,

In thinking last night over what you had been saying in the Fitzwilliam, I see I think what you had been driving at.

The twin law is that the orientation of one of the twins is the same as that of the other would become if the crystal were turned through 180 round the twin axis, and that the twin axis is either (which is the common case) normal to an actual or possible face, ⟨though⟩ or as happens sometimes, but rarely, the axis of a zone even though the plane normal to it be not a possible face.

In the rhombohedral system, everything remains unchanged qs [*sic*] regards the orientation of the molecules when the crystal is turned through 120 about the axis of the rhombohedron. Hence as regards rotation round the axis, the orientation defined by a rotation of 180 is absolutely identical with the rotation defined by a rotation through 180 minus 120, or 60. A cube is a particular case of a rhombohedron, one of the diagonals of the cube being taken as the axis of the rhombohedron; and for a twin axis normal to a face of the regular octahedron a rotation through 180 is identical, as regards orientation, with a rotation through 60. This is the very common twinning in fluor spar.

The law of twinning is not invalidated, nor rendered defective in generality, by the fact that in one particular case the conditions of symmetry render a rotation through 180 identical as regards result with a rotation through 60.

To disprove the law of twinning, it would be requisite to show that in some case rotation through 180 would *not* do. To show that in one case rotation through 60 is as good as rotation through 180 does not convict the law of error or defective generality.

On[2] referring to [W. H.] Miller[3] I see that in amethyst (which is a variety of quartz) the wavy structure is due to repeated twinning, not to alternations of right and left handed crystals. The individuals of a twin crystal of quartz may be of opposite, but are more commonly of the same, handedness.

Yours sincerely,
G. G. STOKES

1 Letters 518, 519, and 520 were all written by Stokes on 13 June 1893. Letter 520 was the third written, because it corrects a statement about Miller contained in both 518 and 519; 519 appears to have been the second, because it (and not 518) contains the comparison of Miller and Moigno mentioned in 520, in which Stokes corrected his 'last' letter.
2 Kelvin has drawn a line down the left side of this paragraph and written in the margin, 'Stokes corrects this in second letter of June 13. K[elvin]'. Actually, as indicated in the previous note, the correction appears in the *third* letter.
3 See letter 516, note 3.

519   STOKES to KELVIN, 13 June 1893
       Kelvin Collection, S486

Lensfield Cottage, Cambridge, 13 June, 1893.
DEAR LORD KELVIN,
As I was returning home from the Senate House, I remembered reading that a Paris optician, it may have been Duboscq, but I rather think it was Hoffmann [*sic*],[1] once and once only came across a crystal of quartz which on being cut perpendicular to the axis furnished a natural bi-quartz, such as is used for the saccharimeter, being formed artificially. Right and left handed crystals were joined together, the junction being along a plane parallel to the axis, and the axes of the two portions being parallel.

I think most likely the junction was not analogous to a twin plane, but was merely a plane of growth. The commonest form is a hexagonal prism with ends of the form of a hexagonal ⟨prism⟩ pyramid, and I imagine that as the crystal grew from its solution, it formed at first a, say, righthanded crystal, and then molecules began to be deposited in a left handed manner. The junction, being an actual face of the growing crystal, was regular. In the very common form of twinned fluor spar, the twin plane is parallel to a face of the octahedron, but the surfaces of growth are parallel to the faces of the cubes, and the junction of the two twins is probably an irregular surface. I have not particularly examined this, but in the portion of space which is common to the two cubes one can tell to which twin such or such a portion of that portion belongs by the direction of the planes of growth. These are indicated by difference of colour or of fluorescence of the portions laid down at different times during the crystallisation, a process during which doubtless the chemical condition of the solution changed, and as a result different impurities were taken up at different ages of the crystal.

Yours sincerely,
G. G. STOKES

P. S. I was near forgetting to add that Moigno 'Repertoire d'Optique ⟨morerne'⟩ moderne' says that the wavy structure of amethyst is due to right and left handed portions.[2] Miller states that it is due to twinning.[3] It was only today or thereabouts that I noticed this last statement. I don't know which is right, but I know that Miller was an extremely accurate man.

1 Jules Duboscq (1817–86) and Dr J. G. Hofmann, optical instrument makers in Paris. There are three letters from the first to Stokes in the Stokes Collection; one from the second.
2 L'Abbé Moigno, *Répertoire d'Optique moderne, ou analyse complète, des travaux modernes relatifs aux phénomènes de la lumière*, 4 vols. (Paris, 1847–50).
3 See letter 516, note 3.

520 STOKES to KELVIN, 13 June 1893
  Kelvin Collection, S488

Lensfield Cottage, Cambridge, 13 June, 1893.
DEAR LORD KELVIN,

I must correct what I said in my last about Miller. On looking again at what he says about amethyst, which I had read very hastily, I see that I misunderstood him. I see now that what he says is quite in accordance with what I had read in Moigno.[1] As I set you wrong, I am desirous of correcting the error without delay, but I do not consider it necessary to go to the general post office in order that my two letters might arrive simultaneously. I will go out and post this in the neighbouring pillar, and then you ought to get it by the second post.

Yours sincerely,
G. G. STOKES

P.S. It is remarkable that the alternate right and left handed structure in amethyst should show itself also in a waviness in a surface obtained by fracture.

1 See letter 519, note 2.

---

521   KELVIN to STOKES, 30 August 1893
Stokes Collection, K297

Aug 30/93
Netherhall.
Largs.
Ayrshire.

DEAR STOKES

We were greatly grieved to see this morning the terrible loss which has come to you, so suddenly.[1] I do not like to write and trouble you just now, but I feel I must just tell you of the deep sympathy with you and Lady Stokes, which we both feel. It is very sad to think of the young life cut off in the very time of beginning what promised to be a happy professional career. We feel deeply for you in your grief.

Believe me, always

Yours most truly
KELVIN

1 This refers to the death of Stokes's son, W. G. G. Stokes.

---

522   KELVIN to STOKES, 25 November 1893
Stokes Collection, K298

8 Belgrave Crescent
Edinburgh
Nov 25/93

DEAR STOKES

I am to have the honour this year of proposing 'The Medallists' and I write to ask you to respond for them all.

The Foreign Sec^{y1} is asking Vant 'Off [*sic*] and Le Bel to say a few words.[2]

We are here from Friday to Monday, and all here send kindest regards to you and Lady Stokes.

Yours always truly
KELVIN

P. S. I enclose a proof of my Address.[3]

P. S. Have you looked particularly at the 'quadrivalence' explanation of the chirality discovered in some carbon-compounds?[4]

P. P. S. I find I have not a copy here which I can send, but I shall send you one from Glasgow on Monday.

1 The Scottish geologist Archibald Geikie (1835–1924), who was foreign secretary of the Royal Society until 30 November 1893, when he was replaced by the surgeon Joseph Lister (1827–1912), who held the position for two years before succeeding Kelvin as president.
2 Jacobus Henricus Van't Hoff (1852–1911) and Joseph Achille Le Bel (1847–1930) were awarded the Royal Society's Davy Medal jointly in 1893 for their research on the optical activity of organic compounds.
3 Kelvin (338).
4 This refers to the work of Van't Hoff and Le Bel. See Kelvin's *Baltimore Lectures* (1904), p. 546n.

523 KELVIN to STOKES, 2 March 1894
Stokes Collection, K299

The University,
Glasgow.
March 2. 1894.

DEAR STOKES

I have been noticing some very curious things with a little radiometer, (See end of next page)[1] both convex and concave sides equally bright. I find that when one side of the glass is hotter than the other the vane tends to set itself perpendicular to the line going from centre of hot to centre of cold. When placed in uniform day light it goes round and round with concave sides foremost.

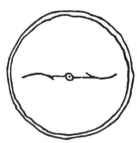

I heard of this kind of radiometer first from you. Can you give me any reference to where your theory of it is to be found or as to what anybody else has said about it? Lady Kelvin joins in kind regards to Lady Stokes and yourself.

Yours very truly,
KELVIN

1 This refers to the figure at the end of the letter.

Lensfield Cottage, Cambridge, 3 March, 1894.

MY DEAR KELVIN,

We have long known the sticking produced by heating the bulb of a radiometer at one spot. It forms an awkward place for the vanes to get past. A general explanation is easy enough. The warmer spot is a place of (differential) molecular bombardment, from which the vanes tend to get away. If there are only two vanes, they tend to set themselves at right angles to the radius drawn from the centre of the spherical bulb to the warmed spot. If the whole of one hemisphere be warmed, the general effect is the same, and the general explanation the same.

You will find the effect of shape fully gone into in Crookes's Bakerian Lecture, Phil. Trans. for 1878, p. 278 and after.[1] Aluminium would absorb I suppose 30 per cent. or more of the radiation falling upon it, and whould [*sic*] thereby get slightly warmer than the bulb, whence the motion you mention in the 2nd (radiation) case.

Yours sincerely,
G. G. STOKES

1 W. Crookes, 'On repulsion resulting from radiation. Part v.', *Phil. Trans.* (1878), 243–318.

Lensfield Cottage, Cambridge, 11 Oct. 1894.

DEAR LORD KELVIN,

I have seen your paper in 'Nature'[1] re the possibility or otherwise of discontinuity arising in a perfect fluid under the conditions treated; or in fact taking the unique solution (supposing the fluid to start from rest) ⟨or in fact⟩ whether the motion so defined is stable or unstable.

Your paper has sent me thinking further about the question, with the result that I think I see my way more clearly, and I am confirmed in my opinion that the motion is unstable.

We agree that if in any position of the boundary the motion were to begin from rest, being generated by the instantaneous motion of the boundary, the motion of the boundary[2] is unique, and is that defined by a continuous velocity-potential. For shortness I will call this the phi motion.

At any moment the motion, be it what it may, may be regarded as compounded of the phi motion and of a motion for which the component velocities are, say, u, v, w. The latter satisfies the so-called equation of continuity and the condition that at the boundary there is no normal velocity. It also satisfies other conditions which I need not enter into which ensure that the expression for dp got from the ordinary hydrodynamical equations shall be a perfect differential. It is easily shown that the kinetic energy is the sum of the kinetic energies due to the phi motion and to the u, v, w motion; and consequently that the phi motion is that for which the kinetic energy is a minimum. But what follows from that? There is the rub.

What is meant by the motion being unstable? *I* should say, the motion is said to be stable when whatever small deviation from the phi motion is supposed to be produced, and the fluid thenceforth not interfered with, the subsequent motion differs only by small quantities from the phi motion, and unstable when the small initial deviation goes on accumulating, so that presently it is no longer small.

I have a right to take for my small initial deviation one in which the fluid close to the edge shoots past the edge, forming a very minute surface of discontinuity. The question is, Will this always remain correspondingly minute, or will the deviation accumulate so that ultimately it is no longer small? I have practically satisfied myself that it will so accumulate, and the mode of subsequent motion presents interesting features.

Yours sincerely,
G. G. STOKES

P. S. I do *not* mean *merely* that the surface of discontinuity will lengthen out, but that u, v, w will not remain small.

1 Kelvin (340).
2 Larmor has inserted *fluid?* after *boundary*.

526 KELVIN to STOKES, 14 October 1894
Stokes Collection, K300

Oct 14/94
Netherhall.
Largs.
Ayrshire.

DEAR STOKES

The same post that brought me yesterday evening, brought me the enclosed proof of the 4th and last instalments of my article in Nature,[1] of which you had seen the 1st and possibly the 2nd, but not the 3^{d} which appeared in last Thursday's number. I think your question, 'what follows that? There is the rub', may be most readily answered by aid of the diagrams Fig^s 4 & 5 of what I now send you, (which will appear in next week's Nature). Suppose the whole of fig 4 (or 5) to be at first all solid, and moving at constant speed through frictionless, incompressible, liquid, in an unyielding outer boundary. Now let the central part (white in the diagram) become suddenly liquid. There results a possible state of fluid which would be permanent if it were *stable*. But as I long ago showed, that a surface of finite slip in a liquid is essentially unstable. And 'what follows? There *is* the rub.' The surface of discontinuity becomes *instantly* ⟨rou⟩ ruffled, and rolled up into an $\alpha\nu\eta\varrho\iota\theta\mu o\nu\ \gamma\varepsilon\lambda\alpha\sigma\mu\alpha$ (by the last word I mean laughing at the doctrine of finite slip): and before our solid in its two parts, which we may suppose held rigidly together has moved through many times its own length the $\gamma\varepsilon\lambda\alpha\sigma\mu\alpha$ is nearly all worked away and left in the wake. Helmholtz here helps us to see how the doctrine of discontinuity, which he too taught, breaks down, in one of the two chief applications of it which he gives. The 'vortex-sheet' constitutes a complexly whirling disturbance which is left farther and farther behind; and the space between the forward and after parts of the solid becomes occupied with liquid having less and less of rotationality, tending *very rapidly* to the ultimate condition of the unique irrotational motion fulfilling the well known *minimum* condition. To save all qualms you may suppose the edge, whichever of Fig^s 4 or 5 you take, to be not a perfect angle⟨s⟩ betw. planes, but to be rounded to curvature of say 10^{-20} of an inch, or if you prefer it, $1/1000$ of an inch. I shall be very glad to hear if you are satisfied. If you write to me posting on or before ⟨Tues⟩ Wed^y (early despatch for north) address Netherhall as above. If you post on Thursday address c/o The Duke of Argyll, Inveraray, if later still, Glasgow.

Yours truly
KELVIN

1 Kelvin (340).

527 STOKES to KELVIN, 23 October 1894
Kelvin Collection, S491

Lensfield Cottage, Cambridge, 23 Oct. 1894.

MY DEAR LORD KELVIN,

I have delayed writing to you, partly because I had friends (who are now gone) staying with me, partly on account of my lectures partly on account of some other investigations (if such slight things deserve the name) about which I was in correspondence with Professor McLeod.[1]

You ask if I am convinced. As to that I am much in the state that I was in before. You appear to be contending against the 'dead water' theory of resistances. You are welcome to do so provided you do not father it upon me.

It is no child of mine. It is directly at variance with both what I have written (see vol. I, p. 54)[2] and what I have always taught in my lectures as to the nature of ordinary resistances, namely, that they are essentially bound up with the formation of eddies. I was not aware that the 'dead water' theory was taught, and if I may guess from your article[3] taught as on my authority, in elementary books, and that it was given in examination papers. I am not acquainted with those books, and I should feel obliged if you would kindly refer me to one, especially if the theory is attributed to me.

It is not correct to say, as you appear to do at the outset, that I laid down the doctrine of discontinuity at a sharp edge. What I *did* say was that the motion *appeared* to be so and so, the word 'appeared' implying that I purposely refrained from asserting that it would be such. I still feel unable positively either to affirm or to deny the possibility. You think the proposition disproved at once by a certain proposition about minimum kinetic energy. But where is that proposition? Does not its demonstration presuppose continuity of motion? Observe I am not referring to the proposition that the particular motion *is* that of minimum kinetic energy, ⟨th⟩ but the proposition that the motion which must take place must be the unique motion of minimum kinetic energy.

I am engaged to dine with [G. H.] Darwin on Saturday, where we may hope to meet.

Yours sincerely,
G. G. STOKES

1 Herbert McLeod (1841–1923) was professor of chemistry at the Royal Indian Engineering College at Cooper's Hill from 1871 to 1901. There are some forty letters from McLeod to Stokes in the Stokes Collection, thirteen dating from 1894.
2 Stokes (13) in *MPP*, I, 17–68.
3 Kelvin (340).

528 STOKES to KELVIN, 27 October 1894
Kelvin Collection, S492

Lensfield Cottage, 27 Oct. 1894.[1]

MY DEAR LORD KELVIN,

As we are shortly to meet, I will mention beforehand the chief points that strike me.

At the opening of your first paper[2] you think to demolish me by saying it is now well known that what I will call for shortness the phi motion is that of minimum kinetic energy. I suppose the positions of the boundaries in the initial and final states given. Well. It IS a minimum, but what then? 'There's the rub'. In the actual motion, why should the k.e. be a minimum? I thought with myself, What Kelvinian theorem leads to this? In your letter you refer to T. & T. Nat. Phil.[3] You don't give the page, but I presume you refer to Least Action.[4] I say the principle of least action does not apply. The boundaries may be supposed to pass from one configuration to another, but the pressure at the boundaries will not therefore be the same; and as the pressure at the boundary does work, the proposition falls to the ground.

With reference to your later post cards I know very well that for a big enough body moving in water, say, the *direct* effect of the viscosity is very trifling. But suppose there is a railway *AB* which at *B* branches off towards *C* and towards *D*. Suppose a train travels without stopping along *AB* and onwards. Will you admit that the muscular exertion of the pointsman at *B* is the merest trifle of the work required to propel the train along *BC* or *CD*? Now I look on viscosity in the neighbourhood of a sharp, though not absolutely sharp, edge as performing the part of the pointsman at *B*.

Suppose a vessel of the shape externally of a circular cylinder with plane ends, and internally of a coaxial cylinder standing for base on a sector of a circle of an angle exceeding 180 deg. For simplicity of conception suppose (though this is not necessary) the wall so loaded as to make the centre of gravity of the whole when the cylinder is filled with liquid lie in the axis. Let the whole be placed ar [*sic*] rest with its axis horizontal on an inclined plane on which it can roll ⟨n⟩ but not slide, and then left to itself. The principle of least action is applicable to the whole system, box and liquid, but not to the liquid along. [*sic*]

But perhaps you think to demolish me by saying, Let the vessel be rigid but massless. Well. There is life in the old dog yet. Two final configurations are not identical merely because they are undistinguishable unless you attend to the personal identities of the particles. So that whether the vessel be massless or not, I don't see that the principle of 13ast [*sic*] action helps us much.

Yours sincerely,

G. G. STOKES

1 Kelvin has written on the envelope, 'Rec^d Oct 27, Stokes and previous letter of date Oct 23'. The envelope is addressed to Kelvin in care of G. H. Darwin in Cambridge.
2 Kelvin (340).
3 Kelvin and Tait, *TNP*.
4 Kelvin has underlined the passage, *presume you refer to Least Action*, and written in the margin, 'no – this explained to Stokes same evening'.

529 KELVIN to STOKES, 29 October 1894
Stokes Collection, K301

> Oct 29/94
> Peterhouse,
> Cambridge.

DEAR STOKES

Will you dine with us this evening at our annual dinner in Hall at 7.30.

> Yours truly
> KELVIN

530 KELVIN to STOKES, 31 October [1894][1]
Stokes Collection, K367

> In train for Colchester
> Oct 31.

DEAR STOKES

If you look at the water in the wake of a screw steamer going through a calm glassy sea, you always see foam produced by bubbles of air rising from below, *not* by splashing of broken water at the surface anywhere round the ship. This proves extraction of air from water below the surface: and we know the explanation to be $\langle \frac{1}{2}pv^2 \rangle\rangle$ $p < \pi + gD$ at some place or many places of water close to the $\langle$ hull (edge of iron)$\rangle$ propeller blades, (and of edges of iron of the hull, when the speed is great). The practical relief from the tendency to infinitely great negative pressure is, the water leaving the solid. You will see something of this in a paper[2] of mine on 'coreless vortices' $\langle$ and R$\rangle$ &c (I forget the title) in the Phil. Mag. sometime about 1888 I think. It was read at the R.S. about the beginning of Feb. and I suppose is also published in the Proc. R.S. I think this will satisfy you that finite slip between liquid and liquid is *never* the relief, when we have flow of liquid across a sharp edge and that there *is in no case any tendency* to the coming into existence of a surface of discontinuity in a liquid. Excuse shakiness due to non-uniformity of motion of my seat (ceased for a few moments by stoppage at Bures).

The mode of motion near the surface of the globe in my 'coreless' paper was very difficult to imagine. But clearly there cannot be any discontinuity in the liquid not even when a stone is thrown into water.

> Yours (after this parting shot.
> The 'coreless' paper and drawing,
> were completed in train from
> London to Glasgow.)
> KELVIN

1 The date is determined by the content, which fits that of the previous several letters.
2 Kelvin (283).

531 STOKES to KELVIN, 1 November 1894
Kelvin Collection, S493

Lensfield Cottage, Cambridge, 1 Nov. 1894.

MY DEAR LORD KELVIN,

The old dog's heart is beating still. My attention having been called anew to O. Reynolds's work in his *former* paper,[1] a happy thought struck me this morning as to an application of his principle – that the conditions of dynamical similarity may be extended to the determination of the conditions under which eddies just commence. Partly from this fresh idea and partly from considerations which I had lately been thinking of, I ⟨fell⟩ feel convinced now that the conjecture I threw out in p. 311 of my vol. I (the long foot-note)[2] to which you refer so far from being absurd is actually true, and that the limiting state of things for a slightly viscous fluid and a slightly blunted edge, when the viscosity and bluntness are both supposed to vanish, is really indeterminate, and that the limiting state of things is altogether different according as you first suppose the viscosity to vanish, the edge remaining slightly blunted, and then suppose the bluntness to vanish and the edge to become sharp, or else first suppose the edge to become perfectly sharp, and then suppose the viscosity to vanish. On the first supposition you get the phi motion, with a great velocity near the edge, a velocity which increases indefinitely as you suppose the bluntness to vanish. On the second supposition you get a generation of rotational motion propagated inwards from the bounding surface, and especially from the neighbourhood of the edge, and if the motion be continued in one di[r]ection you get a tail of fluid with rotational motion carried along in the direction of the general motion. As the viscosity diminishes the tail gets narrower and narrower, but not therefore shorter, and the state of things approaches more and more nearly to that of a vortex sheet or surface of discontinuity which is paid out from the edge. Your speculations about vortex atoms led you to approach the limit in the first way; my ideas, derived from what one sees in an actual fluid, led me to approach it in the other way. I am not concerned with a steady discontinuous motion as I always supposed the motion to be eddying, though after what has been done by others I would not deny that there may be a conceivably steady, although unstable, mode of motion involving a surface of discontinuity.

Yours sincerely,
G. G. STOKES

1 See O. Reynolds, 'An experimental investigation of the circumstances which determine whether the motion of water shall be direct or sinuous, and of the law of resistance in parallel channels', *Phil. Trans.* (1883), 935–82.

2 Stokes (21) in *MPP*, I, 237–313.

532 STOKES to KELVIN, 8 June 1895
Kelvin Collection, S494

Lensfield Cottage, Cambridge, 8 June, 1895.

DEAR LORD KE[L]VIN,

I was hasty in retracting, as I be[l]ieve I did, what I said about an extension of the very simple particular case of your problem, or perhaps you would say of a particular case forming for a special reason an exception to your problem, that I had in view. Your problem is that of the mean kinetic energy of two perfectly elastic bodies, balls say, which move within a perfectly smooth tube rigidly closed at both ends. The very particular case I took was that in which the two balls have their velocities in such ratio ⟨n⟩ that their centre of gravity when the balls are moving towards each other is at rest, simplified still further by the supposition that the distances of the point of collision from the two ends are directly as the velocities, or inversely as the masses, of the balls. In this case it is clear that the velocities of the two will each be constant, the mutual collisions will always occur at the same spot, and the kinetic energies will be as the masses directly and the squares of the masses inversely, that is, instead of being equal will be inversely as the masses.

The 'extension' of this simple case is, while retaining the same ratio of velocities to start with, to suppose the point (*A*) of mutual collision to be differently situated. In this case the collisions with the ends will not be simultaneous, and after the first the centre of gravity will no longer be at rest. But if the point *A* be not too far from its former position the rebounds from the ends will both have taken place before the second collision of the balls with one another, and the second rebound will restore the centre of gravity of the two to rest, so that the state of things will be the same as before, only that the collision of the balls will take place at a different point, *B*, after which the motion will go on repeating itself, the collisions taking place alternately at the points *A* & *B*, and the velocities of both balls remainin[g] constant, and the energies, and therefore the mean energies, being inversely as the masses.

But it may be objected that this is a very special case; and perhaps if it were but slightly departed from there would be a periodic change which would make the mean energies obey Maxwell's law, though if the departure from the assumed conditions were but slight the period would be extremely long. Let us take then another test case in which there is a long period which is followed and which is so chosen as to work out pretty easily. Let M, m be the masses, and let us suppose that M is enormously great compared with m, while (at least to start with: whether it will so continue will be shown by the solution) the velocity of m is far greater than that of M, as would be the case for instance if the kinetic energies were equal, or if they varied inversely as the masses. Then m will make a vast number of rebounds, alternately from M and from the end of the tube on M's side, in the interval between two successive rebounds of M from the end of the tube. Hence as regards M's motion we may take an increment, dt, of the time t so large as to cover a great many rebounds of m, and yet so small as to be treated as a differential element; just as in hydrostatics or hydrodynamics we may treat the motion of the fluid as continuous in spite of the existence of ultimate molecules. This enables us to substitute differential equations for equations of finite differences, and renders the solution comparatively simple. The motion is evidently of such a nature that M is gradually driven back from a position of momentary rest till it reaches the end of the tube, when it rebounds with the velocity it then had, and the previous motion is repeated in the reverse order, and so on. I find for the ratio of the mean kinetic energy of m to the mean kinetic energy of the whole $\dfrac{\phi}{\tan \phi}$, where $\tan \phi = \dfrac{\sqrt{2ac - a^2}}{c - a}$, $c =$ length of tube, $a =$ distance from end on M's side to point of M's momentary rest.

Hence, according to the value of the ratio a/c, m's share of the total mean energy may be anything from 0 to 1, so that the ratio of the mean energies of M & m may be anything at all. Either then the proposition breaks down, or the problem you have posed does not give a fair test of what takes place in three dimensions, and with molecules of two kinds unrestricted in number. Maxwell I think always regarded the problem as far more difficult for a mixture of two gases than for one. It seems probable that the law may be true, or very nearly so, for an assemblage of a vast nujber [*sic*] of each of two kinds of colliding bodies moving in space of three dimensions, but I have not much faith in the alleged law of partition of energy between the energy due to translation and the internal energy of molecules.

Yours sincerely,
G. G. STOKES

533 STOKES to KELVIN, 8 June 1895
Kelvin Collection, S495

Lensfield Cottage, Cambridge, 8 June, 1895.

DEAR LORD KELVIN,

Could you give us an address at the Victoria Institute some time in the course of the month?[1] We had one provided for the Anniversary Meeting, which is usually held some day in June, but unfortunately the person who was to have given it is ill. Thinking that we were provided *this* year, I did not press you for it when we met, but hoped you might give one some other time. It would be a great boon to us if you would consent. You are quite free to choose your subject. What you said to me at Greenwich about the designed planting of the trees &c. might be enlarged into an address. I merely mention this lest you should think that you have nothing. As I said you are quite free to choose your subject, and if you like it may be wholly scientific. You do not need to write it; there will be a good reporter present. You may choose the day within wide limits so as to suit your own convenience.

Hoping for a favourable reply, I remain

Yours sincerely,
G. G. STOKES

1 Stokes was president of the Victoria Institute. Kelvin did address the Institute, but not until 1897 (Kelvin (363)).

534 STOKES to KELVIN, 1 July 1895
Kelvin Collection, S495A

Lensfield Cottage, Cambridge, 1 July, 1895.

DEAR LORD KELVIN,

Opening my pocket book to make an entry, I found in pencil against July 4, 'Lord Kelvin 9 a.m.'. This looks like an engagement for something, but I confess if it were the thing had quite gone out of my head. If there was any engagement, please send me a line; if not, don't trouble to write.

I thought I should have been in London on July 2, 3, 4, 5 for a meeting of the Lay House, but the Archbishop[1] has decided that the Convocation of the Province of Canterbury will not meet, so the Lay House won't meet either. I am going up on the 4th for our annual Pembroke dinner.

Yours sincerely,
G. G. STOKES

1 Edward White Benson (1829–96), who took his B.A. at Cambridge as eighth classic in 1852, was Archbishop of Canterbury from 1883 to 1896.

535 KELVIN to STOKES, 2 July 1895
Stokes Collection, K302

July 2/95
28, Chester Square,
S.W.

DEAR STOKES

You agreed to breakfast with us here on the 4th as you thought you were to be in London at the time. But now I hope you will come on the 5th instead, at 9 am, as you must be in town on account of the Pembroke dinner of the 4th.

Don't be at the trouble of writing but *come*.

Yours very truly
KELVIN

536 KELVIN to STOKES, 8 July 1895
Stokes Collection, K303

July 8/95
28, Chester Square
S.W.

DEAR STOKES

I have sent your letter for A. Mallock[1] to his address, which is 3 Victoria Street Westminster.

I am exceedingly obliged to you for the warning, and correction *re* quartz. I had seen $OZ=51°\ 47'$ ⟨on⟩ at the beginning of the article in Miller–Philipps[2] [*sic*] and not noticed the '*zb*' on the next page till you called my attention to it. I am glad now to know that it is an error corrected in the errata.

It happens that I had in pencil filled in the '*b2ī ī*' a year ago in the R.S. edition, and I now see this omission also among the errata!

I hope you are pushing on Vol III[3] vigorously.

Yours very truly
KELVIN

1 Henry Reginald Arnulph Mallock (1851–1933), who became a fellow of the Royal Society in 1903, was a consulting engineer to the Board of Ordnance. There are twenty-eight letters from Mallock to Stokes in the Stokes Collection, sixteen of which date from July to October 1895.
2 William Phillips, *An Elementary Introduction to Mineralogy*, new edn with alterations and additions by H. J. Brooke and W. H. Miller (London, 1852). Henry James Brooke (1771–1857) was a businessman and amateur crystallographer, who amassed large collections, wrote articles for the *Encyclopaedia Metropolitana*, and became a fellow of the Royal Society in 1819.
3 Of Stokes's *MPP*.

Lensfield Cottage, Cambridge, 17 July, 1895.

DEAR LORD KELVIN,

As I was returning by train, it struck me that what Minchie [*sic*] Smith[1] said about the relation of manifestations of electricity to mist fell in extremely well with the idea that the separation of the electricit[i]es which appear to be developed in condensation is due to gravity.

The commonest observation of the phenomena of thunderstorms combined with the obvious nature of the cumulus cloud seems to show pretty conclusively that the *origin* of the electricity is referable to the condensation of water from vapour, whatever the reason of the development of the two electricities thereby may be. Now heavy rain in lo [*sic*] large drops, or hail as the case may be, is a most common accompaniment of thunder & lightning. These large drops, and even the smaller drops by the coalescence of which they were formed, would fall rapidly, and thereby tear asunder the positive and negative electricities contained in the first instance in the air and water.

As to the nacreous clouds, the luminosity cannot be an electric discharge, as Smith suggested; it is plainly diffraction due to excessively minute globules of water, just in the initial stage of condensation. It is illustrated by an experiment Shaw[2] showed at our soiree. I do not know whether you saw it, as you had to receive the people. The globules are at first too small to be seen at all, or rather I should say to reveal their presence by any optical effect whatsoever. The mist is sensibly perfectly transparent for light of all wave lengths. As the globules incr3ase [*sic*] in size, they become large enough to cause diffraction (through a very wide angle) in the shorter waves, while the mist is still sensibly perfectly transparent for the red. As the globules grow the high diffraction passes on to the red, and on still further growth we have light which is sensibly white immediately about the luminary, and for some way on, and then we have the usual coloured rings forming the 'corona'. Would you tell Smith this is [*sic*] you meet him, and if you don't would you kindly give me his address (if you know it) that I may tell him by letter?

Yours sincerely,

G. G. STOKES[3]

---

1 Born and educated in Scotland, Charles Michie Smith (1854–1922) spent most of his career in India, holding a series of positions including the directorship of the Kodaikánal and Madras Observatories from 1899 to 1911. For a brief discussion relating to the topic mentioned here, see his 'On Indian thunderstorms', *Brit. Assoc. Rep.* (1895), 626.

2 William Napier Shaw (1854–1945) was sixteenth wrangler and placed in the first class in the natural sciences tripos in 1876. He held various positions at the Cavendish Laboratory and

was director of the Meteorological Office from 1905 to 1920. See his 'The motion of clouds considered with reference to their mode of formation', *Quarterly Journal of the Royal Meteorological Society*, **21** (1895), 166–80.

3 Kelvin has written at the bottom of the page, '*Keep*'.

538   KELVIN to STOKES, 19 July 1895
   Stokes Collection, K304

28, Chester Square,
S. W.
July 19. 1895.

DEAR STOKES,

I was very glad to receive your letter of the 17th, and much interested in it. I am sending it to Michie Smith (India Office, for address). He is probably going to Scotland about this time, but no doubt it will be forwarded to him duly.

I enclose a recent communication[1] of mine to the Glasgow Philosophical Society which may interest you. It contains a good deal on the subject of your letter so far as it relates to electrification of air.

We are off to Aix-les-Bains tomorrow where our address will be Hotel Britannique.

Yours very truly,
KELVIN

11 pm July 19.

P. S. Yours of today received. I have written accordingly to M[r] Rix[2] withdrawing Mallock's paper,[3] and asking him to receive it under later date, as communicated by me in its amended form. If the zero of torsion was verified after each experiment, as I suppose it was, it would be impossible I believe that any error so great as $\frac{1}{2}$ per cent of the measured force, could result from elastic 'fatigue'.

It is very good of you to help Mallock as you are doing; and I am exceedingly glad to hear that you have found correc- [The rest of the letter is missing.]

1 Kelvin (344).
2 Herbert Rix was assistant secretary of the Royal Society from 1885 to 1896.
3 H. R. A. Mallock, 'Experiments on fluid viscosity', *Phil. Trans.*, series A (1896), 41–56. Received 26 July 1895.

July 22/95
28, Chester Square,
S. W.

DEAR STOKES

Your letter which I received on Saturday night must have crossed mine to you of Friday night. Mr Rix understands that Mallock's first paper[1] is withdrawn, and that when it comes back to the R.S. in amended form it is to be received as communicated by me, under fresh date. There will be no meeting of the Council till October; but no farther sanction than was given at its last meeting is needed. The appointment of referees was prospective, and the paper was to be dealt with by the officers and referees in the vacation, to save time. It is a good thing that this was arranged for, as the paper, and the R.S., have already got the benefit of your consenting to be referee. I called on Mallock this morning to speak to him about it, but did not find him in, so left a note for him, in answer to which I find the enclosed[2] this evening. I am glad to know from you that the correction diminishes the discrepanc[i]es, ⟨and⟩ not as he supposes increases them. We have been unexpectedly detained in London; but we leave for Aix tomorrow morning.

Yours very truly
KELVIN

1 See the previous letter, note 3.
2 See H. R. A. Mallock to Kelvin, 22 July 1895, Kelvin Collection, M71A, in which Mallock wrote:

> I have heard from Sir G. Stokes and am most thankful to him for pointing out the mistake I had made. (I had taken the shear in the fluid as measured by dv/dr instead of $dv/dr - v/r$.) The correction of the error however makes the values for the coeff of viscosity deduced from my series (1) and (3) more different from one another and from Poiseu[i]lle's than my wrong formula did.

Lensfield Cottage, Cambridge, 23 July, 1895.

DEAR LORD KELVIN,

A line of explanation. Mr. Mallock did not say in his paper[1] *how* he had made the comparison of his results with theory, and it was the merest guess on my part how he had done it. Towards the end of the paper he referred to a former result in Proceedings for Dec. 189 [*sic*] 1888.[2] On examining it I found that the formula he there worked with was wrong. Presumably he worked the same way in the late paper, and some numbers written on one of his diagrams, which at first I could not make head or tail of, showed that my conjecture derived from examining Proc. ⟨I'⟩ 1888 was right. That point being made out, it was clear that the effect of the alteration would be to *increase* the values of mu deduced from his results in the ratio of the sum of the radii to double the outer, therefore to increase the discrepancies.

A pleasant time of it in Aix to you and Lady Kelvin.

Yours sincerely,
G. G. STOKES

1 See letter 538, note 3.
2 H. R. A. Mallock, 'Determination of the viscosity of water', *Proc. Roy. Soc.*, 45 (1888–89), 126–32.

541 KELVIN to STOKES, 20 October 1895
Stokes Collection, K306

Oct 20/95
The University,
Glasgow.

DEAR STOKES

In answer to your letter of the 18th I have sent a small donation (£2) to the funds of the Christian Evidence Society.[1]

Yours very truly
KELVIN

I hope to see you in Cambridge about the 29th.

1 Stokes was vice president of the Christian Evidence Society, and there is a good deal of correspondence in the Stokes Collection involving the society. Included in the correspondence are several copies of a form letter written by Stokes as vice president in October 1895.

542 STOKES to KELVIN, 1 December 1895
Kelvin Collection, S498

Lensfield Cottage, Cambridge, 1 Dec. 1895.

DEAR LORD KELVIN,

I left my lodging a few minutes after 7, and got here for breakfast about 10-20. I found a printed card with notice of Mr. Ingram's lecture tomorrow evening, at the foot of which it was printed that I would take the chair.[1] So, you see I could not have accepted your kind invitation to dinner.

As I listened to your address,[2] I liked very much what you said of religious opinions in speaking about Huxley.

I have given your kind message to Mary, or, to be quite exact, a message either identical with or equal to your[s]; for I cannot trust my memory as to the exact words. Give my kindest regards to Lady Kelvin.

Yours sincerely

G. G. STOKES

1 Although this sounds like a meeting of the Victoria Institute – whose meetings Stokes often chaired as president – it is not recorded in the *Journal of the Transactions of the Victoria Institute*. Ingram may be Henry Manning Ingram (1824–1911) who corresponded a good deal with Stokes. Ingram was a low wrangler in 1847 and was rector of Aldrington, Sussex, from 1879 to 1893.
2 Kelvin (347), his presidential address to the Royal Society, in which he discussed the recently deceased Huxley on pages 109–10.

543   KELVIN to STOKES, 1 February 1896
Stokes Collection, K307
Partially printed in Thompson, 11, 956.

The University.

Glasgow.

February 1. 1896.

DEAR STOKES,

Considering the equations for motion in an elastic solid,

$$\left.\begin{array}{c} \varrho\,\dfrac{d^2\xi}{dt^2}=(k+\tfrac{1}{3}n)\,\dfrac{d\delta}{dx}+n\,\nabla^2\xi \quad \text{\&c.} \\[2mm] \text{where}\quad \delta=\dfrac{d\xi}{dx}+\dfrac{d\eta}{dy}+\dfrac{d\zeta}{dz} \end{array}\right\} \tag{1}$$

have you noticed or can you tell me if any other person has noticed the following solution or its result for light?

$$\left.\begin{array}{c} \zeta=0;\quad \xi=\dfrac{d\psi}{dx}\cos\dfrac{2\pi}{\lambda}\left(t\sqrt{\dfrac{n}{\varrho}}-z\right);\quad \eta=\dfrac{d\psi}{dy}\cos\dfrac{2\pi}{\lambda}\left(t\sqrt{\dfrac{n}{\varrho}}-z\right) \\[3mm] \text{where } \psi \text{ is a function of } x, y \text{ such that} \\[2mm] \dfrac{d^2\psi}{dx^2}+\dfrac{d^2\psi}{dy^2}=0 \end{array}\right\} \tag{2}$$

except throughout a cylindric tunnel or tunnels parallel to OZ.

It is useful for explaining the velocity of propagation of alternate currents of high frequency between two straight parallel conductors of any shapes of cross-section which may be supposed to have two ends O, O', close to us and no other ends.

To take the very simplest idea; – consider two tunnels in an infinite

631

homogeneous elastic solid beginning with O, O' and ending nowhere. Make a dynamite blast anywhere in the neighbourhood of OO'. The greater part of the energy will be taken by a condensational-rarefactional wave spreading uniformly in all directions if the explosion be made in a spherical cavity at a distance from O and O', large in comparison with their distance from one another. But wherever it is made both condensational-rarefactional and distortional spherical waves of all types of nodal multiplicity will spread out. *And* (except in cases of special adjustment) there will always be also a special plane wave expressed by equations (2.), with front perpendicular to the tunnels.

One application to light is of course known:– a light placed at one end of an infinitely long, absolutely uniform tube of glass with air or vacuum outside and inside it. Beyond the distance of a few diameters from O, no light is lost by transmission through space away from the tube. All that is not lost is transmitted along the tube chiefly through the air inside it. The best known case is simply a solid glass rod.

The case of a single tunnel or of two parallel tunnels through homogeneous glass filling all space except the tunnels and a source of light in one of the tunnels, or anywhere near them both, startles me very much and I don't venture (at all events for want of time) to write to you about it just now.

In respect to[1] the Röntgen X-rays,[2] are you a longitudinalist or an ultra-violetist or a tertium-quidist?

Have you noticed how Lenard[3] is punished for following Hittorff[4] [*sic*] and others in their perversity in respect to Varley & Crookes' discovery of the molecular torrent from the Cathode? The absurd supposition of a Cathode undulatory ray and no torrent of molecules lost the discovery of the X-rays to Lenard.

See Perrin in this week's 'Nature.'[5] I got Lockyer[6] to translate it and put it in.

I had a slight attack of pleurisy which came[7] suddenly on Monday. I am feeling much better now and the Doctor is well satisfied with progress but he won't let me out of his hands on any account yet, and I don't know what he will say when he hears that I have been dictating this, also a short article[8] for 'Nature' on 'Maxwell's infinite velocity for the propagation of electrostatic force' for which, look out next week.

Yours truly
KELVIN

1 Thompson's version has *of* instead of *to*.

2 See W. C. Röntgen, 'Ueber eine neue Art von Strahlen', *Sitzungsberichte der Physikalisch-Medizinischen Gesellschaft zu Würzburg* (1895), 132–41, translated into English in *Nature* (23 January 1896), 274–6, and in *The Electrician*, **36** (24 January 1896), 415–17. There is a reprint of the German version of the paper, annotated by Kelvin, in the Kelvin Collection, PA 431.

3 Philipp Lenard (1862–1947), after teaching at various German universities, was professor of experimental physics at Kiel from 1898 to 1907 and at Heidelberg from 1907 to 1931.

4 Johann Wilhelm Hittorf (1824–1914) was professor at Münster of physics and chemistry from 1852 to 1876 and of physics from 1876 to 1890.

5 J. Perrin, 'New experiments on the kathode rays', *Nature* (30 January 1896), 298–9, taken from *Comptes Rendus*, **121** (1895), 1130–4. Jean Baptiste Perrin (1870–1942) took his doctorate from the École Normale in 1897, after which he taught physical chemistry at the Sorbonne.

6 Joseph Norman Lockyer (1836–1920), director of the Solar Physics Observatory and professor of astronomical physics at the Royal College of Science from 1890 to 1913, was the first editor of *Nature*, holding the position for half a century.

7 Thompson's version inserts *on* after *came*.

8 Kelvin (349).

544 KELVIN to STOKES, 3 February 1896
Stokes Collection, K308

The University.
Glasgow.
February 3. 1896.

DEAR STOKES,

The enclosed which I only found this morning, in connection with the subject of my Saturday's letter has surprised me. I suppose it will not surprise you or Rayleigh to whom I am writing also. Consider as velocity-potential of simplest source of sound $\phi = \dfrac{C}{r} \sin m(r - vt)$. Take, in a straight line $X'OX$ a row of i such sources alternately differing in phase by a half period at consecutive distances equal to half the wave-length. The result will be loud sound at great distances from O in the two opposite directions OX, OX' and very faint sound at great distances in any direction inclined to OX or OX' at more than quite a small angle.

The velocity-potential for great distances from O is,

$$\frac{d^i \phi}{dx^i} = \frac{K}{r} \cos^i \theta \, \frac{\sin}{\cos} \, m(r - vt),$$

where $\cos \theta = \dfrac{x}{r}$.

Suppose for example $i = 100$, we have $(\cos 5°)^{100} = .68$, $(\cos 10°)^{100} = .22$, $(\cos 15°)^{100} = .031$.

I suppose a speaking trumpet realises part of this principle: and would realise a very large part ⟨of it is⟩ if its length were 20 or 30 or 100 wave lengths of the sound for which it is used.

Do you know whether the loudness in the direction towards which the speaking trumpet is pointed is greater, relatively to the loudness in other directions, for shrill musical notes than for grave ones?

Yours truly,
KELVIN

P. S. The solution (2) of my Saturday's letter requires of course a non-penetrative supplemental solution to fulfil boundary conditions at the surfaces of the tunnels. For ψ, I take

$$\Sigma m \log D - \Sigma m' \log D'$$

where D denotes distances from parallel lines in one tunnel and D' from parallel lines in the other, and $\Sigma m = \Sigma m'$.

I am obliged to choose thus for ψ in order to make the total energy per wave length, finite in the special kind of plane wave expressed by (2).

545 STOKES to KELVIN, 10 February 1896
Kelvin Collection, S499

Lensfield Cottage, Cambridge, 10 Feb. 1896.[1]

MY DEAR KELVIN,

The reason why I was so long in replying to your two letters of the 1st and 3rd inst. was that I wished first to go fully into the solution given in the former, and my lecturew [*sic*] and a good deal of correspondence and other engagements came in the way. However I will not wait longer. I may say at once that I have not seen the solution you give in your letter of Feb. 1 for the tunnel or tunnels in an elastic solid. I have not come across it, nor anything like it that I remember, and I am sure I should have remembered it if I had done so. As to the result you mention in the other letter, where you have sources alternately plus and minus at a half wave interval in a straight line, the result does not seem to me surprising. It is a good deal similar to what we have in a grating. Take for example a grating in which the interval is all but a wave length, and we get a result a good deal similar. Of course I mean only in some general aspects.

As to thr [*sic*] Röntgen rays, my mind was divided between transversal vibrations, which on the whole I thought the most probable, normal vibrations, the existence or [*sic*] which in the ether I greatly doubt, in fact I am decidedly against it, and a 'tertium quid', which I thought might be a sort of push, like what you have in an incompressible fluid. I did not think this very likely, but it might be worth while to examine the law of decrease with the distance. Vibrations should give the inverse square; for the 'push' one would expect the inverse cube. [J. J.] Thomson told me he has set one of his men to work at the law connecting the intensity with the distance.

When I had written so far the post brought me the list of papers for the R.S. on Thursday. I see you are down for longitudinal waves in the ether.[2] I am sorry I cannot go to hear your paper. I have an engagement in London that day up to 4, but we have a dinner in Pembroke, and I have asked guests, so I must return by the 5 p,m, [*sic*] train.

I was so satisfied that the ray-like things that come from the kathode, and which are acted on by a magenet [*sic*], are streams of molecules, or perhaps atoms, that when I came accidentally across the expression 'Kathodostrahlen', [*sic*] I supposed they were called rays only in a metaphorical sense, as a convenient term. On mentioning this some little time ago to Thomson, he told me that there were several who took them for actual rays of some kind. On subsequently reading some German papers I found that the writers were so strongly of that opinion that they rather I think looked down on those who thought otherwise. I had not when I spoke to Thomson, but have now, read Lenard's paper.[3] Röntgen seems to think that Lenard has settled the question that the Kathodostrahlen are real rays of some kind; though Röntgen distinguished, which Lenard did not, the X-rays from the Kathodostrahlen.

I wonder what is your idea of the way in which, in Lenard's experiments, the 'Kathodostrahlen' passed, or seemed to pass, through an aluminium window into a vacuum as nearly perfect as he could make it. My notion is that it is something like the way in which, in a row of ivory balls in contact, if the first be struck the last flies off; not that I take so gross a merely mechanical notion as that. To account for the ordinary phenomena of the molecular stream, the rapidly-moving molecules (or atoms) must be supposed to ne [*sic*] electrified. My notion is that in the common case of a current (electric) flowing along a wire something takes place in the wire similar to, if not even of the very same nature as, what takes place in an electrolyte when a current is passing through it; that there are motions of ions, or what answer to ions, in both directions; and the same again in a tube containing rarefied gas; gas which if of suitable density will show the stratified discharge.

Yours sincerely,
G. G. STOKES

P. S. From the account you gave of yourself in your last I I [*sic*] had been thinking of you as by this time practically well. I hope I have not been too sanguine. It may be that some remains of the attack of bronchitis are still about you at least, that the doctor does not yet give you a carte blanche to do just what you like.

1 Kelvin has written at the top of the letter, 'Stokes Rec^d Feb 11'. His secretary has written on the envelope, 'Received Feb. 11. 1896 Stokes. Sent to Lord Rayleigh'.
2 Kelvin (352).
3 See P. Lenard, 'Ueber Kathodenstrahlen in Gasen von atmosphärischem Druck und im äussersten Vacuum', *Annalen der Physik und Chemie*, 51 (1894), 225–67, and 'Ueber die magnetische Ablenkung der Kathodenstrahlen', *ibid.*, 52 (1894), 23–33.

546 KELVIN to STOKES, 12 February 1896
Stokes Collection, K309
Printed in Thompson, II, 957–8.

The University.
Glasgow.
February 12. 1896.

DEAR STOKES,

I am very much obliged to you for your letter of yesterday. Rayleigh gives me a reference to §301 of his book on Sound volume II[1] where there is, particularly in equation (12), something for condensational-rarefactional waves analogous to what I wrote to you regarding transverse vibrations in an elastic solid in my letter of Feb. 1.

As to the true Kathodenstrom, it is wonderful how the Germans have called it Kathodenstrahl, having allowed themselves to be misled by Hittorf and Goldstein.[2] They, everyone of them that I know of *except Helmholtz*, have insisted with something like strong partisan spirit upon a ray of undulatory light from the Cathode and have blindly refused to accept Varley's conclusion of a torrent of molecules, corroborated as it is by Crookes. I enclose a marked copy of my address[3] of 1893 which may show you, or remind you of, some dates and references on the subject.

As to the Röntgen rays, you will see in 'Nature' for Jan. 23, page 275, second column,[4] that Röntgen himself made the experiment which you tell me J. J. Thomson[5] thinks of making and that he found, as nearly as he could test it, an intensity varying inversely as the square of the distance. This, of course, if confirmed, is decisive against the hypothesis of 'push' in an incompressible medium.

I feel strongly disposed to Röntgen's own supposition of condensational-rarefactional waves, but still I see tremendous difficulties.

Thanks for your enquiries. I am now 'practically well' except that the Doctor still rigorously orders the leg to be kept horizontal, and so for the present I am kept in bed. The pleurisy is nearly quite gone away.

Yours always
KELVIN

1 Rayleigh, *The Theory of Sound*, 2 vols. (London, 1877–78). See Rayleigh to Kelvin, 6 February 1896, Kelvin Collection, R44, in which he wrote:

> On the other question there is something like it for air in The. of Sound vol ii §§268, 300, 301. On speaking trumpet §280. But this is only for aerial vibrations.

2 Eugen Goldstein (1850–1930) was a physicist at the Potsdam observatory and published several papers on cathode rays.

3 Kelvin (338).

4 See letter 543, note 2.

5 Kelvin has added a footnote here reading, 'I have written him a post-card calling his attention to this'. See J. J. Thomson to Kelvin, 16 February 1896, Kelvin Collection, T536, and Kelvin's answer of February 18th printed in Thompson, II, 958–60.

547 STOKES to KELVIN, 17 February 1896
Kelvin Collection, S500

Lensfield Cottage, Cambridge, 17 Feb. 1896.[1]

MY DEAR KELVIN,

I was in London on Thursday, but could not stay for the R.S. meeting, as there was a feast in the hall of Pembroke. I had seen that Abney[2] proposes to call the Rontgen Photographs 'electrographs'. I called at the R.S. about noon, and saw your paper.[3]

I am not quite clear how much you imply by the term 'normal vibrations'. If you mean vibrations produced by resistance to compression, I do not think that action on a plate such as you suppose would establish them.

Suppose that you had two parallel disks rigidly connected, say by a pillar in the middle, immersed in a perfect incompressible fluid, the whole being at rest. Let now the disks be moved to and fro by an external force in a direction perpendicular to their plane. Suppose the distance apart of the disks to be very small compared with their radii. Then except near the edges the fluid between would move sensibly in the same manner as the disks. If the motion of the disks is thought of as a vibration, the fluid between may *in a certain sense* be spoken of as executing normal vibrations. But these are not vibrations of a sound-like character. Now the off-and-on electrifications of two parallel plates of which one is charged intermittently and acts by induction on the other (suppose the plates in a perfect vacuum) may or may not produce a to and fro motion in the ether between. If it does, that does not establish the existence of sound-like normal vibrations. And if a sensitive photographic plate between is found to be affected, that does not even prove that there are to-and-fro normal motions of any kind; for I don't know what the physical interpretation of electric (electrostatic) force in relation to ether and matter is. Or at least I don't know, and I am not aware that anyone else does; but I am not strong in electricity.

I have since referred to the passage you gave me the reference to in the translation of Rontgen's paper.[4] Rontgen sent me a copy of his paper, which I read, naturally with very great interest. But at the time of reading the possibility of a 'push' theory had not occurred to me, and it seemed to lie between transversal vibrations of excessive frequency, which is what I most inclined to, and normal vibrations, which Rontgen inclined to. Putting Rontgen's results along with some of Tyndall's, which struck me many years ago, when he read his ta [*sic*] paper,[5] I was led to form a (to me) new idea as to the conditions of refraction. Tyndall working with a rock salt prism and thermopile had found refraction beyond the red extending far beyond what was to be expected from Cauchy's work as the limit of all refraction; and moreover the effect did not cease rather suddenly, as might have been expected from Cauchy's work, but gradually trailed away to insensibility. Putting this along with Rontgen's work, I was led to imagine that refraction might depend on the excitement of molecular motions which go on along with the etherial [*sic*] vibrations, and virtually increase the inertia of the ether; and that the possibility of these molecular motions going on may depend on the vibration-frequency of the various possible vibratory movements of molecules or groups of molecules being neither enormously greater nor enormously less than that of the particular etherial vibrations with which we are dealing. In Tyndall's experiments he may have got approximately below the frequencies of molecular motions. In Rontgen's work, the electrically charged molecules streaming from the kathode came suddenly against the glass wall of the vessel, where they may very well have excited vibrations of such high frequency that the transversal waves they produce change too quickly (i.e. from + to −tive) to disturb even the component parts of most compound molecules, and accordingly the etherial vibrations go through without sensible refraction, and in most cases without much absorption.

You recollect the dynamical illustration I mentioned to you of fluorescence. It related to an infinitely long row of equal and equidistant masses strung on a weightless string at a certain tension. You recollect the radical distinction between the permanent motions of the masses corresponding to a permanently regular disturbing force according as the period of the force was greater or less that [*sic*] the period of the shortest free vibration of the masses. I have not investigated the problem of the motion of the masses in case the disturbing force, though perhaps pretty regular, in fact sensibly regular, for a few hundred or thousand vibrations, is not permanently so, though it does not look as if the investigation would be of any particular difficulty. But it seems likely enough that some interesting result would come out. I tried a case of less simple distribution of masses, and a result came which seemed prettily to illustrate the alternations of comparative transparency and opacity that one finds so frequently in solutions of coloured substances.

Yours sincerely,
G. G. STOKES

1 Kelvin has written on the envelope, 'Stokes, rec^d Feb 19 Answ^d Feb 24 & 25/96'.
2 William de Wiveleslie Abney (1843–1920) joined the Royal Engineers in 1861, becoming
captain in 1873. In 1877 he entered the Science and Art Department, South Kensington, and
held a series of positions there until 1903. The chemical side of photography was his main area
of research. There are some sixty letters from him to Stokes in the Stokes Collection.
3 Kelvin (352).
4 See letter 543, note 2.
5 J. Tyndall, 'On calorescence', *Phil. Trans.* (1866), 1–24.

548 KELVIN to STOKES, 24 and 25 February 1896
Stokes Collection, K310
Partially printed in Thompson, II, 1062–3.

The University,
Glasgow.
February 24. 1896.

DEAR STOKES,

I am sorry not to have been able to thank you sooner for your letter of the
17th which has interested me exceedingly. Your illustration of the case of
electrostatic action between two parallel discs supposes the fluid between
them to be incompressible. Suppose, however, the fluid to be air and the
period of the vibration to be considerably less than the time sound takes to
travel the distance between the plates; the commencement of a series of such
vibrations would produce the 'longitudinal waves' and its continuance the
'condensational-rarefactional' vibrations, which I speak of in the last three
lines of my R.S. paper[1] of Feb. 10 (copy enclosed). Even if such vibrations are
possible in ether however, it seems scarcely[2] probable that the spark in the
arrangement which I suggest could produce a sudden enough effect in the
space between *AA* and the roof to do much in the way of exciting them.

I have been trying almost incessantly since some time before Nov. 28. 1846
(art. XXVII, vol. 1. of my Mathematical & Physical papers)[3] for a mechanical-
dynamical representation of electrostatic force, but hitherto quite in vain.
Many others, including Maxwell, have tried more or less for the same, but
with no approach to a glimpse of what might become a success. It seems highly
probable that there may be longitudinal waves in ether but hitherto this idea
does not help us to explain electrostatic force.

As to the Röntgen light what you say of high frequency seems to me of very
great importance but you need not confine it to 'transversal vibrations'. It is
equally applicable to waves of longitudinal vibrations if there are any in ether.
Excessively high frequency gives according to the molecular theory which I
learned from you before 1852 the same propagational velocity in all transparent mediums as in vacuum. I enclose a formula cut out of a sheet of my
Baltimore Lectures (which has been in type since 1885, but which in
consequence of your letter I have sent today to the Pitt Press[4] for final revise)

639

$$\frac{T^2}{\lambda^2}=\frac{1}{l}\left[\varrho-C_1 T^2\left\{1+\frac{C_1 T^2}{m_1}\left(\frac{\kappa_1^2 R_1}{\kappa_1^2-T^2}+\frac{\kappa_2^2 R_2}{\kappa_2^2-T^2}+\cdots\right)\right\}\right].$$

This, if $\frac{\varrho}{l}=1$, is the expression for the square of the refractive index as it is affected by the presence of molecules arranged in the way we[5]

T is the vibrational period,

λ, the wave-length,

ϱ & l, the rigidity and density of the ether,

m_1, the mass of the first interior shell,

C_1, $1/\beta$ of the mutual force between it and the rigid lining of the hollow in the ether around it, per unit of relative displacement; $1/\beta$ being the ratio of sum of volumes of hollows to total volume and being *very small*.

I should explain that the formula relates to waves in ether as influenced by the compound molecule represented in the accompanying diagram, being my realisation of the vibratile molecule which I first learned from you. The number of molecules like this in a cubic wave-length is supposed to be exceedingly great, practically infinite.

The outermost circle represents a rigid spherical lining of the hollow whose mass is equal to that of the ether which would fill it. The interior circles represent rigid shells and a central nucleus of matter connected with one another and with the lining by massless springs. The central nucleus is infinitely massive and the masses of the shells are less and less in their order outwards from it. κ_1, κ_2 etc. denote the periods of the unforced fundamental vibrations of the molecules when the rigid lining is held fixed; and R_1, R_2 the ratios of the energy of m_1 to the total energy in these ⟨circumstances⟩ vibrations. The formula was given in the Baltimore Lectures for waves of transverse vibrations, but it is equally applicable to longitudinal, if for l we substitute $k+\frac{4}{3}l$, where k denotes the compressibility modulus.

You will see that when T is a very little smaller than any one of the κ's, μ^2 is negative (In my Baltimore Lectures I tried to explain metallic reflection by taking μ a pure imaginary). The adjustment of values of C_1, m_1, κ_i, R_i, to give ordinary refraction and dispersion in water, glass, ⟨etc.⟩ air, and other colourless transparent ponderables, not sensibly disturbed by anomalous dispersion, is I believe quite practicable, though not at first sight very obvious. But our present affair according to what you tell me in your letter is to consider periods very much smaller than the smallest of the κ's. For this the refractive index is unity. Cela saute aux yeux, if you look at the formula!!! Thus all Röntgen's own demands may be practically fulfilled either by transverse or longitudinal waves of frequencies which need not be much greater than five or ten times that of the extreme visible violet light.

But now, here comes a strong reason for choosing high frequency transverse as at present more probable than high frequency longitudinal. [Unless[6] the compressibility modulus is less than $-1/3$, which can scarcely be said to be probable at present (although we cannot say it is impossible), the propagational velocity of longitudinal waves is greater than that of transverse waves. At present I think we may say it is probably much greater if not quite infinite as ordinarily assumed. Hence it is probable that, for the same vibrational-frequency, the wave-length is much longer for longitudinal than for transverse. Now we find in Comptes Rendus for Jan. 27, 1896 page 187,[7] an experiment by Perrin in which Röntgen light gives no diffraction fringes in an arrangement showing a very sharp shadow in which, when visible green light from the same vacuum tube is added to the Röntgen light interference ⟨bands⟩ fringes are clearly photographed. Perrin's inference as to the Röntgen light is: 'Si donc le phénomène est périodique, la période est très inférieure à celle de la lumière verte employée.' This inference is correct on the highly probable supposition that the propagational velocity of the Röntgen light is not less than that of Old light; but the thing absolutely proved by the observation is that the wave length of the Röntgen light, if it consists of waves at all, is much less than that of the green light of the experiment. The frequency required to give the short enough wave length would be *very much greater* if the Röntgen rays are longitudinal than if they are transverse, supposing, as seems most probable, the propagational velocity of the longitudinal to be *very much greater* than that of the transverse. Hence we have to go much further from known things in the way of frequency, besides going to altogether unknown things in the way of longitudinal in ether, to account for the Röntgen light by high frequency longitudinal than by high frequency transverse. It seems to me that the combined force of these two reasons is very strong in favour of high pressure transverse as the real explanation of the X-rays; and I adopt it henceforth accordingly unless you instruct me otherwise.

Electrostatic force still languishes unexplained. I wish you would turn your attention to it and tell me how to explain it; or even give me a hint how to find a way to get towards an explanation of it.

I am feeling perfectly well now; the pleurisy quite gone and almost forgotten. But the Doctors are quite absolute that I must give the leg rest for at least a fortnight longer. This is a great disappointment to me, as I thought I should be released this week, instead of being kept in bed, as I am. But they say that if I am rigorously obedient I shall be perfectly well and able to go about with perfect freedom before very long, which is cheering.

Yours very truly
KELVIN

1 Kelvin (352).
2 Kelvin has added a footnote here reading, 'Feb. 25. Since writing this yesterday I withdraw the word "scarcely". Witness experiment described in my Electrostatics & Magnetism art. XVII'. (Kelvin (131A) in *PEM*, 239–41.)
3 Kelvin (25) in *MPP*, I, 76–80.
4 Kelvin has added a footnote here reading, 'Since you have impelled me to take this step I have reciprocated by asking Clay to get the Syndics to join him in putting irresistible pressure on you to bring out your volume III without any further delay'. The third volume of Stokes's *MPP* was published in 1901.
5 From the beginning of the formula to this point has been clipped from page 106 of Kelvin's *Baltimore Lectures* (1904) and pasted onto the letter. The expression 'if $\frac{\varrho}{l} = 1$', has been inserted by Kelvin's secretary and is not in the final printed version. Also, in the final version, C_I has been changed to c_I. The figure in the text comes from page 118 of the *Baltimore Lectures* (1904).
6 Kelvin's bracket. The letter contains no closing bracket.
7 J. Perrin, 'Quelques propriétés de rayons de Röntgen', *Comptes Rendus*, 122 (1896), 186–8.

549   KELVIN to STOKES, [26 February 1896][1]
Stokes Collection, K369

Glasgow

Formula yesterday's letter requires largely simplifying amendment not affecting our conclusions I wrote by post.

KELVIN

1 This is a telegram from which the date has been torn. It must date after Kelvin was raised to the peerage, and I have given it this date because of its similarity to the next letter.

550   KELVIN to STOKES, 26 February 1896
Stokes Collection, K311

The University.
Glasgow.
February 26. 1896.

DEAR STOKES,

I am happy to say the formula does not seem to require any amendment. It had been in type since 1885 and was struck off in 1892, but I could not pass an examination on it when I wrote you yesterday; so please, in my explanations, make the following corrections:—

m_1 is equal to N times the mass of the first interior shell,

C_1 is N times the mutual force specified in my yesterday's statement: N, being the number of molecules per unit bulk of the ether.

Instead of 'infinitely massive' substitute 'of greatest mass.' In reality I don't need to fix the order of magnitude of the masses, or of the strengths of the springs but I described them in my lectures[1] as I thought suitable for a mechanical representation of the action of molecules on ether, which we want.

I was staggered this morning to find that when T is very great the formula apparently did not give $\dfrac{T^2}{\lambda^2} = \dfrac{1}{l}\,[\varrho + m_1 + m_2 + m_3 + \text{etc.}]$ as it manifestly ought to do.[2] This however I now see is all right, at all events for the case of just one interior shell; as in this case we have $\dfrac{m_1}{C_1} = \kappa^2$, and the formula becomes:—

$$\frac{T^2}{\lambda^2} = \frac{1}{l}\left[\varrho - \frac{m_1 T^2}{\kappa^2}\left(1 + \frac{T^2}{\kappa^2 - T^2}\right)\right] = \frac{1}{l}\left[\varrho - m_1 \frac{T^2}{\kappa^2 - T^2}\right].$$

This is right, and it becomes $\dfrac{1}{l}\,(\varrho + m_1)$ when $T = \infty$.

The general formula will come all right no doubt with any number of shells for the case of T very large, but I have not yet had time to verify.

Yours

KELVIN

1 Kelvin's *Baltimore Lectures* (1904).
2 Kelvin's brackets here and in the equation below.

---

551 STOKES to KELVIN, 28 February 1896
Kelvin Collection, S501

Lensfield Cottage, 28 Feb. 1896.[1]

MY DEAR KELVIN,

I must not write long, as I have a paper and a half to prepare for the Bell Scholarship, and the examination is very close. I thought you would have been about by this time; I had not heard of the ailment in the leg.

Normal vibrations in the ether did not fit in with my own speculations. My own mind goes along with the very strong terms in which, in a letter to Bentley quoted by Faraday and others, ⟨he⟩ Newton repudiates the idea of action at a distance across a perfect void.[2] Now the only compressibility that we know anything about is that of ponderable matter, which involves and depends on ponderable matter not being a plenum, but consisting of separate molecules. How they act on one another we know not, but in all probability the ether has a great deal to do with their mutual action. If the ether be compressible, the only examples of compressibility that we know anything about would lead us to attribute discontinuity to the ether, to suppose that it too is made up of discrete things, molecules shall I call them? But how do these 'things' act on each other? Is it by a sort of impact and rebound? That would lead us to attribute again structure and molecular constitution to these supposed molecules of ether. Is it by action at a distance? that leads us to the old alternative of action across a perfect void, or an ether of the second order to account for the supposed action of one on another of two molecules of the ether of the first order. Either supposition reminds me of the rhyme

'. . . . . and dogs have fleas that bite 'em,
And big fleas have little fleas, and so ad infinitum'.

My mind inclines me to scratch off the fleas, and rest in the idea of a plenum of incompressible ether, which our present knowledge does not authorise us in going beyond.

The consideration you mention of the length of wave required for normal waves ⟨req⟩ rendering all the more difficult of explanation the absence of fringes of interference in the Röntgen ⟨wa⟩ rays on the supposition that they are due to normal vibrations, is one which had not occurred to me. Indeed I had not seen Perrin's paper[3] till you mentioned it. There is one source of absence of fringes in ⟨perrin&s⟩ Perrin's experiment the efficacy of which we cannot well judge of as he does not even give a rough estimate of the actual width of his 'very narrow' slit. Now the slit being presumably near the part of the tube which is the source of the Röntgen rays, each longitudinal element of the slit is to [be] regarded as acting independently, and giving a system of fringes, and the illuminations due to these have to be superposed. (If the source in the wall of the Crookes tube were distant from the slit the thing would be more complicated, as there would be two successive diffractions.) Now the shift of position on the plate in passing from the right to the left edge of the slit (supposing for the sake of explanation that the slit and aperture are vertical) is twice the breadth of the slit (according to the distances actually used by Perrin), and therefore the fringes if very narrow might well be blotted out by confusion unless the slit were very narrow indeed.

I have some speculations about the statical condition of electricity, but it would take a good deal of writing to explain, and I must leave it for another time.

I hope Lady Kelvin is well. I suppose she had something in the way of assisting in nursing you when you were ill.

Yours sincerely,
G. G. STOKES

1 Kelvin's secretary has written on the envelope, 'Sir George Stokes. Received Feb. 29. 1896'. Kelvin has written on the envelope:

Sent to Lord Rayleigh and rec^d back Mar 14

Enclosed also Lord Rayleigh's letter of Mar 13 [This letter is in neither the Kelvin Collection nor the Kelvin Papers at Glasgow.]

Lond Ap 25. Put R's letter of March 13 into GGS envelope of March 11 [This refers to the next letter dated March 9th, but the envelope of which is post marked March 11th.]

2 The letter from Newton to Bentley is published in H. S. Thayer, ed., *Newton's Philosophy of Nature* (New York, 1953), 50–3.

3 See letter 548, note 7.

552 STOKES TO KELVIN, 9 March 1896
Kelvin Collection, S502

Lensfield Cottage, Cambridge, 9 March, 1896.[1]

MY DEAR KELVIN,

I write to call your attention (in case you should not have noticed it) to a paper in the Comptes Rendus for March 2, p. 525.[2] If the explanation of the diffusion which the authors give after the small print on that page be the true one, which seems very likely, we have here additional evidence of the smallness of the lengths of wave in the Röntgen rays.

It is a pity the authors did not test their explanation by taking reflection from the surface of mercury, where we have a metallic surface polished by Nature.

Abney believes that the Röntgen rays denote a purely electrical action.[3] I don't know how he reconciles that view with the rectilinearity of propagation as established by the experiments to which you called my attention.

Some time ago I completed the reprinting of my paper[4] on pendulums (including a small additional note) with the exception of 2 or 3 pages which I have yet to write, and the paper[5] which comes next in order is printed, and ready for making up into pages when the paging of the pendulum paper is ascertained, and the next[6] to that (which happens to be 'On the colours of thick plates' is left for the compositors to be getting on with. So you see I am going ahead now that I have given up re-computing numerically the reduction of Baily's (and other) experiments in[7] the pendulum paper.[8]

I hope you are by this time out of bed and about.

Silvanus Thompson wrote to me announcing a discovery he had made – that a solar phosphorus exposed for a considerable time to ordinary light was a source of Röntgen rays, or at least rays which traverse opaque substances. I see by the Comptes Rendus that he has been anticipated.[9]

I still think that the Röntgen rays are transversal vibrations of extreme frequency. I don't mean to say that I look on that as established, but only as being (to me) the most probable account of their nature.

Yours sincerely,
G. G. STOKES

1 Kelvin's secretary has written on the envelope, 'Sir Geo. Stokes. Received March 12 1896'. Kelvin has written on the envelope, '⟨R⟩ Sent to Lord Rayleigh March 12 Returned to K March *x*'.

2 Armand Imbert and Henri Bertin-Sans, 'Diffusion des rayons de Röntgen', *Comptes Rendus*, **122** (1896), 524–5. The *Royal Society Catalogue of Scientific Papers* lists nine joint papers by Imbert and Bertin-Sans, published mostly in the *Comptes Rendus*. It also lists a few papers by Imbert on muscles and a few by Bertin-Sans with a Joseph Moitessier on blood.

3 Kelvin has encircled this sentence and written, 'Nonsense K'.

4 Stokes (47) in *MPP*, III, 1–141.

5 Stokes (46) in *MPP*, III, 142–54.

6 Stokes (48) in *MPP*, III, 155–96.

7 Kelvin has underlined the passage, *now that I ... experiments in*, and written, 'This res⟨olve⟩ult I ⟨urg⟩ obtained a year or two ago K'.

8 Kelvin has drawn a line down the left side of this paragraph and written, 'This is answer to a final application (very urgent) of pressure which I made about a fortnight ago'.

9 See the correspondence between Thompson and Stokes in Stokes's *Memoir*, II, 495–9, and H. Becquerel, 'Sur les radiations émises par phosphorescence', *Comptes Rendus*, **122** (24 February 1896), 420–1, which Stokes cited to Thompson in *Memoir*, II, 496. Silvanus Phillips Thompson (1851–1916) was professor of applied physics and electrical engineering at the City and Guilds Technical College, Finsbury, from 1885 to 1916. He did publish a few papers in 1896 on X-rays. Also, of course, he is Kelvin's biographer, beginning the biography in consultation with Kelvin a year and a half before Kelvin's death. There are some twenty letters between Thompson and Kelvin in the Kelvin Collection, four of which date from the period of their collaboration on the biography. By the date of this letter, Becquerel had presented two more articles: 'Sur les radiations invisibles émises par les corps phosphorescents', *Comptes Rendus*, **122** (2 March 1896), 501–3, and 'Sur quelques propriétés nouvelles des radiations invisibles émises par divers corps phosphorescents', *Comptes Rendus*, **122** (9 March 1896), 559–64.

553 KELVIN to STOKES, 9 March 1896
Stokes Collection, K312

The University.
Glasgow.
March 9. 1896

DEAR STOKES,

I have been prevented by one thing following another, day after day, from sooner acknowledging your letter of the 28th ult., in respect to ether.

I do not see how you can consider rigidity, whether like that which we know in jelly or virtual rigidity due to resistance to rotation, as the one essential property of ether: and how you can say that compressibility requires either 'action at a distance' or 'a second ether' to explain it. It seems to me that infinite resistance against compression is a harder assumption than finite compressibility, that is to say, yielding, but resisting with an increasing force as density increases. Therefore it seems to me difficult to believe that *there are not* longitudinal waves in ether. What do you say to this? We are however, I suppose, both agreed that Röntgen's X-rays are more probably extreme ultra-violet rays of transverse vibration than anything else we can think of just now. Would you like to send a note to this effect to the R.S. or, it will be a tremendous feather in my cap, shall we write a joint note?[1]

Here is another affair which surprised me in the 'Glasgow Herald'[2] (referring to a letter by Ramsay in 'Nature' of Feb. 20.) a few days before my last letter to you. It was a leader, and I can't conceive how the Editor or writer got the information. I can't think of anybody in Glasgow who can have suggested it. But I heard there was a little feeling at the Glasgow Philosophical Society 'Graham Lecture,' which was given by Ramsay in Glasgow on the 8th of January, on Argon,[3] that he had not made it clear that Lord Rayleigh was the true discoverer of Argon, and that his part was his having been allowed to take part in announcing the discovery and help Rayleigh in initial work regarding it. I thoroughly agree with the 'Glasgow Herald' that the kindest thing the public can do for Ramsay is to 'remember the able way in which' he 'helped to work out Lord Rayleigh's discovery, and to forget his extraordinary annoyance at any other attempt to follow on the same path.' The scientific judgment of the matter must certainly be that Rayleigh's twelve years of persevering work in the redetermination of the densities of the principal gases included the discovery of Argon. His searching and exhaustive experiments, on Nitrogen from different sources, prove beyond all doubt that what is left of common air, when Oxygen, vapour of water, and Carbonic acid are extracted from it, is denser than Nitrogen. This was done and published before Ramsay came on the field at all, and I think it is very unfortunate for Ramsay's reputation that he allowed Rayleigh to associate his name with the announcement of the discovery that the atmosphere contains a fifth constituent, previously unknown and unimagined.

When Rayleigh's work and results in respect to density were published, it remained to take the known methods of Cavendish, by the electric spark, and the known methods of chemists, by combination with magnesium or or [sic] other chemical, to extract the Nitrogen after extracting the other four known constituents, and examine the residue. It turns out that Cavendish himself did find a refractory residue about the size of a pinhead, after three weeks application of his own method, and this, we now know, is really the fifth constituent, to the discovery of which Rayleigh's determinations of densities led. It is rather disturbing sometimes to one's equanimity to find Daily Telegraphs, Spectators, etc. speaking of 'Lord Rayleigh's assistance to Ramsay in his discovery of Argon'; 'Ramsay's discovery of Argon' etc. etc.; but the history of the affair is sufficiently *made*, and sufficiently known among chemists and scientific men generally, to leave no doubt as to the judgment of the scientific world in respect to the discovery.

Yours always truly,
KELVIN

1 They did not write a joint paper on the nature of X-rays, but see Kelvin (350) and (353) and Stokes (130), (131), (132), and (134).

2 Kelvin enclosed the following clipping from the *Glasgow Herald* of 22 February 1896:

An interesting question is raised and a somewhat melancholy sight presented by a letter which Professor William Ramsay has written to a leading scientific periodical.[a] Professor Ramsay is chiefly known to the public, outside chemical circles, by his association with Lord Rayleigh in the recent discovery of the new element argon.[b] He has more than once allowed it to be guessed that he was not altogether delighted by the way in which the world of science greeted the achievement of 'the Argonauts,' as he and his partner have been jestingly called; and he now enunciates the sum of his discontent in a perfectly distinct but unmelodious fashion. The discovery of argon was first announced, it will be remembered, in a somewhat bold manner, whilst much of the corroborative detail still remained to be worked out. Many chemists of high standing immediately submitted the announcement to free criticism, and implied their right to test it by all the experimental methods at their disposal. Mr Ramsay now asks whether such a course was 'consistent with the highest view of scientific morality,' and shows that he holds that it was not. He singles out for condemnation the words of the late President of the Chemical Society, Dr Armstrong,[c] who laid down a doctrine with which few unprejudiced persons will disagree. 'After having been told so much,' he said, 'chemists could not be expected to remain under the imputation that they had been eyeless for a whole century, and they would undoubtedly inquire into the matter. Although no one would seek to take the discovery out of the hands of those who had announced it, chemists unquestionably had the right, not only to exercise entire freedom of judgment, but also to critically examine the statements which had been made.' Beyond, perhaps, the split infinitive, a layman can see nothing objectionable in this declaration. Mr Ramsay thinks differently. His share in the discovery of argon was, as he now claims, sacrosanct and above all uninspired criticism, and he shows his bias by comparing those men of science who ventured to apply any independent tests to it, to the business adventurers who infringe patents and make a livelihood by stealing the product of more lively brains. He has chosen rather an unfortunate parallel. Every business man knows, what ought to be familiar to the scientist, that any man who can honestly improve upon an invention is at liberty to patent his improvement, and not only may but often does thereby take the wind out of the sails of the original inventor. Hundreds of instances occur to the mind, of which the steam engine and the sewing machine afford perhaps the most notable. From a scientific point of view, Mr Ramsay's contention is even less to be praised. It has often been declared by the opponents of modern science that it is in reality as obscurantist in its tendencies as was mediaeval theology. This is a sweeping libel; but such plaintive appeals as Mr Ramsay has now issued would go far to substantiate it, if they were common. It is only a short step from his threat that 'scientific men will provide their private laboratories with a good lock,' to the method of publishing discoveries in undecipherable anagrams which was occasionally adopted by Galileo and Huyghens in days when it was not safe to be frank with the world. Every one agrees that a discoverer deserves all the laurels that he can fairly earn; but the surest way for him to dim their green is to manifest that dog-in-the-manger spirit which is aggrieved that his discovery should be submitted to the criticism or the improvement of others. Where would science be now if Kepler had warned Newton off his premises, or Mr Wallace had refused to let Darwin work out their common idea? The present protest, in fact, is so ill-advised and so unscientific that it is hardly necessary to say more about it. The kindest thing the public can do is remember the able way in which Mr Ramsay helped to work out Lord Rayleigh's discovery, and to forget his extraordinary annoyance at any other attempt to follow on the same path.

a. W. Ramsay, 'Science and morals', *Nature*, 53 (20 February 1896), 366. William Ramsay (1852–1916) was professor of chemistry at University College, London, from 1887 to 1912.

b. Rayleigh and Ramsay, 'Argon, a new constituent of the atmosphere', *Phil. Trans.*, series A (1895), 187–241.

c. Armstrong made his comment during discussion following presentation of J. Dewar, 'The relative behaviour of chemically prepared and of atmospheric nitrogen in the liquid state', *Proceedings of the Chemical Society*, 10 (1894), 222–5. Armstrong's remark is on page 225. Henry Edward Armstrong (1848–1937) was from 1884 to 1911 professor of chemistry at the Central Institution, South Kensington, which merged with the Imperial College of Science and Technology in 1907.

3 W. Ramsay, 'On argon and helium', *Proceedings of the Glasgow Philosophical Society*, 27 (1896), 92–116.

Lensfield Cottage, Cambridge, 12 March, 1896.[1]

MY DEAR KELVIN,

I don't think I have yet mentioned to you (forgive the repetition if I have) an idea which occurred to me when I read ⟨his⟩ Silvanus Thompson's letter[2] announcing his discovery (in which I found he had found afterwards that he had been anticipated) that a solar phosphorus after mere exposure to light is a source of an influence which is capable of acting on a sensitive plate across a substance which is opaque to light, an influence accordingly which is presumably the same as the X-rays. I mentioned it to him in my reply. It seems to me that the result presents a striking analogy with calorescence.[3] In calorescence, the active agent is ethereal vibrations of so low frequency as to place them beyond the red. These presumably in the first instance produce molecular vibrations of similar period or nearly so, but the motion thus excited in molecular groups or molecules, in sharing itself among neighbouring molecular groups or molecules gives rise to molecular motions of shorter period, which communicate to the ether vibrations of such periods as to fall within the visible spectrum.

Now in a solar phosphorus we have comparatively restricted molecular groups capable of being excited in the first instance by ethereal vibrations of pretty high frequency, the effect of which accumulates till there is considerable molecular agitation, which however does not readily communicate itself to wider molecular groups. When this considerable but localised agitation is established, it may be that in the permqnent [sic] state there are some molecular vibrations of high frequency belonging to the system of agitation, which excite ethereal vibrations for which black paper are transparent.

As compared with Tyndall's calorescence, we here start with the vantage ground of highly localised and consequently quickly vibrating molecular groups. When I mention 'vantage ground', I mean with reference to the production of vibrations of excessively short period as the object to be attained.

Yours sincerely,

G. G. STOKES

P. S. The two kinds of disturbance I have in my mind may I think in a rough sort of way be compared to the periodic and the secular planetary disturbances.

I find that in the attempt to convey one's own ideas to the mind of another, one's own ideas grow and get clearer.

---

1 Kelvin's secretary has written on the envelope, 'Sir George Stokes. Received March 13. 1896'.

2 See letter 552, note 9.
3 See letter 547, note 5.

555 KELVIN to STOKES, 12 March 1896
Stokes Collection, K313[1]

The University.
Glasgow.
March 12. 1896.

DEAR STOKES,

I am tremendously interested in what you say regarding Imbert and Bertin-Sans' paper[2] in the Comptes Rendus which I had just received but not read before receiving your letter yesterday.

I had received a letter from Lord Blythswood of date Feb. 28,[3] of which I send you a leaf enclosed describing an experiment which seems to prove decisively reflection of Röntgen light from polished speculum metal. I have written to him today telling him of your suggestion that experiments should be tried on reflection from a mercury surface, because *it* is molecularly smooth, and we cannot be sure that this is true of the best polished solid metals; and suggested to him that he should have this done by his assistant at Blythswood if possible. Meantime, however, I have offered to communicate a paper to the R.S.[4] (which I hope will be in time for next week) describing what he has already done for reflection of Röntgen light from polished speculum metal.

I had noticed that Sylvanus Thompson's very interesting discovery had been anticipated by d'Arsonval in the Comptes Rendus of March 2.[5]

I think you should write to d'Arsonval and suggest the reflection from mercury as you tell me in your letter of yesterday, you thought of doing.[6]

Notwithstanding what you say in your letter of yesterday I shall try and write a note for the R.S.[7] giving your reasons and mine (learned originally from you) for thinking it most probable that Röntgen light consists of transverse vibrations of very high frequency. If I succeed in writing it I shall send it to you for approval, adhesion, correction or rejection.

Yours very truly,
KELVIN

P.S. What you tell me in your letter of the 9th 'Abney believes' is as wise as his suggestion that photographs by Röntgen light should be called 'electrographs.'

1 K314 in the Stokes Collection is a press copy of K313.
2 See letter 552, note 2.

3 The following is the enclosed part of Blythswood's letter, at the top of which Kelvin has written, 'One leaf of a letter which I received from Lord Blythswood on Feb 29/96. Sent to Sir G. Stokes March 12/96. K[elvin]'.

Reflection

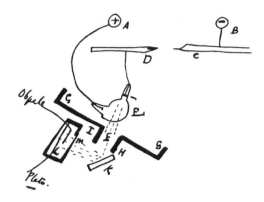

AB Poles of W[imshurst] M[achine]. *C.D.* Spark gap. *E* Vacu[u]m Tube. *F* X Rays. *GG* Heavy Lead screen 18^{in} × 12 into a 2^{in} *H* Hole at *H*[sic] into a lead Pip[e] one inch Long at *I*. *K* Speculum Mirror angle 45°. *L* Closed Metal box. *M* black card board Window.

This was the arrangement and I got clear and good Photographs which as soon as they are printed I will send you.

Reflection is positively Proved

I am tomorrow going to try whether there ⟨are⟩ is any difference as to the absorption of different colors by placing card board colored Red and black on the mirror. If this is the case with a ⟨convex?⟩ concave Mirror one ought to get Images of things as with light.

You may rely on all this as quite conclusive as far [as I have gone.]

Kelvin has written *Wimshurst Machine* above Blythswood's *WM* and has supplied *as I have gone* as the first words on the next page (not enclosed) of Blythswood's letter. The remainder of Blythswood's letter is not in the Kelvin Collection or the Kelvin Papers at Glasgow, but there are ten letters from him to Stokes in the Stokes Collection dating from March through May of 1896. Archibald Campbell Campbell (1835–1908) became the first Baron Blythswood in 1892 and a fellow of the Royal Society in 1907. He published a few scientific papers.

4 Blythswood, 'On the reflection of Röntgen light from polished speculum-metal mirrors', *Proc. Roy. Soc.*, **59** (1896), 330–2.

5 A. d'Arsonval, 'Observations au sujet de la photographie à travers les corps opaques', *Comptes Rendus*, **122** (2 March 1896), 500–1. Arsène d'Arsonval (1851–1940) was director of the laboratory for biophysics at the Collège de France from 1882 to 1910.

6 There is no correspondence between Stokes and d'Arsonval in the Stokes Collection.

7 See Kelvin (353).

556 STOKES to KELVIN, 13 March 1896
Kelvin Collection, S504

Lensfield Cottage, Cambridge, 13 March, 1896.[1]

MY DEAR KELVIN,

I have a good deal to write to you, and have not time to catch this post with it. I just write to say that I do not by any means think that Lord Blyth-[s]wood's experiment proves the reflexibility of the X-rays. It is equally consistent with the hypothesis of reflexibility or that of absorption and emission. The choice between these is of radical importance as to the nature of the Röntgen rays, and admits I think of pretty easy decision, indeed in one way very easy. So you had best not trouble him with the mercury experiment, at any rate till you hear agaon. [*sic*] For the arrangement must be essentially different from that he used in order to decide.

Yours sincerely,
G. G. STOKES

1 Kelvin's secretary has written on the envelope, 'Sir George Stokes. Received March 14 1896'.

557 STOKES to KELVIN, 13 and 14 March 1896
Kelvin Collection, S505

Lensfield Cottage, Cambridge, 13 March, 1896.

MY DEAR KELVIN,

I will say in the first place for fear I should forget it that the results obtained by Henri Becquerel, Silvanus Thompson and others[1] as to the emission of something which, so far as is known, has the properties of the Röntgen rays, by means of certain phosphori which have been merely exposed to ordinary light, not subjected to rediations [*sic*] produced directly or indirectly by an electric discharge, seem to me pretty well to give the coup de grâce to the idea of normal vibrations. For ordinary light contains no sensible quantity of Röntgen rays, inasmuch as, so far as our means of testing enable us to decide, its effects are quite stopped by screens of black paper &c., and yet it excited in certain phosphorescent bodies something which appears to be Röntgen's rays, or I should rather say excited them so as to give out such rays. Now it seems most improbable that the transversal vibrations of which light consists, be the source the sun, or clouds illuminated by the sun, or the flame of a candle, or even an electric discharge as such, should so set the constituent parts of molecules in a state of agitation such as to cause them to produce normal vibrations in the ether. We have however the analogy of calorescence in support of the supposition that they might give rise to agitations of shorter periods that [*sic*] the exciting vibrations.

Now for reflection. There are experiments seeming to indicate reflection of the X-rays made, both by Röntgen himself, by MM. Imbert & Bertin-Sans, and by Lord Blythswood.[2] These however, so far as the statements as to results yet made (such statements at least as I have come across) go [*sic*] admit of explanation on two totally ⟨diss⟩ different suppositions; namely, (1) that the X-rays are reflected, (2) that they are absorbed by the metal, and that the metal then emits other X-rays, not necessarily, or even probably, of just the same refrangibility as the exciting rays. On supposition (2) I should rather have expected that the exciting rays and the X-rays given out would rather be related in the way that ordinary rays exciting a solar phosphorus are related to the rays that it gives out.

The two suppositions are radically different, and lead to wholly different ideas as to the relation of the X-rays to matter.

Supposition (1) further devides [sic] itself into (1.a.), regular reflection and (1.b.) reflection like that of light by ground glass.

Lord Blythswood's arrangement would not distinguish between these three suppositions, which are respectively analogous to (1.a.) reflection from a looking glass; 1 (1.b.) [sic] reflection of light from white paper; (2) emission of radiant heat from a body (suppose blackened card) which had been warmed by radiant heat.

A modification of Lord Blythswood's arrangement would serve to distinguish between (1.a.) on the one hand and (1.b.) or (2) on the other. But as the results of MM. Imbert and Bertin-Sans pretty well exclude (1 a.), unless it be for a surface of mercury, and as it seems to me that (2) is the most probable, I hasten to mention what had occurred to me for testing this.

Use a machine, be it a Wimshurst or an induction coil, that does not discharge too rapidly, say not more that [sic] 5 or 6 per second. Use for test, not a photographic plate, but a powerfully phosphorescent substance of which the phosphorescence ceases almost instantaneously when the exciting rays are cut off, such as several of the platinocyanides, or several of the salts of uranium. Any one of these would do. Arrange matters as was done by MM. Imbert and Bertin-Sans, or by Lord Blythswood, only the object must not be shut in on all sides, as it has to be viewed through a tube, blackened inside to defend the eye from stray light. The object is protected from any light coming from the mirror by a screen of black paper. The observer being in position, looking at the phosphorus, let the machine play. If the X-rays are reflected, whether regularly or irregularly, the phosphorus will show an intermittent illumination. If it does not, we must conclude that the effects which have been observed have been erroneously attributed to reflection, and that they are really due to absorption and emission. In that case I should expect that when the machine began to play, at first no illumination would be seen, but as the play went on luminosity would slowly come on (if not too faint to be seen) and would approximate asymptotically to a maximum; and if the machine were now stopped the luminosity would fade, probably I think not very rapidly. In the fading stage, if a not too thin screen of metal, such as lead or brass or zinc, were interposed between the mirror and the phosphorus, the illumination ought to cease, to be resumed when the screen was removed.

It is conceivable of course that the effect might be of very brief duration, even though it were one of absorption and radiation, like the transitory phosphorescence which is called fluorescence. Of course as regards the 'effect' I am not speaking of the test phosphorus, but of the mirror regarded as a phosphorus as regards X-light.

Should the experiment turn out as I expect, it would be interesting to see whether if a plate of metal, such as lead or platinum, when held for some time close to the spot in the exhausted bulb on which the kathodic 'rays' fell, would when quickly carried into a dark room render luminous a crystal, say, of a platinocyanide, which was laid on the metal, on the face which had been turned towards the bulb, and at the spot which was nearest to the green patch on the wall of the bulb. If the effect was too feeble to be shown by the luminosity of a phosphorus, it might perhaps be shown by means of a sensitive plate laid upon the metal, and after a sufficient sojourn developed.

March 14. So far last night, or rather the commencement of the small hours of the morning. I resume before breakfast.

In my proposal for distinguishing between reflection (whether regular or irregular) on the one hand and absorption and emission on the other, I have been supposing that on the latter hypothesis the emission would go on so long that its change may be looked on as secular, so that it would be sensibly constant over the interval from one discharge of the machine to the next, thought [sic] there might be sensible variations if the machine were worked for a minute then let rest for a minute, then worked for a minute, and so on.

As I have said, Lord Blyth[s]wood's arrangement does not distinguish between the three hypotheses (1 a.), (1 b.), (2), but with a change it may be used to distinguish between (1 a.) on the one hand and (1 b.) or (2) on the other. The failure to make the distinction as it stands depends on the identity of direction of the active rays on the three suppositions, or rather the identity of the place where they strike the sensitive plate, and that again depends in part on the object which limits the rays (invisible) of the beam being placed close to the sensitive plate. The following is the arrangement which I would propose if the result of the first experiment should be to show that the effect is due to reflection of some kind, and not, as at present seems to me the more probable, to absorption and emission.

For the sake of description I will suppose the plane of the paper in Lord Blythswood's figure, which I return herewith, to be horizontal. Limit somewhat the phosphorescent spot of the glass wall of the tube by a vertical aperture with cheeks of brass or lead, selecting the brightest part for that opposite to the aperture. Place a second aperture between the bulb abd [sic] the mirror, as close as may be to the mirror. Arrange the mirror so that the regularly reflected light shall be reflected, not to the middle of the black window, m, but a little to one side. Cover half, say the upper half, of the window by a plate of lead or brass or zinc. Now start the machine, and let it play for a suitable time. Now stop the machine. Shift the screen over *m* so as to cover the under half. Turn the mirror a little round a vertical axis so that the regularly reflected light shall fall to the other side of the middle of the window to what it did before, taking care that the intersection of the mirror by a line drawn through the middles of the two apertures shall be practically in the same point of space as before, at any rate that there shall be no sensible displacement in a direction perpendicular to the reflected rays, (a slight displacement in the direction of those rays would not much matter). Now start the machine, and let it play as before. Develop the plate.

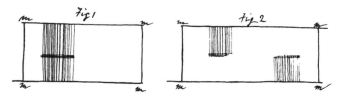

In the figures, *mmmm* denotes the projection of the black window on the plate. The ink shading denotes the umbra (it will appear as such in the developed negative) if the widths and distances are such that there is an umbra at all, the pencil shading the penumbra.[3]

If the result of the first experiment should be to show that the intermittence of the test phosphorus under its black paper screen is just the same whether the active rays come direct from the bulb or else from the reflecting (?) mirror, we must either discard the idea of absorption and emission, or attribute to the mirror a sort of fluorescence as to Röntgen rays. In that case the results would probably be different with mirrors of different metals, and some might be found in which there was a distinct ⟨in⟩ difference of intermittence between the effects of the direct and the reflected (?) rays. But I think this quasi-fluorescence very improbable.

Should there be reason to discard (2), and should the second experiment give a result as in fig. 1, it would then be right to try mercury in place of speculum metal.

Yours sincerely,
G. G. STOKES

P. S.[4] I was forgetting to say that I saw in a newspaper that Professor Joly[5] had obtained reflection of the Röntgen rays. The method was not stated, and I have not seen his paper. Röntgen's own experiments on reflection are at least as explicable on the supposition of absorption and emission.

I would not make the apertures very narrow, as unless (1 a.) be the thing, which does not seem likely, there would be great weakening from cutting off diffused light, and it would be discouraging after the trouble to get nothing at all on the plate. I should be disposed to choose the breadths of the two so as to leave a little umbra.

1 See letter 552, note 9, and letter 559, note 4.
2 See letter 543, note 2; letter 552, note 2; and letter 555, note 3.
3 In the two figures, the four or five central vertical lines – in each of the three sets of vertical lines – are in ink. The vertical lines on either side of them are in pencil.
4 Kelvin has written in the margin, 'Stokes Rec^d Mar 14'.
5 John Joly (1857–1933) became professor of geology at Trinity College, Dublin, in 1897. His finding that X-rays are reflected from the surface of mercury is reported in an article in *Nature* summarizing several men's work: 'Recent work with Röntgen rays', *Nature*, 53 (2 April 1896), 522–4.

558 KELVIN to STOKES, 16 March 1896
Stokes Collection, K315

The University.
Glasgow.
March 16. 1896.

DEAR STOKES,

When I sent you the leaf of Lord Blythswood's letter,[1] the photographs which he promised me had not come and I knew nothing more than the very slight statement on that leaf. I have since ⟨received⟩ seen the photographs and heard from him more of what he had done. He placed a circular disc of lead on the mirror and the photograph showed perfectly its shadow. He put a circle of pasteboard instead of the lead disc and it showed nothing. In one experiment he had two mirrors of speculum metal put together and the result showed the line between them quite clearly on the photograph. You will see thus that he has absolutely proved true reflection from his surfaces of polished speculum metal. I am asking him to send you prints of his photographs and I hope you will receive them in the course of a few days. I understand that he has sent prints with his paper[2] to the Royal Society. He is from home just now but will be back tomorrow and will try the mercury surface. It will be interesting to see whether it also reflects the Röntgen light. I think most probably all polished metallic surfaces will be found to give good reflection, but probably different metals in very different proportions: I suppose Aluminium very little. I should not be at all surprised if mercury gives much more than speculum metal. I hope Lord Blythswood will go on and try polished platinum, polished silver and polished gold. After having been an amateur in Mechanics and electrical experiments for many years he is delighted to be able now to do something for Science.

Yours very truly,
KELVIN

P.S. Since writing I have received the two photographs which I send you. I shall be obliged by your returning them at your leisure. The line of separation *AB* between the two mirrors is very faint but unmistakable.

1 See letter 555, note 3.
2 See letter 555, note 4.

559   STOKES to KELVIN, 16 and 19 March 1896
Kelvin Collection, S506

Lensfield Cottage, Cambridge, 16v [*sic*] March, 1896.[1]

MY DEAR KELVIN,

I think Röntgen's own experiments, as mentioned in his original paper,[2] conclusively disprove regular reflection. I feel confident that Lord Blythswood would have obtained the same results as he did if he had used speculum metal which was only ground, not polished. Thie [*sic*] leaves open the two alternatives of scattered reflection or absorption and emission. Röntgen himself regards the effect as analogous to reflection in a muddy medium. But I think there are very strong theoretical objections to this, and I feel a good deal of con [*sic*].

Resumed March, 19.[3] I had written so far when the letter 'e' in my machine broke down, and before I resumed I got your letter announcing Lord Blyth[s]wood's supposed result demonstrating regular reflection of the Röntgen rays. That led me off in a different direction, and then the actual photographs were a smashing blow to my 'con'. But now that it appears that the supposed result was due to Lord Blythswood's assistant having disobeyed his instructions, I may almost complete my word with 'fidence'. Well, I was going to say that I felt a good deal of confidence in the supposition that the supposed reflection obtained by Röntgen and others was due to a sort of phosphorescence or fluorescence of the metal as regards Röntgen rays.

H. Becquerel professes to have established the reflection. But in the first experiment C.R. p. 561, l. 9,[4] the steel mirror was close to the plate, and the result would be the same on the hypothesis of absorption and emission; and in the second, next par., the rays exciting the plate were not filtered through aluminium or black paper, and there is no evidence that he was working with the Röntgen rays at all; it may very well have been, and I am disposed to think it was, visible rays he was working with, in the sense in which invisible nebulae have been photographed by a long exposure.

Yours sincerely,
G. G. STOKES

1 Kelvin's secretary has written on the envelope (S507A in the Kelvin Collection), 'Sir George Stokes. Received March 20, 1896'.

2 See letter 543, note 2.

3 The next two letters are dated 17 March 1896.

4 H. Becquerel, 'Sur quelques propriétés nouvelles des radiations invisibles émises par divers corps phosphorescents', *Comptes Rendus*, 122 (9 March 1896), 559–64.

560   STOKES to KELVIN, 17 March 1896
Kelvin Collection, S507

Lensfield Cottage, CambridgC, 17 March, 1896.[1]

MY DEAR KELVIN,

The pull-wire of the letter that lies between d & f got broken, and I have sent it to London to be repaired, so please excuse e doing duty for it for the time.

I have just received your letter of yesterday with the ⟨concloscd⟩ enclosed photographs from Lord Blythswood, which I return. They furnish me with the first unmistakeable proof of the regular reflection of the Röntgen rays that I have come across. From Röntgen's own statements, combined with what I have seen elsewhere, I was inclined to think that they did not undergo regular reflection. I had seen in a newspaper a sta[t]ement that Joly[2] had proved their reflexibility. I knew he was a very good hand, but I had not, nor have I now, seen the evidence.

Lord Blythswood's results open up some very interersting [*sic*] enquiries.

(I) What degree of imperfection of polish will the Röntgen rays tolerate? If they are of very high frequency we might expect that their regularity of reflection would be interfered with by a degree of imperfection of polish which would be ins[e]nsible to light, so that with light the polish would appear perfect. If on the other hand their wave length be greater than that of light, a speculum very finely ground which would not suffice to give a regular reflection of light might yet give one of the Röntgen rays. This would bear on the question, Are they normal or transversal?

Again, Is the reflection of the nature of that of light on glass implying a considerable diff[er]ence of velocity of propagation, or is it of the nature of the quasi-metallic reflection shown by certain intensely absorbing substances, such as various aniline colours? This would require an axamination [*sic*] of a good many different substances. But I must not trouble you with the writing of my lame machine. Moreover I cannot get on so fast with it, having to think a bit instead of going on almost without thinking about the manipulation.

Yours sincerely,
G. G. STOKES

1 Kelvin's secretary has written on the envelope, 'Sir George Stokes. Received March 18. 1896'.

2 See letter 557, note 5.

561 KELVIN to STOKES, 17 March 1896
Stokes Collection, K316

The University.
Glasgow.
March 17. 1896.

DEAR STOKES,

I am sorry to say there is a doubt after all as to the photographs I sent you yesterday. Lord Blythswood has just been in to tell me that he found the two lead discs had been laid, not, according to his instructions, on the mirror; but inside the dark box and close to the receptive plate. So that photograph proves nothing. The faint straight line on the other which I sent you would be decisive in proving regular reflection if it corresponds properly to the border line between the two mirrors.

Blythswood has returned home today and is going to try, tomorrow if possible, the experiment with the lead discs placed truly according to his former instructions. He is going to send the result to me and I shall write or telegraph to the R.S. if it either confirms or disproves the reflection which is the subject of his paper.[1] He has been troubled with the vacuum tubes breaking, and is not quite sure whether he will be able to manage the experiment tomorrow.

Yours,
KELVIN

1 See letter 555, note 4.

562 STOKES to KELVIN, 23 March 1896
Kelvin Collection, S508

Lensfield Cottage, Cambridge, 23 March, 1896.[1]

MY DAER [*sic*] KELVIN,

I take for granted that Lord Blythswood did not get the same result when the experiment was repeated according to his directions as he seemed to have got at first, or I should have heard of it. I was not however at the R.S. when his paper[2] was read. So far as evidence has come before me at present, I do not believe that the X rays are reflected by metals, at any rate that if reflected at all it is only in a small proportion. As far as I know, I think it most probable that the apparent reflection, which Röntgen regarded as similar to reflection in a turbid medium, is really of the nature of phosphorescence or fluorescence with regard to the Röntgen rays. It would not I think be difficult to test this experimentally.

Hutchinson[3] of Pembroke has verified Becquerel's result that certain compounds of uranium after being exposed to ordinary light or during exposure to ordinary light, give out something that affects a photographic plate across aluminium foil. The mineral scheelite (tungstate of calcium) fluoresces under the action of the Rontgen rays.

Yours sincerely,
G. G. STOKES

1 Kelvin's secretary has written on the envelope, 'Sir George Stokes Received March 24, 1896'.
2 See letter 555, note 4.
3 Arthur Hutchinson (1866–1937) placed in the first class in part II of the natural sciences tripos in 1888 and was a fellow of Pembroke from 1892 to 1928 and master from 1928 to 1937. His verification is summarized in 'Recent work with Röntgen rays', *Nature* 53 (2 April 1896), 522–4. This article notes work by several men including Hutchinson, whose findings are reported on page 524. Hutchinson referred to Edison's telegram given in the next letter, note 2.

563   KELVIN to STOKES, 25 March 1896
Stokes Collection, K317

The University,
Glasgow.
March 25. 1896.

DEAR STOKES,

I enclose a copy of a note which I sent to Sir Joseph Lister to be read immediately after the reading of Lord Blythswood's paper on Thursday last.[1] I hope you will not disapprove of my reference to you which it contains. I have not yet heard from Blythswood that he has made the promised confirmatory experiments. Until they are made we cannot feel confidence in the conclusion to be drawn from his experiments communicated last Thursday. He is, as you will no doubt understand an amateur experimenter, but I shall be very glad if with his grand apparatus he brings out some really important results. I am much interested in what you tell me of what Hutchinson of Pembroke has been doing. You may have seen in 'Nature'[2] that I had a telegram last week from Edison announcing the discovery of the merits of Tungstate of Calcium. A postscript to my note communicating it to 'Nature' will no doubt appear tomorrow.[3]

Yours,
KELVIN

1 For Blythswood's paper, see letter 555, note 4. The published version (Kelvin (353)) of the enclosed draft is substantially the same as the draft except for one sentence. Whereas the draft reads:

This, as Sir George Stokes has suggested in letters which I have received from him in the last few days, might be due to the reflecting surface though polished for ordinary light being rugged for light of the exceedingly short wave length which may be attributed with probability to the Röntgen X rays: or due to fluorescence induced in the surface by the X-light; or something analogous to cal[or]escence,

the published version reads:

This, as Sir George Stokes has suggested in letters which I have received from him in the last few days, might either be due, as indicated by MM. Imbert and Bertin-Sans, to the reflecting surface, though polished for ordinary light, being rugged for light of the exceedingly short wave-length which may be attributed with probability to the Röntgen X rays; or else to a sort of phosphorescence, or possibly fluorescence, with regard to X light, produced in the substance of the mirror.

See the next four letters, especially the next.

2 Edison's telegram to Kelvin reads: 'Just found calcium tungstate properly crystallised gives splendid fluorescence with Röntgen rays far exceeding platino-cyanide rendering photographs unnecessary'. (*Nature*, 53 (19 March 1896), 470.)

3 I do not find this postscript in *Nature* for either March 26th or April 2nd.

564 STOKES to KELVIN, 26 March 1896
Kelvin Collection, S510

Lensfield Cottage, Cambridge, 26 March, 1896.[1]

MY DEAR KELVIN,

Thanks for the copy of the note you added to Lord Blythswood's paper.[2] I had not noticed anything on the second of his photographs that you sent me.

What you said about my views does not exactly represent them. In the first place as to the possible roughness for X-rays, though the surface is polished for ordinary light, I think that as the idea was mentioned in print by MM. Imbert and Bertin-Sans[3] it would be proper to mention them. I did not myself think fluorescence so likely as phosphorescence[4], though if experiments instituted with a view to testing X-phosphorescence should lead to a negative result, the failure might be due to the phosphorescence being so brief as to deserve the name of fluorescence, and it is conceivable that the thing might yet be established by dealing experimentally in accordance with that supposition, so that I did not wish to exclude fluorescence. As phosphorescence is not like the metallic reflection of gold or ⟨aniline dyestuffs⟩ aniline colouring matters dependent on what takes place at a distance from the surface comparable with a fraction of a wave length, I think it would be better, to avoid confusion in the minds of persons who are not very well up to the subject, to avoid the word 'surface' in speaking of it. Lastly, what I said of calorescence related to a different phenomenon altogether, namely, the giving out of X-light as a result of merely exposing s [*sic*] certain phosphori to ordinary daylight.[5] I would therefore leave that out.[6]

If not too late, I would suggest to read instead of 'as Sir George Stokes . . . . or calorescence' the following: – 'as Sir George Stokes has suggested in letters which I have received from him in the last few days, might either be due, as indicated by MM. Imbert and Bertin-Sans, to the reflecting surface though polished for ordinary light being rugged for light of the exceedingly short wave length which may be attributed with probability to the Röntgen rays, or else to a sort of phosphorescence or possibly fluorescence with regard to X-light produced in the material from which an attempt was made to obtain a regular reflection of the Rontgen rays.'

My mind has rather turned from the idea of excessively rapid vibrations excited within molecules, or in groups of neighbouring molecules, by the impact (that term being supposed to be generalised from its mere mechanical signification) of molecules shot from the kathode on the wall of the bulb, rapid vibrations which communicate themselves to the ether, to the idea of a vast succession of independent pulses in the ether, each charged molecule producing such a pulse when it gets to the wall. Contrasted with the other idea, this would be like the sound arising from the hedge[7] fire of a regiment as contrasted with the ring of rapidly (I mean as to succession, not velocity) struck bells. This falls in with the almost complete absence of reflection and refraction *provided* we suppose that the diminished velocity of propagation of light in Glass, water &c. as compared with vacuum is due to the ether and matter forming a compound vibrating system, the complex system of molecules vibrating harmonically in unison with the ether.[8]

Yours sincerely,
G. G. STOKES

P.S. I will write to the Assistant Secretary of the R.S.[9] asking him to defer the sending to press of your note till he hears from you.[10]

What I said with reference to the analogy of calorescence had reference to Becquerel's experiment[11] showing that the mere exposure to ordinary light of certain solar phosphori caused them to give out something that affected a photographic plate through aluminium foil or black paper.[12] It did not refer to the diffused reflection (if reflection it be) from metals.

1 Kelvin's secretary has written on the envelope, 'Sir George Stokes. Received March 27. 1896. Sent to Lord Rayleigh March 27. Received back by K[elvin] March 29'.

2 Kelvin (353), added to Blythswood's paper cited in letter 555, note 4.

3 See letter 552, note 2.

4 Kelvin has underlined *fluorescence* and *phosphorescence* and written in the margin, '*I* always think of fluorescence as *being* ⟨simply⟩ phosphorescence of very short duration. K Mar 27'. *Simply* is written very lightly and appears to have been erased.

5 Kelvin has drawn two lines down the left side of the letter (from *related to* to *ordinary daylight*) and written in the margin, 'This is just what I understood Stokes to mean. K'.

6 Kelvin has written in the margin, 'I don't see why, but I do so. K'.

7 Kelvin has underlined *hedge* and written in the margin, 'Though a retired Captain of 1st L.R. rifle volunteers I don't know what this means. K'.

8 Kelvin has drawn a line down the left side of the letter (from *forming* to *ether*) and written in the margin, 'This is exactly as I have represented Stokesian theory in my Baltimore Lectures.

Would you (R) care to have an advance copy of 112 pages which have been in type for 8 years. If so write a P.C. to the Pitt Press and say I wish them sent to you. K'.

9 Robert William Frederick Harrison was assistant secretary of the Royal Society from 16 January 1896 to 1920.

10 Kelvin has written in the margin, '⟨He will get the corrected proof tomorrow morning from me. K⟩ No. I am sending two proofs to Stokes, one [of] them with alternative corrections and he is to send the one he chooses to Rix'. Actually, as implied by the previous note, Herbert Rix's term as assistant secretary ended on 16 January 1896. But see letter 574.

11 Kelvin has inserted here, '(and Sylvanus' [sic] few days later one)'. For Becquerel and Thompson, see letter 552, note 9.

12 Kelvin has drawn a line down the left side of this paragraph and written in the margin, 'I knew this quite well'.

565 STOKES to KELVIN, 26 March 1896
Kelvin Collection, S509

3 Trinity St Cambridge[1]
26 March 1896

MY DEAR KELVIN,

I think Lord Blythswood's photo with the 2 plane mirrors goes far to prove that the regular reflection must at any rate be very small compared with some other effect, be it scattered reflection or phosphorescence of the metal. It is a

pity he did not incline the mirrors a little to one another thus

or thus ⌣ as in the one case we ought to have a central band

of double effect and in the other of nil effect so far as regular reflection was concerned. I suppose he adjusted them to have their reflecting surfaces parallel.

The 'hedge fire' is common to the two very different ideas I broached; but in other respects the two are very different: according to the first the struck glass wall of the bulb is like a target which vibrates from the impact of the bullets; according to the second the Röntgen rays are an effect in the ether alone, arising from the charged molecules reaching the wall, and the vibrations of the target are a concomitant effect, rendered visible to the eyes by the phosphorescence of the glass, Röntgen's results[2] with 1. Crookes' bulb 2. black paper or wood 3. photographic gelatine film (or was it glass?) 4. aluminium foil 5. pieces of Pt, Cu, Zn seem more favourable to the first view.

Yours sincerely
G. G. STOKES

1 Kelvin's secretary has written on the envelope, 'Sir Geo. Stokes. Received March 27. 1896. Sent to Lord Rayleigh March 27. Received back by K. March 29. Second letter of yesterday'.
2 See letter 543, note 2.

566 KELVIN to STOKES, 27 March 1896
Stokes Collection, K318
Partially printed in Thompson, II, 961.

The University.
Glasgow.
March 27. 1896.

DEAR STOKES,

I am exceedingly interested in all you have been been [sic] writing to me about phosphorescence, fluorescence and calorescence. I enclose two corrected proofs[1] and an empty envelope. Put one of the two, whichever you please, into it, not both as this would puzzle Mr Rix. I plead for the shorter one giving your three possibilities as stated in your former letter. My understanding of the statement in print is precisely in every detail what you describe in your first letter of yesterday: and I would be sorry to see it included but you are the judge and must decide what you think best.

I have instructed the Pitt Press to send you advance corrected proofs, (which have been in print 8 years,) of the ⟨the⟩ first 112 pages of my Baltimore Lectures. You will find the formula I gave you a few weeks ago on page 106,[2] also a good deal of fluorescence and phosphorescence jangling about in one half or other of most of the lectures. I am afraid you will be very much shocked to see such a rigmarole as having been given in University lectures. I hope it will not plague you to have them in your hands and to keep them till you get the rest of the volume from the Pitt Press which I hope may be within a year from now.

Yours
KELVIN

1 Kelvin (353).
2 See letter 548.

567 STOKES to KELVIN, 27 March 1896
Kelvin Collection, S511

3 Trinity St Cambridge 27 March 1896[1]

MY DEAR KELVIN,

My chief wish was to *omit* the calorescence, because I don't think it applicable to this phenomenon, though I *do* to that of H. Becquerel (uranium salt emitting X rays merely from exposure to ordinary light).[2] I have therefore adopted the longer revision,[3] except that I have adopted an improvement in your shorter revision by writing after the words 'produced in the' the words 'substance of the mirror' instead of 'material from which an attempt was made to obtain a regular reflection of the Röntgen rays'.

We go home on Monday.

I think Rontgen's 2nd exper^t in (8) sets aside calorescence for *this* phenomenon.[4]

Yours sincerely
G. G. STOKES

1 Kelvin has written on the reverse of the letter, 'Stokes Rec^d Mar 30'. The envelope provisionally placed with the letter is post marked 29 March 1896, but Kelvin has written on it, 'Stokes Rec^d March 5'.
2 See letter 552, note 9.
3 Kelvin (353).
4 See letter 543, note 2.

568   STOKES to KELVIN, 31 March 1896
Kelvin Collection, S512

Lensfield Cottage, Cambridge, 31 March, 1896.[1]

MY DEAR KELVIN,

Have you seen in the Comptes Rendus for March 23, page 718 of the volume, that Prince Galitzine and M. Karnojitsky[2] [*sic*] have found (assuming the correctness of the experiments) that traces of polarisation by tourmalines have been found in the X-light? J. J. Thomson told me some time ago that he had got indications of polarisation, but later he said that they had repeated the experiment, and could not be sure of the result. I have always myself been in favour of transversal vibrations of very high frequency.

I have had a long letter from Lord Blythswood,[3] and have written a long letter to him, followed by a shorter one going tonight. I think his own experiments disprove more than a very minute reflection, if any at all, and the point is to make out the nature of the process by which X-rays are sent back ⟨to⟩ from the mirror. To me it seems most probable that it is by X-phosphorescence or X-fluorescence. I told Lord Blythswood of one experiment I should like very much to see tried.

Yours sincerely,
G. G. STOKES

1 Kelvin's secretary has written on the envelope, 'Sir George Stokes. Received April 1896'.
2 B. Galitzine and A. de Karnojitzky (as spelled in *Comptes Rendus*), 'Recherches concernant les propriétés des rayons X', *Comptes Rendus*, 122 (23 March 1896), 717–18. Aleksandr Nikolaevič Karnožickij (as given by the *Royal Society Catalogue of Scientific Papers*) and Boris Borisovich Golitsyn (as given by the *Dictionary of Scientific Biography*). Golitsyn (1862–1916) graduated from Strasbourg and began teaching at the University of Moscow in 1891, eventually becoming known for his work in seismology.
3 See Blythswood to Stokes, 28 March 1896, Stokes Collection, B454.

Lensfield Cottage, Cambridge, 1 April, 1896.[1]

MY DEAR KELVIN,

If there be anything in the views of M. Lafay (C.R., p. 713)[2] the thing is most important as regards the nature of the X-light. But I cannot help thinking that there may have been a hitch in the experimental arrangement to which the result may have been due. The second screen was presumably insulated from earth, being connected with the negative terminal of the inductorium, which I suppose was not to earth.

The only way I see of explaining the result obtained without supposing that the author has hit on something altogether new is as follows. Nothing is said as to the leads from the inductorium to the second screen, on which presumably the silver foil rested, nor of the electrostatic capacity of the screen and leads. At each break of contact of the inductorium there would be a to-and-fro current from the terminal to the screen. There would be reaction between this current and the powerful magnetism of the field, and this current would be modified by reversing the current actuating the electro-magnet. The inductorium works both the Crookes tube and the second screen, and a change in the to-and-fro current to the screen might make a change in the current of the Crookes which might have the effect of causing a minute change in the place where the 'kathode rays' inpinged [sic] on the glass; beside which the magnetic force consequent on the screen current might have an influence on the kathode rays, though perhaps not much, as the reversal of the current of the electro-magnet made no difference when the screen was not temporarily electrified.

This notion of a possible way of dispensing with the author's idea as to the cause of the result might be tested by keeping the second screen negatively electrified by insulating it (it doubtless was insulated except from the terminal of the inductorium) and connecting it with the inner coating of a negatively charged Leyden jar, which is kept charged independently so far as may be necessary to make up for the leakage produced by the Röntgen rays.

The slits were far too broad to determine the position of the shadow of the wire merely by them; much must have depended on the place where the kathode rays struck the glass wall; and as the Crookes was about 45 mm. from the wire, and the wire was at a distance from the phtotgraphic [sic] plate equal to 150 mm. plus the distance (not stated) of the poles of the e.m. from the wire, any minute displacement of the point of impact of the kathode rays would be much magnified on the photographic plate.

I am curious to know what you think of Lafay's experiment.

Yours sincerely,
G. G. STOKES

1 Kelvin's secretary has written on the envelope, 'Sir George Stokes. re. Experiment of M. Lafay "Comptes Rendus" March 23 p. 713. Received ⟨M⟩ April 2. 1896'.

2 A. Lafay, 'Sur un moyen de communiquer aux rayons de Röntgen la propriété d'être déviés par l'aimant', *Comptes Rendus*, **122** (23 March 1896), 713–15. Lafay was professor of physics at the École Polytechnique.

570 KELVIN to STOKES, 4 April 1896
Stokes Collection, K319

The University,
Glasgow.
April 4. 1896.

DEAR STOKES,

I think that most probably it will turn out as you say you 'cannot help thinking that there has been a hitch in Lafay's experimental arrangement.'[1] It does seem almost infinitely improbable that the Röntgen X-rays should in passing through a thin silver foil, if and not unless this foil is negatively electrified, acquire a property of being altered in direction by magnetic force perpendicular to their direction.

I think it quite likely that when every detail of Lafay's arrangement is sufficiently described his supposed result would be found nugatory. But if it still holds good it will be intensely interesting and must be scrutinised in the way you propose and in any other way that may occur according to the circumstances.

Yours
KELVIN

1 See the previous letter, note 2.

571 STOKES to KELVIN, 4 April [1896][1]
Kelvin Collection, S514

Lensfield Cottage, Cambridge, 4 April, 1886.[2]

MY DEAR KELVIN,

I am afraid I made a silly oversight in a proposal I made to you, and suggested you should send on to Lord Blythswood, relative to a proposal for distinguishing between regular reflection on the one hand and diffuse reflection or else phosphorescence on the other.[3] I drew a figure relating to it like this.

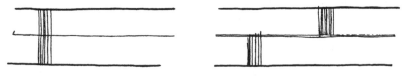

I hope you have not communicated it to Lord Blythswood.[4] If you have, please write him a line to retract it.

I determined the place of the band on the screen due to regular reflection by joining the virtual image of the first slit or aperture with the second, and producing the joining line to meet the screen or photographic plate, while the place of the shadow, or rather projection, of the second slit was got by joining the spot where the light limited by the first slit fell on the mirror with the second slit, and producing the joining line to meet the photographic plate. I stupidly forgot that there were no regularly reflected rays that could come as drawn from the image, as the part of the mirror from which they would be reflected is in shade of the cheek of the first slit. If you should have communicated this proposal to Lord Blythswood please to write to him at once to stop it, lest by any chance he should take trouble in trying an experiment which must be abortive.

I called, I think, your attention to a paper in C.R., p. 718,[5] showing polarisation of the X-rays. This disposes of the idea of normal vibrations.[6]

Lord Blythswood has sent me 3 positive copies of a photo munbered [sic] 116, the same I believe as you have had.[7] It shows a disk of about 1.6 in. diameter in the middle *very* slightly more luminous than the surrounding field. I believe I could not see it, or could only just see it, in the photo you sent. In the first he sent me I felt almost certain I saw it; the two later copies, one especially showed it in a way that left no doubt. The photos prove that there is a minute regular reflection, but that the bulk of the light is returned by the mirror by some other process. I have suggested to him an experiment with a view to try whether ⟨is⟩ it is by X-phosphorescence.

Yours sincerely,
G. G. STOKES

1 Stokes has misdated the letter.
2 Kelvin's secretary has written on the envelope, 'Sir Geo. Stokes. Rec^d & Ans^d April 5. 1896'. Kelvin has written at the top of the letter, 'Rec^d & answ^d Ap 5 (by Sec^y F.!) no copy kept'.
3 Kelvin has written in the margin, 'answ^d'.
4 Kelvin has underlined this sentence, drawn a line down the left side of this paragraph, and written in the margin, 'no, but did give your suggestion to try inclining one of his mirrors rel^{vy} to the other'.
5 See letter 568, note 2.
6 Kelvin has written at this point, '(Prince Galitzine & Mr de Karlojitzky [sic][)]', and in the margin, 'Yes, aeolotropy of absorptivity quite expectable. Result decisive for transverse!'
7 Kelvin has written in the margin, 'No, I have not seen this – glad you find it proves a small proportion of regularly reflected light'.

April 5/96
The University,
Glasgow.

DEAR STOKES —

I had not communicated to Lord Blythswood the plan to which you refer in your letter of yesterday so there is nothing to correct or retract. I did give him your suggestion about inclining one of the mirrors relatively to the other slightly in either direction round the line of intersection of their planes, and I hope he will do this. It will give a very clear and decisive test.

I have not seen his number⟨s⟩ 116 yet. I am glad to hear that you think it proves a small proportion of the light to be regularly reflected!

I see several people (one of them, if I remember right, Tesla)[1] have been publishing results which they think proves reflection, but none of them even thinking of the question of whether it is regular reflection or induced fluorescent glow that they have got.

I read carefully the C.R. page 718[2] to which you referred me and wondered that, when the velocity of the X rays is so nearly equal in metals, glasses, wood &c there could be any effect in the way of double refraction. But I saw that as the Tourmaline effect depends on colotropy of absorptivity, and as there are great differences of absorptivity in different substances for the X rays, we may quite expect that Tourmaline could be a polarizer, & a test for polarization, of the X rays. And the paper in the C.R. seems to show a thoroughly good inves⟨i⟩tigation, so I suppose we may consider it as settled by the Prince Galitzine and Mr de Karnojitzky (? Poles) that Röntgen rays consist of transverse vibrations!! I am glad we had both come to that conclusion as probable.

Yrs
KELVIN[3]

1 Nikola Tesla (1856–1943), who was born in Austria-Hungary and became an American citizen, is known for inventing an alternating current motor which dispensed with commutators. I have found no reference to a paper by him on X-rays.
2 See letter 568, note 2.
3 Except for Kelvin's signature, the letter is in Lady Kelvin's hand, and she has written at the end of the letter, 'My love to Lady Stokes! FAK'.

Lensfield Cottage, Cambridge, 6 April, 1896.[1]

MY DEAR KELVIN,

Röntgen[2] himself recognises the power of metals, especially (among those tried) zinc, to send back x-light otherwise than by regular reflection. He seems most inclined to favour the idea of a sort of molecular reflection. I do not give in to the idea of molecular reflection. The alternative lies between reflection from a rough surface and X-phosphorescence or X-fluorescence, fluorescence being merely phosphorescence of very brief duration. I look on Lord Blythswood's photograph No. 116, a copy is enclosed, as showing that there *is* regular reflection, albeit very small, from polished speculum metal. In this photo a wide aperture in lead (aperture say $1\frac{1}{2}$ in. diameter) in the centre of curvature of a ⟨convex⟩ concave mirror of speculum metal allowed the X-light from a Crookes tube to fall on the speculum, which was slightly inclined, just to separate the reflected light, if any, from the incident, and the reflected was received at the same distance on a photographic plate, passing through blackened card and aluminium. The image of the aperture is faintly seen, but unmistakeably, though the difference between this and the ground is very small compared with the latter, as shown by the difference between the ground and the shadow of the wheel. This photo in my mind pretty well disposes of the idea of scattered reflection, and leaves nothing for it as regards the diffused light (X-light) but phosphorescence.

I think we may apply Fresnel's formulae to the reflection, even though the material be metal, for metals are not excessively opaque with regard to the X-light, so that we must regard them as optically vitreous. The intensity of the reflected light would therefore be $\dfrac{(\mu-1)^2}{(\mu+1)^2}$,[3] that of the incident being unity. Röntgen got a probable though somewhat doubtful indication of refraction through aluminium, though the index can hardly be as great at [*sic*] 1.05. 1.05 would give at a perpendicular incidence a reflection of only 0.0006, which in the photograph would be utterly swallowed up by the diffused X-light. But the index for speculum metal would in all probability be greater than for aluminium. If it were 1.2, the intensity of the reflected [light] would be 0.01, which seems something like what the photo indicates.[4] I think I will propose to him to repeat the experiment with the difference of using a much smaller hole. Suppose the hole had been of $1\frac{1}{2}$ in. diameter, and were reduced to $\frac{1}{4}$ in. The reflection would be as strong, but the image would have the 1/36th of the former area, whereas for the diffused light the area on the plate would be the same as before, but the intensity only the 1/36th of what it had been.

I think it would be possible to show polarisation of X-light by an arrangement shightly [*sic*] different from that of Malus for glass.

Yours sincerely,
G. G. STOKES

1 Kelvin's secretary has written on the envelope, 'Sir Geo. Stokes. Rec^d April 7. 1896'.
2 See letter 543, note 2.
3 Stokes has made a correction in the denominator, deleting one or two symbols now illegible.
4 Stokes has written in the margin, 'I have another copy of the photo'.

574   KELVIN to STOKES, 24 April 1896
Stokes Collection, K321

28, Chester Square,
S.W.
April 24. 1896.

DEAR STOKES,

I enclose a copy of a note I have just written for 'Nature'.[1] I hope you won't disapprove of the way I have used your name. It leaves it open for us if you will agree, to write a joint note for the R.S. on the nature of the X-rays.

I was exceedingly sorry to miss the opportunity yesterday of having some talk with you. I wish I had thought at the right time to ask you to wait for a little when I went upstairs with Sir Joseph Lister to shake hands with Mr Rix and say good-bye to him as Assistant-Secretary. But I hope we shall have a good talk at Cambridge, in May, or, still better, will you not dine with us here before the Gentlemen's Conversazione on the 6th?

Yours
KELVIN

P.S. Don't you think Galitzin[e] and Karnojitzky[2] are to be trusted as having *seen* ⟨the⟩ an effect by crossed tourmalines, though two or three others have tried for it and *not seen* it?

1 Kelvin (350) in *Nature*, **54** (1896), 12–13. There are a variety of small differences between the draft and the published version, but the three most important changes are: (1) in the footnote on page 13, *exceedingly* replaces *almost infinitely*; (2) in the footnote, the reference to Sagnac has been added; and (3) at the end of the article, the passage after the semicolon, beginning 'but if viewed', has been added. See letters 576 and 577. Sagnac's article cited by Kelvin in his (350) is 'Sur la diffraction et la polarisation des rayons de M. Röntgen', *Comptes Rendus*, **122** (1896), 783–5. Georges Marc Marie Sagnac (1869–1928) was an assistant in physics at the University of Paris from 1894 to 1900 and later was professor of physics at Lille and then Paris.
2 See letter 568, note 2.

671

575 Stokes to Kelvin, 25 April 1896
Kelvin Collection, S516

Lensfield Cottage, Cambridge, 25 April, 1896.[1]

My dear Kelvin,

I hope you will consider seriously whether you cannot give us an address at the Victoria Institute.[2] You may write it or not write it as you like. There is a good reporter present, so that if you prefer not to write it you can have it well taken down, and can afterwards correct the press. You can choose your own subject, and to a considerable extent your own time.

This morning's post brought me a very interesting paper from Röntgen, his No. 2.[3] I dare say he has sent you one, but as it probably would go to Glasgow you would not have got it yet. I have not yet heard from Lord Blythswood, that is, since he was here, but I dare say he is getting on. An idea occurred to me which I suggested to him to try. At a nearly perpendicular incidence it is only a very minute fraction of the X-rays coming from speculum metal on which X-rays fall that come by regular reflection. The rest come in some other way, which I think most probably is a sort of X-phosphorescence. The idea is that as reflection is a surface effect and phosphorescence is a substance effect, we might get nearly rid of the latter so as better to study the former by using a reflecting film of silver or gold chemically deposited on glass, or perhaps aluminium with a film of gold or silver on it.

Yours sincerely
G. G. STOKES

1 Kelvin's secretary has written on the envelope, 'Sir Geo Stokes. Received April 26. 1896. Answered April 29 1896'.
2 Kelvin did not address the Victoria Institute until the next year. (Kelvin (363).)
3 W. C. Röntgen, 'Ueber eine neue Art von Strahlen', *Sitzungsberichte der Physikalisch-Medizinischen Gesellschaft zu Würzburg* (1896), 11–16, 17–19, translated into English in *The Electrician*, **36** (24 April 1896), 850–1.

576 Kelvin to Stokes, 29 April 1896
Stokes Collection, K322

28, Chester Square,
S.W.
April 29. 1896.

Dear Stokes

I am very sorry but I am afraid I have absolutely no subject at present on which I could give an address at the Victoria Institute, as I am wholly occupied with endeavours to bring out my Baltimore Lectures and some other work too long delayed, none of which contains anything that would be suitable towards such an address. Besides at present and I am afraid for many weeks to come I must keep very quiet as Sir Joseph Lister is quite imperative that I must keep my troubled leg as much as possible in a horizontal position and avoid all fatigues as much as possible.

I enclose a corrected proof of the little note for 'Nature' of which I sent you a press-copy last Friday.[1] I have made a little alteration on the footnote of which I have no doubt you will approve. I did not like the 'almost infinitely' myself; but, your name being mentioned in the same line, I hope you will approve of the 'exceedingly.'

I have been reading with great interest in the 'Electrician' of last week Röntgen's second paper[2] to which you call my attention.

He seems to make out (though as he says himself not quite confidently) that the conductivity-producing effect of the Röntgen light is in the air and not in solid paraffin. What do you think of this?

Yours
KELVIN

1 Kelvin (350).
2 See the previous letter, note 3.

577 STOKES to KELVIN, 30 April 1896
Kelvin Collection, S517

30 April 1896[1]
The Athenaeum
Pall Mall S.W.

MY DEAR KELVIN,

I had not much hope that you would be able to give us (Vict. Inst.) a lecture but I thought I would try.

I return you the proof.[2] I think 'exceedingly' is an improvement.

It is remarkable how full the Comptes Rendus are of the Röntgen rays and how little there is in Wiedemann's Annalen.[3] At the R.S. today I looked over the numbers for this year and found only one paper – by Goldhammer[4] – who favours transversal vibrations of high frequency.

J. J. Thomson some time ago made out that the electricity-discharging effect of the X rays depends on the air an[d] other surrounding gas.[5]

Yours sincerely
G. G. STOKES

1 Kelvin's secretary has written on the envelope, 'Received May 1. 1896'.
2 Kelvin (350).
3 Gustav Heinrich Wiedemann (1826–99), professor of physical chemistry and later of physics

at Leipzig from 1871 until his death, took over editorship of the *Annalen der Physik und Chemie* after Poggendorff's death in 1877.

4 Dmitrij Aleksandrovič Goldhammer, 'Sur la nature des X-rayons', *Annalen der Physik und Chemie*, 57 (1896), 635–8. Goldhammer (1860–1922) was professor of physics at Kazan.

5 See J. J. Thomson and E. Rutherford, 'On the passage of electricity through gases exposed to Röntgen rays', *Phil. Mag.*, 42 (1896), 392–407.

578 KELVIN to STOKES, 1 May 1896
Stokes Collection, K323

28, Chester Square,
S.W.
May 1. 1896.

DEAR STOKES,

If you are coming to London for the Gentlemens' [*sic*] Soiree I hope you will dine with us next Wednesday. I wish we could have asked you to take a bed here but alas, it so happens, on account of a Drawing room to be attended on Thursday, that all our rooms are occupied.

We shall have dinner at 7-30, but if you could come here at 7, or earlier, we would have some time to talk over Röntgen and other matters.

Yours
KELVIN

579 KELVIN to STOKES, 19 June 1896
Stokes Collection, K324

In train for London
June 19/96

DEAR STOKES

I yesterday tried for the retardation of transparency of a book for X-light described by Quincke[1] as having been found by an experiment (which however I think he had not seen himself.) I found *none*; none perceptible. The full illumination was certainly reached within about 1/8 sec.

I looked at a fluorescent screen kept *aglow* by an X-source beyond. Then shut my eyes for some little time. Then on a signal from me a[n] assistant interposed a book between the screen and the X-source; and said 'now': I opened my eyes at the instant and saw the screen *aglow*, with light fainter than before. It kept ⟨*aglow*⟩ glowing without any perceptible change.

The effect described by Quincke was probably due, (1ˢᵗ) to contrast according to which a sudden diminution of light by interposition of the book, would seem like annulment of the light (to a bad observer) and (2ⁿᵈ) gradual increase, in the course of 5ˢ or so, of the sensibility of the eye, by which what seemed darkness came to be seen as light.

674

I wrote yesterday to Lord Leigh[2] in support of Arthur's candidature. It happens that I ⟨have just⟩ had a letter two days ago from Mr Irvine, vicar of [blank space] church Warwick, (congratulating me on Jubilee!)[3] I see he is one of the Governors. I hope to write tomorrow thanking him and putting in a word for Arthur.

Give our kindest regards to Lady Stokes.

Yours
KELVIN

1 I have not found this reference. The *Royal Society Catalogue* lists no papers by Quincke on X-rays; nor does Quincke appear in the relevant volumes of *Nature*, which regularly reported on European and American research on X-rays.
2 William Henry Leigh, second Baron Leigh (1824–1905). He was a governor and trustee of Rugby School, so perhaps Arthur had applied for a position there.
3 Alexander Campbell Irvine, who received his B.A. from Oxford in 1848, was vicar of St Mary's Church, Warwick.

580   KELVIN to STOKES, 23 June 1896[1]
Stokes Collection, K325

The University,
Glasgow.
June 23, 1896

SIR GEORGE G. STOKES BAR^t

Lord Kelvin is much gratified by welcome letters containing congratulations on the occasion of the Jubilee of his Professorship, and highly valued good wishes, and kind words, which have come to him from many friends. He is very sorry that it is impossible for him to write in reply to each. He desires now to express his heartfelt thanks to all, for the great kindness and sympathy which he has received.

1 This is a form letter with Stokes's name inserted.

581   STOKES to KELVIN, 2 October 1896
Kelvin Collection, S518

Lensfield Cottage, Cambridge, 2 Oct. 1896.[1]

MY DEAR KELVIN,

I looked last night into the plate of snow crystals in the Encyclopedia Metropolitana,[2] which I have got. I think it shows pretty clearly that the direction of growth of a crystal of ice deposited from vapour of water is very largely influenced by pointedness of form. I imagine that outlying points are favourable to the escape, by radiation, of the latent heat of solidification, and so favour a growth of the crystal in places where the crystal projects.

675

About the simplest form is that of a plain very thin hexagonal plate. It would seem that caeteris paribus a crystal grew more readily in a direction perpendicular to the axis than in the direction of the axis. We frequently, apparently, have a hexagonal plate as a nucleus, and when this has attained a certain small size we have outgrowths from the 6 *corners*, giving rise to a 6-rayed star. But it is quite possible that the rays are not twinned crystals at all, but merely a continuation of the same molecular orientation which exists in the hexagonal plate nucleus.

We cannot do much in this country ⟨do much⟩ in the way of making out the crystalline forms of ice, further than that it belongs to the rhombohedral system of crystallization, and shows the faces of a hexagonal prism, and faces perpendicular to the axis. One or more of the figures seem to indicate a growth along faces of the rhombohedron.

We must leave the investigation of the angle of the rhombohedron and of the various forms crystallographically considered to those who are more favourably situated as to climate. The investigator should be acquainted with crystallography, and if not living in a strictly Arctic country should at least be in such a place as Siberia, or central Russia, or perhaps even Berlin.

Shortly after my return home, Lady Stokes saw in the newspaper the death of a daughter of the Duke of Argyll's, Lady Elizabeth Clough-Taylor, who died at Inveraray after a rather short illness. Kindest regards to Lady Kelvin.

Yours sincerely,

G. G. Stokes

1 Kelvin has written on the envelope, 'Stokes Oct 3. Crystals of ice. To be answered. answ[d] from Garth'.
2 See plate three entitled 'crystals of snow and hail' in G. Harvey, 'Meteorology', *Encyclopaedia Metropolitana*, eds. E. Smedley, H. J. Rose, and H. J. Rose, 20 vols. (London, 1845), V, 1–174*. (The asterisk is in the original.) George Harvey (d. 1834) was a lecturer in mathematics at Woolwich and became a fellow of the Royal Society in 1825.

582 KELVIN to STOKES, 17 October 1896
Stokes Collection, K326

Oct 17/96
Garth,
Aberfeldy,
Perthshire.

DEAR STOKES

I was much obliged to you for your letter about ice-crystals, and I should have written sooner to thank you for it, but have been prevented by a trip to Foyers[1] (Aluminium factory) and the beginning of my University work this week in Glasgow.

If the six-rayed structure of snow, commonly represented as six little rods in one plane, joined by a central portion, were all of one homogeneous structure, the rods would be, almost certainly as appears to me, rectangular prisms, not hexagonal as commonly and, (almost no doubt,) correctly, supposed. The fact that the 22° halo is much oftener seen than the 46°, seems to prove beyond all doubt, the existence of right angles, but a great preponderance of angles of 60°, in the ice crystals high up in air. We don't know enough to judge whether these crystals are ⟨like⟩ grouped to make snow flakes or are simple little separate bars. When the ⟨22°⟩ 46° halo is ⟨not⟩ seen, and the 22° not (as on the first occasion I rem[em]ber having seen and attended to an ice halo) I suppose the crystals must have been very short hexagonal prisms, or 'hexagonal plates'. In some circumstances the tendency may be to grow in plates; and in ⟨varied⟩ other conditions as to temperature, height ⟨in the air⟩ above the ground, moisture in the air, &c the tendency may be to grow in long thin hexagonal rods ⟨whether⟩ ended by plates perpendicular to their lengths, or perhaps by three or six planes.

There ought to be more of thorough crystallographic investigation of ice than has yet been made, whether, as you suggest, by Scandinavian, Canadian, or other Naturalists blest with long and severe frosts in winter, or by less happily placed people, who might work by aid of the cold chambers produced by the ice-making machines now so much in use.

If you have any views as to the proba[bi]lities in respect to ice crystals in the higher regions of the air I shall be very glad to learn of them from you and as we are to be at Cambridge from Friday ⟨Saturday⟩ ⟨week⟩ the 30th till the following Monday or Tuesday you can tell me then. So don't be at the trouble of writing. We return from here to Glasgow next Tuesday.

Yours always
KELVIN

P.S. When the orientations (I mean angular position) of ⟨each⟩ of [sic] the crystals depend considerably on gravity the thin bars would tend to have their lengths ⟨more nearly⟩ horizontal, and thin plates their large faces horizontal. This is no doubt the explanation of 'parhelions,' and 'mock suns'. ⟨But⟩ And the comparative rarity of these phenomena seems to prove (or absolutely proves?) that the orientations are ⟨influ⟩ determined chiefly by whirlings about of currents of air and are not allowed to be determined gravitationally by fallings of the crystals ⟨thro⟩ relatively to the air. This seems to prove exceeding smallness of the crystals.

1 'The first works built by the British Aluminium Company used hydro-electric power and were located at Foyers, Inverness-Shire, Scotland, and the production of aluminum was started there in June, 1896'. (J. D. Edwards, F. C. Frary, and Z. Jeffries, *The Aluminum Industry*, 2 vols. (New York and London, 1930), 1, 46.)

Lensfield Cottage, Cambridge, 21 Nov. 1896.[1]

MY DEAR KELVIN,

I am lecturing on viscosity, and a possible physical application occurred to me of a problem of which I gave the solution 46 or 48 years ago which never occurred to me till the other day.

In my paper on pendulums,[2] I gave the result for a sphere moving uniformly in a viscous fluid, the conditions being such as to permit of our neglecting the square of the velocity. It led to an interesting physical result, namely, affording the explanation of the suspension of the clouds, which is mainly due to the viscosity of the air. I pointed out the modification of the solution to make it applicable to the ascent of a bubble in water or oil, which however at the time I regarded merely as a sort of pretty Senate-House problem.

But a physical application occurred to me the other day which I had not thought of before. How do we know but that as regards the viscosity of fluids there may be a special viscosity at the common surface of two fluids, which bears to the body-viscosity the sort of relation which in hydrostatics the surface tension at a free surface or the common surface of two liquids bears to the hydrostatic pressure p? If there be, the ascent or descent of a sphere of one fluid in a mass of another fluid would seem to afford a hopeful means of determining it. We should calculate the resistance in terms of the coefficients of viscosity of the two fluids, supposed known, equate it to the apparent weight, positive or negative, of the sphere in the surrounding fluid, and see whether the observed velocity agreed with the calculated within the limits of error of the experiments, or whether it wqs [sic] distinctly smaller. The latter result would point to the existence of a superficial viscosity.

The nature of the motion is such as to cause a constant renewal of the common surface, and so guard against the result being attributable to a scum. It is true that the extension or contraction of the surface in a meridional direction would be the same as in a direction perpendicular[3] to the meridian, so that there would be no shear of the surface, but only uniform expansion or contraction. But I am inclined to think that if there be such a thing as a superficial viscosity, it would come in rather in change of area than in shear.

I have worked out the expression for the resistance to the sphere, which I find to be

$$2\pi V a \frac{2\mu^2 + 3\mu\mu_1}{\mu + \mu_1}$$

where V is the velocity and a the radius of the sphere, and μ, μ_1 are the coefficients of viscosity of the outside and inside fluid respectively. The resistance is of course to be equated to the apparent weight (positive or negative) of the sphere.

The spheres must be small, both in order that the capillary tension may have sufficient command to keep them sensibly spherical, and that the velocity may be small enough to allow us to neglect anything depending on its square, besides that the velocity must be slow enough to prevent eddies. I think it would be possible to deliver the spheres slowly and uniformly, slowly in order that that [*sic*] the motion in the trail of one sphere should have time to subside before the next sphere was delivered. The spheres would be caught in a beaker, erect or inverted as the spheres moved downwards or upwards, till a volume of the sphere-liquid was collected large enough to measure with the requisite accurqcy, [*sic*] and then the total volume of a large and known number of sensibly equal spheres would give the volume of one.

I have always felt puzzled to account for the effect or [*sic*] oil in calming the waves (it is true the somewhat small waves only) on water. Of course the oil is much more viscous than water, but it is said that though the oil spreads out so thin as to show the colurs [*sic*] of thin plates and even too thin for that, it still produces a calming effect. It seems to me that the difference between the coefficients of viscosity of oil and water, though doubtless pretty large, can hardly account for the fact as due to body viscosity when we are dealing with a stratum of oil of a thickness or [*sic*] 2 or 3 wave-lengths of light.[4]

Have you any explanation of the calming effect of oil? If it be due to surface viscosity, it seemes [*sic*] to me more likely that the common surface of water and oil is where it chiefly comes in, rather than at the free surface of the oil, i.e. at the common surface of oil and air.

I hope by this you have pretty well got over your face troubles. Do you know whether the Duke of Argyll is now well? I saw a good while ago in the papers that he was not able to go to the funeral of his daughter, but I have not seen anything about it since. Kindest regards to Lady Kelvin.

Yours sincerely,
G. G. STOKES

1 Kelvin's secretary has written on the envelope, 'Sir George Stokes. Received Nov. 22. 1896. Sent to Lord Rayleigh Nov. 27. Returned from [Lord Rayleigh] Dec. 1. Press copy of letter to Lord Rayleigh enclosed. On the resistance of a liquid sphere moving in a liquid in terms of the two viscosities'. Kelvin has written at the top of the letter, 'Return to K'. The press copy of Kelvin's letter to Rayleigh, dated 27 November 1896, is in the Kelvin Collection, R46. In it Kelvin wrote:

See also enclosed letter from Stokes p. 3 [i.e., the second- and third-to-last paragraphs of letter 583]. Has not Osborne Reynolds published something about the mitigating effect of oil on waves? [See letter 584, note 1.] He certainly gave a short lecture on the subject to the passengers of the 'Servia' on the occasion of the entertainment evening when we were going to America for the B.A. in 1884, but I have not been able to find any published paper of his on the subject. The result is, I think, without doubt, due to doing away with the tendency to the formation of the ripples which are produced when wind blows over the surface of non-oily water, but I do not quite see how to connect this with the diminished capillary surface tension produced by oil and I do not think it can be explained by any kind of surface film viscosity of the oil. *You* know the true reason, I believe. So please tell me or give me a reference so that I may answer Stokes.

Rayleigh's answer is not in the Kelvin Collection or the Kelvin Papers at Glasgow, but was received by Kelvin before he wrote the next letter to Stokes.

2 Stokes (47).

3 Kelvin has drawn a line down the left side of part of this paragraph, underlined *same as in a direction perpendicular*, and written in the margin, '? Dec 10. K.'

4 Kelvin has drawn a line down the left side of this paragraph.

584 KELVIN to STOKES, 10 December 1896
Stokes Collection, K327

The University.
Glasgow.
December 10. 1896.

DEAR STOKES

I have delayed and delayed answering your letter of Nov. 21 until I should be able to look up Osborne Reynolds (B.A. Report 1880 p. 489),[1] Aitken (Proc. R.S.E. Jan. 29, 1883),[2] and Rayleigh (Proc. R.S. June 5, 1890)[3] regarding the calming effect of oil on troubled waters, references given me by Rayleigh in answer to a letter of which I enclose a press copy.[4]

I do not find complete satisfaction in any of these but they all agree with Osborne Reynolds in attributing the calming effect to augmentations and diminutions of surface tension produced by thinnings and thickenings of the oil film when the surface of the liquid stretches and contracts. His paper (title obviously wrong, and only 9 lines of print) is as follows:–

'On the Effect of Oil in destroying Waves on the Surface of Water.'
By Prof. Osborne Reynolds, M.A. F.R.S.

'This paper contained a short account of an investigation from which it appeared that the effect of oil on the surface of water to prevent wind-waves and destroy waves already existing, was owing to the surface-tension of the water over which the oil spread varying inversely as the thickness of the oil, thus introducing tangential stiffness into the oil-sheet which prevented the oil taking up the tangential motion of the water beneath. Several other phenomena were also mentioned. The author hopes shortly to publish a full account of the investigation.' Reynolds' statement about 'taking up the tangential motion' is not very clear, nor, I think, correct, and I don't understand his 'tangential stiffness.' I cannot find anything of his published on the subject except those few lines.

I think you will be much interested in reading (or re-reading) Aitken's and Rayleigh's papers. I find nothing quite clear in them as to any sufficiently great augmentation of surface-tension by stretching to account for the extremely strong anti-ripple effect of a very thin stratum of oil. I shall be very glad to hear from you what you think of this.

I am much interested in your expression[5] for the resistance of a liquid sphere moving through a liquid, in terms of the two viscosities.

We heard that the Duke of Argyll had rather a severe attack of gout since we were at Inveraray but that he is now much better.

Our kind regards to Lady Stokes.

Yours,
KELVIN

1 O. Reynolds, 'On the effect of oil in destroying waves on the surface of water', *Brit. Assoc. Rep.* (1880), 489–90.
2 J. Aitken, 'On the effect of oil on a stormy sea', *Proc. Roy. Soc. Edinb.*, 12 (1884), 56–75. John Aitken (1839–1919) lived in Darroch, near Falkirk, Scotland.
3 Rayleigh, 'On the superficial viscosity of water', *Proc. Roy. Soc.*, 48 (1890), 127–40.
4 See the previous letter, note 1.
5 Kelvin has added a footnote here reading, 'It proves the correctness of the last sentence of §43 of your paper "On the effect of Internal Friction . . .".' (Stokes (47).)

585 STOKES to KELVIN, 8 February 1897
Kelvin Collection, S520

Lensfield Cottage, Cambridge, 8 Feb. 1897.[1]

MY DEAR KELVIN,

There is an interesting paper in the Comptes Rendus for Feb. 1, p. 253,[2] which gave me quite a new idea as to the facts of the case as to the mode in which oil prevents mischievous waves out in the ocean. I used to think that the oil kept the waves from breaking, and wondered where sufficient energy for that purpose could come from. But the words at p. 2[5]3 'Les lames étaient brisées à 3m ou 4m du bord' showed that the protection is afforded, not by preventing the waves from breaking, but by causing them to break before they arrive at the ship, and so to do the ship no harm.

In the theoretical highest possible wave, the velocity of the water just at the crest is equal to the velocity of propagation – a terrific velocity for striking a ship – but falls off rapidly downwards from the crest. But practically no such tremendous velocity is encountered; the conditions for its production become too ticklish before that condition is reached, and the crest breaks. It seems that the effect of the oil is to introduce a change of conditions which makes the ticklish motion more ticklish still, and thereby causes the breaking to take place sooner and to a greater extent.[3] The effect of the oil is to give a harmless direction to the energy, causing it to be expended in making eddies in the sea

681

astern of the vessel (as she rides before the wind) instead of smashing the bulwarks and sweeping overboard some of the sailors.

Yours sincerely,
G. G. STOKES

P. S. I dare say oil may cause directly a subsidence of the ripples on a pool, but how it could master the powerful waves of the ocean so as to prevent them from breaking was always a puzzle to me when I supposed that such was the fact.

1 On the envelope has been written:

Sir George Stokes. Received Feb. 10. 1897. re 'Oil on troubled waters'. Mayall 1.0874D. Answered Feb. 25. 1897. See p[ress] c[opy] book.

Kelvin's secretary has written everything except *1.0874D*, which appears to be in Kelvin's hand and which resembles numerical results reported on page 268 of R. H. D. Mayall, 'On the diffraction pattern near the focus of a telescope', *Proc. Camb. Phil. Soc.*, 9 (22 February 1897), 259–69. Robert Hume Davison Mayall (1870–1946) was second wrangler in 1891 and was a lecturer in mathematics at Sidney Sussex College, holding a university lectureship in mathematics from 1926 to 1935.

2 Baretge, 'Sur les effets du filage de l'huile', *Comptes Rendus*, **124** (1 February 1897), 253–4. I have found no information on Baretge other than this one paper.

3 Kelvin has put inverted commas around the passage, *introduce a change . . . a greater extent.*

586 KELVIN to STOKES, 25 February 1897
Stokes Collection, K328

The University,
Glasgow.
February 25. 1897.

DEAR STOKES,

I am much obliged to you for calling my attention to the note by M. Baretge in the Comptes Rendus for Feb. 1.[1] Your interpretation of the observations to the effect that the oil prevents the mischievousness of the waves by causing them to break before they reach the ship is quite new to me: and is just the opposite to what I have hitherto thought. I had always thought that it was by freeing the surface of ripples and diminishing the effect of the wind on the water thus smoothed, that the mischievousness of waves was diminished. Do you think that the waves were really caused by the oil to break at a safe distance from the ship? Do you see any physical and dynamical explanation of how the oil could 'introduce a change of conditions which makes the ticklish motion more ticklish still and thereby causes the breaking to take place sooner and to a greater extent?' It seems that the application of the oil may turn out to be much more practically useful than sailors have generally judged it to be.

Two days ago I received from Moissan[2] a specimen of Uranium, and have seen with my own eyes its effectiveness in discharging an electrified conductor which is more like magic than anything I have ever seen or heard of in Science.

Yours very truly,

KELVIN

1 See the previous letter, note 2.
2 Ferdinand Frédéric Henri Moissan (1852–1907), who won the Nobel Prize for chemistry in 1906, was professor of toxicology and later inorganic chemistry at the École Supérieure de Pharmacie and, from 1900, of inorganic chemistry in the Faculty of Sciences in Paris. See Moissan to Kelvin, 20 February 1897, Kelvin Collection, M151.

587 STOKES to KELVIN, 1 March 1897
Kelvin Collection, S521

Lensfield Cottage, Cambridge, 1 March, 1897.[1]

MY DEAR KELVIN,

M. Baretge's paper[2] was quite a revelation to me. As I read it I seemed to have a picture of the whole thing before my eyes, and it all appeared so reasonable compared with anything I had thought of before. In very high waves the motion is on the brink of instability, at least when the viscosity of water, small as it is for such motions, is taken into account. Suppose the motion irrotational, and imagine the waves at their highest theoretical limit. Neither of these suppositions will be practically true; for in the first place the previous 'white horses' will have had the effect of mixing up the swiftly moving water near the crests with the less quickly moving water further down, producing a forward motion near the surface besides the onward motion which is an accompaniment of the wave motion, regarded as taking place irrotationally, which belongs to the waves now reduced in height by the breaking, thereby reducing the very formidable velocity of the water near the cresta [sic]. And in the second place the theoretical limit is never practically attained; the motion is by no means so regular as to permit of that. But for the sake of explanation suppose the highest possible wave attained.

Supposing the ideal highest possible wave were attained, at the crest the water would be moving forward with a velocity equal to the velocity of propagation – a most formidable velocity for water to impinge with against a ship. But th9ugh [sic] we can't get to the ideal limit, in high waves of considerable length measured in a direction perpendicular to the ridges a very formidable velocity may be reached near the crests. But the motion borders on instability, and the impediment offered by the viscosity of the oil may suffice to make the quickly-moving water near the crest shoot ahead and then tumble over, mixing the swiftly moving water with water lower down which moves with a moderate velocity only, so that the average velocity is reduced to what is no longer formidable to the ship's stern.

It is I think quite impossible that the defensive action of the oil can be explained by the mere prevention of ripples on the surface, and thereby preventing the wind from getting quite so great a grip on the water. Big oceanic waves like what we are dealing with are of gradual production, and when they become big are propagated with a high velocity. Till such a wave got near the ship it would be out of reach of the influence of the oil; and once it came within reach of the influence of the oil it would be so near the ship, and its velocity of propagation would be so great, that the wave would be upon the ship before the slight loss of grip of the wind on the water would not be worth mentioning as regards the augmentation of disturbance which would be saved.

With respect to uranium, I should very much like to know what your experience is as to the necessity or non-necessity of a previous exposure to rays of high refrangibility, or to Röntgen rays. In Becquerel's earlier papers he seemed to regard previous exposure as necessary, but later on he mentioned facts which seemed to indicate that the effect was produced irrespective of previous exposure.[3] But he has nowhere, so far as I recollect, asserted that it was unnecessary.

Yours sincerely
G. G. STOKES

1 Kelvin's secretary has written on the envelope, 'Sir Geo. Stokes. Re M. Baretge's paper on calming effect of oil on waves. also Uranium discharge of elect.[y] Received March 2. 1897'.
2 See letter 585, note 2.
3 See letter 552, note 9, and the next letter, note 1.

588   KELVIN to STOKES, 4 March 1897
Stokes Collection, K329

The University,
Glasgow.
March 4. 1897

DEAR STOKES

It seems that Becquerel found the metallic Uranium not to have lost its marvellous virtue when kept for months in the dark (from last March till last November.)[1] I have had no opportunity of testing this yet as I only received it from Moissan about 10 days ago. Since I got it, it has not been exposed to any light except ordinary daylight. Its 'rays' I find pass through aluminium sheet, and copper sheet of perhaps $\frac{1}{4}$ millimetre thickness, and through tinfoil.

When the Uranium is held within a few inches of the outside of a closed aluminium box within which is insulated a copper disc connected with the insulated electrode of an electrometer by a fine wire passing through a hole in the box, the box being metallically connected with the metal case of the electrometer, the electrometer shows a reading deviating from its metallic zero[2] about the same as would be found by connecting the copper and aluminium by a drop of water.

Yours always truly,
KELVIN

1 H. Becquerel, 'Sur diverses propriétés des rayons uraniques', *Comptes Rendus*, **123** (23 November 1896), 855–8.
2 Kelvin has added a footnote here reading, 'that is to say the indication of the electrometer when its metal case and insulated electrode are metallically connected'.

589 STOKES to KELVIN, 6 March 1897
Kelvin Collection, S522

Lensfield Cottage, Cambridge, 6 March, 1897.[1]

MY DEAR KELVIN,

Thanks for the information about uranium. I had seen in the Comptes Rendus that Becquerel[2] had found the photographic effect from uranium compounds which had been long in the dark, and also from *fused* nitrate of unranium [sic], where one would have supposed that any effect from a previous exposure would have been destroyed by subjecting the salt to fusion (the so-called watery fusion). It certainly looks as if previous exposure to rays of high refrangibility, or to X-rays, was not essential, but that the Becquerel rays were emitted as a result of the agitation which takes place at ordinary temperatures. It is of course well known – Canton[3] showed it a century ago or more – that a phosphorus after exposure till it has ceased to shine will give out light when heated, though that is then spent, and the phosphorus will not show it again without a fresh exposure. And if the uranium that had lain so long in the dark discharged an electrified body only on condition that the uranium was warmed a bit, one could well believe that it may have produced the effect only as a consequence of a previous exposure. But as I understand the uranium in the trial was just in the condition in which it had been as it lay in its drawer in the dark.

Suppose uranium is exposed to rays of high refrangibility, and after a minute of [sic] so is tested as to its discharging power. Does it in that case act far more vigorously than when it had been taken out of its drawer without having been exposed? The phosphorescence of uranium compounds, unlike that of various sulphides, becomes insensible in an extremely small fraction of a second after the exposure has ceased. What does experiment say as to the effect

685

a minute or two after exposure as compared with the activity when the uranium has merely lain in a drawer?

Yours sincerely,
G. G. STOKES

1 Kelvin has written on the envelope, 'Stokes. March 8/97. Glow of uranium &c. Phosphorus'.
2 See the previous letter, note 1.
3 John Canton (1718–72) was elected a fellow of the Royal Society in 1749, received two Copley Medals in 1751 and 1765, and 'invented a strongly phosphorescent compound "Canton's phosphor" made of sulfur and calcined oyster shells'. (*Dictionary of Scientific Biography*.)

590 KELVIN to STOKES, 16 April 1897
Stokes Collection, K330

April 16/97
Netherhall.
Largs.
Ayrshire.

DEAR STOKES

I have obeyed your injunction, in not answering your letter of the 6th by return of post. It came last week when I was in London for two days and Lady Kelvin brought it to meet me in Selkirkshire on my return. If you think it would be a suitable subject I might give a lecture to the Victoria Institute 'On the Age of the Earth as an Abode fitted for Life.'[1]

Early in June, or quite early in July might be chosen according to the convenience of the Institute.

I *must* try to get it written out before hand but this is always a great difficulty for me.

I hope you and Lady Stokes had a pleasant visit to the Isle of Man and all went well on 'the eventful day' with much happiness in prospect for the young couple.[2]

I am very glad you are going to give a paper[3] to the Camb. Phil. Soc on the Röntgen, Le Brun [*sic*],[4] and Becquerel rays. Uranium is a marvellous enigma. Don't you think the effects of the rays in producing quasiconductivity (actual conductance) to air and other gases, for electricity must be due to abnormally high velocities to some few of the molecules? The conductance is certainly *by* the molecules, as seems to me: because it is less and less, as the gas is rarefied, and approaches *nil* with nothing but ether left. Ether without molecules tearing through seems to be an absolutely perfect insulator of electricity.

I am to give a Friday evg lecture to the Royal Institution 'on Contact Electricity of metals' on the 21st of May.[5] I shall have to *ask* (not tell I am

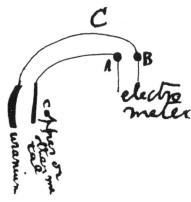

afraid) the source of the energy manifested in successive deflections shown by the electrometer when metallic contacts are successively made, and broken. If Zinc or aluminium is the 'other metal' the electrode A acquires a *negative* charge (up to nearly the same as if ⟨it were⟩ red and blue of diagram were connected by a drop of water.)[6] It takes about $\frac{1}{4}$ or $\frac{1}{2}$ minute to reach very nearly the limit when red & blue are in one or other gas at atmospheric pressure; and the limiting value seems nearly the same for common air, hydrogen, carbonic acid. When the pressure is reduced to 10 mm the deviation from metallic zero on breaking connection at C becomes exceedingly slow; and seems to tend to being infinitely slow when the gas is exhausted to the utmost. I hope you will see how all this is to be explained.

Do you know that when uranium is rubbed hard with sand paper it emits a *very* strong and peculiar odour (something like garlic)?

Can volatility of the metals, (or of the uranium alone?) be concerned?

Yours very truly
KELVIN

1 Kelvin (363).
2 Stokes's son, A. R. Stokes, was married on 7 April 1897 to Mary Winifred Garbett of the Isle of Man.
3 Stokes (134).
4 See the paper by the French psychologist Gustave Le Bon (1841–1931), 'La lumière noire', *Comptes Rendus*, **122** (1896), 188–90. Stokes did not comment on Le Bon in his (134), but Becquerel did in his 'Explication de quelques expériences de M. G. Le Bon', *Comptes Rendus*, **124** (1897), 984–8. Le Bon answered Becquerel in 'Sur les propriétés de certaines radiations du spectre. Réponse aux objections de M. Becquerel', *Comptes Rendus*, **124** (1897), 1148–51.
5 Kelvin (364).
6 In the diagram in the text, the thick line above *uranium* is in blue, while the thick line to the left of *copper* is in brown, presumably Kelvin's 'red'.

4 Windsor Terrace Malahide[1]
19 April 1897

MY DEAR KELVIN,

I got your letter on returning from church yesterday, the Sunday delivery here being about noon. The subject you propose for the Victoria Institute will be extremely suitable.[2] I wrote yesterday to Capt[n] Petrie[3] the hon. Secretary telling him, and giving your present address in case he should wish to write.

With respect to the remarkable behaviour of metallic uranium, I have long thought from what Becquerel wrote, even before he had worked with the metal itself, that exposure to rays of high refrangibility was not essential, in which case the source of energy which supplied the Becquerel rays was the molecular motions which go on at ordinary temperatures.[4] These of course are continually replenished by the incident radiations of the ordinary kind. For simplicity's sake suppose the body suspended like Mahomet's coffin and in vacuo, so that there is no loss or gain of energy except by absorption and radiation. Then in the permanent state there is a balance between the energy received from the ether by absorption and yielded to the ether by emission. But while the *quantity* of the two energies is the same, their *qualities* are in all ordinary cases entirely different. By quality, I mean the nature of the ethereal disturbance. Take for example a black-bulb thermometer in sunshine, or indeed any object in a room into which daylight enters through a window. It is only in the ideal case of a body enclosed in an adiabatic envelope that the absorbed and emitted energies (radiant energies they are) agree in quality as well as quantity. Suppose a lump of uranium in vacuo in a room. It continually absorbs radiation of light and invisible heat, and, it may be, ultra-violet as well, the last depending on the circumstances of the exposure. It emits heat rays and Becquerel ⟨waves⟩[?] rays. The latter are always going on but require some kind of tell-tale to show their presence. The tell-tale may be a photographic plate. If the lump be not in vacuo, but have a gas round it, the presence of the Becquerel rays may be shown by the effects they produce on the gas. Two effects have been found which are to a certain degree connected. One is that of discharging an insulated charged conductor, a property agreeing with that produced by the action of the Röntgen on gas, and which in the case of gas rendered active by the Röntgen rays (and therefore presumably by gas rendered active by the Becquerel rays) lasts for some time, seconds or perhaps minutes; I do not exactly remember for how long it has yet been traced, but certainly for some such time as a second at least. The other effect is that of producing a permanent potential. I have seen conflicting statements about this, and I believe you are the first to make the experimental conditions definite by opposing another metal, and thereby obtain definite results.[5] I think the effect was tried with one or more gases ⟨befo⟩ besides air, but I don't recollect that experiments were made before yours on the effects of exhaustion.[6] I *may* have read of such and forgotten it, for I cannot keep all the experimental details I have read in my head.

I don't the least believe that the effect on the gas is to give a swift motion of translation to a few molecules. I think it is either dissociation or, perhaps more probably,[7] putting the molecules into a sort of condition of strain in which the ether takes part; a state of strain involving a deformation of the molecule.

I never had uranium in my possession; I don't know whether I ever saw it; and I was not aware of the smell you mention. Whether it is volatilised or mechanically divided into *very* fine powder I cannot say. If volatilised I think it must almost immediately be oxidised. I suppose it is the dust of uranium or oxide of uranium chemically acting on the ends of the olfactory nerves that produces the smell.

I expect to leave this for Cambridge on Friday afternoon.

Yours sincerely
G. G. Stokes

P.S. I forgot to mention two things. I dare say as a boy (not very likely later) you may have rubbed together wave-worn quartz pebbles, picked up on the sea shore, to see the light, and noticed the smell given out. I don't know what it is due to.

I feel pretty confident that the Becquerel rays are vibrations of considerable irregularity; coming in series not long enough to have the properties of harmonic vibrations.

1 Kelvin has written on the envelope, 'Stokes. Ap 21/97. Becquerel Rays. Rontgen Rays. Smell of quartz rubbed together. Keep'.
2 Kelvin (363).
3 Capt. Francis W. H. Petrie (d. 1900) was secretary of the Victoria Institute, and the Stokes Collection contains numerous letters from him to Stokes regarding the Institute's affairs.
4 Becquerel experimented with compounds of uranium before using uranium itself. In his sixth paper on the subject, he reported that the effect from the element was stronger than that from its compounds. ('Émission de radiations nouvelles par l'uranium métallique', *Comptes Rendus*, 122 (18 May 1896), 1086–8.)
5 See Kelvin, Beattie, and Smolan (3). John Carruthers Beattie (1866–1946) received a D.Sc. from the University of Edinburgh in 1896, was professor of physics at South African College, Capetown, from 1897 to 1918, and was vice-chancellor and principal of the University of Capetown from 1918 to 1937. There are a few Beattie letters in the Kelvin Collection plus a testimonial Kelvin wrote for him in 1904. Maryan Smoluchowski, Ritter von Smolan (1872–1917) received a Ph.D. from the University of Vienna in 1894 and an LL.D. from Glasgow in 1901. He was professor of experimental physics at the University of Cracow.
6 See Kelvin, J. T. Bottomley, and Maclean (1). Magnus Maclean (1857–1937) was professor

of electrical engineering at the Royal Technical College, Glasgow. There are fifteen Maclean letters in the Kelvin Collection.

7 Kelvin has underlined the passage, *it is either . . . more probably.*

592 STOKES to KELVIN, 20 April 1897
Kelvin Collection, S524

4 Windsor Terrace Malahide[1]
20 April 1897

MY DEAR KELVIN,

I am weak in electricity, so my notions go for little, but I have long thought that ether without matter was a perfect insulator. I think an electric current is something in which ponderable matter is essentially concerned, and that it must not be identified with a mere flow of ether, as in electro-magnetic waves, although in this case the flow is reciprocating. I mean that even making abstraction of the reciprocating character of the current of ether in electro-magnetic waves, I do not think we have a right to identify ⟨it⟩ the flow with an electric current.

In making some speculations about comets' tails in my Burnett Lectures (Aberdeen) I adopted Sir John Herschel's supposition (in his Cape Observations) that the sun is an electrically charged body.[2] This demands that the ether be a perfect insulator.

Did the idea ever occur to you that the stratified discharge in a ⟨negatively charged⟩ moderately exhausted tube might be a sort of visible picture of Grotthus's [*sic*] theory of electrolysis?[3] That the strata, where as we know there is a development of light and heat, might be places where the dissociation and fresh combination take place, while the dark intervals are places where the ions are merely travelling in both directions?

Yours sincerely
G. G. STOKES

1 Kelvin has written on the envelope, 'Stokes. Ap 22/97. Flow of Electricity. Comets' tails. Keep'. Below this he has written, 'Gray send RSE (? of last summer) [Instabilities of fluid motion]'. The brackets are Kelvin's and the reference is to Kelvin (354). Gray has written below Kelvin's instructions, 'Sent'. John Gray, Kelvin's assistant, for whom there are several entries in the *Index* to the Kelvin Papers at Glasgow, especially for 1897 and 1898.

2 The reference to Herschel is on pages 214–15 of the 1892 edition of Stokes's *Burnett Lectures*.

3 Theodore (Christian Johann Dietrich) von Grotthuss (1785–1822) presented his theory of the electrolysis of water in 1805, according to which 'molecules of water and salt are polarized and, under the influence of the electric poles, form in the solution electromolecular chains whose members at each end are discharged at opposite poles of the current'. (*Dictionary of Scientific Biography.*)

593   KELVIN to STOKES, 27 April 1897
Stokes Collection, K331

The University,
Glasgow.
April 27. 1897.

DEAR STOKES

I have written to Capt. Petrie saying I would be glad if he would fix June 2 for the date of my lecture.[1]

We hope to come to Cambridge for two days on Sat. May 8. Your last two letters are full of very interesting and important things about which I hope we shall have a thorough going talk.

Yours always truly,
KELVIN

1 Kelvin (363).

594   KELVIN to STOKES, 21 July 1897
Stokes Collection, K332

Netherhall
Largs, Ayrshire
July 21. 1897.

DEAR STOKES,

I found yours of the 16th waiting my arrival here last night. The distinction of 'pitch,' and quasi-musical sound, which we hear in the sound of a hammer reflected from a flight of steps or reflected obliquely from a paling illustrates Lord Rayleigh's theory[1] (so far as I can recollect it) of the non-periodic character of white light and the colour which we perceive in white light reflected or transmitted obliquely from a grating. I doubt however whether white light from any source is composed of constituents each as far from being periodic as Rayleigh supposes. What do you think?

In sunlight or any white light showing a spectrum with fine black bands, there must certainly be approximate periodicity through many hundred or many thousand periods. If you care to look at page 98 of my Baltimore Lectures you will see a conversation with Rowland[2] on the subject! What do you think of the character of the light from white hot melted rock or solid platinum or iron?

As to the diffraction of the ether wave due to a single impulse I find quite a satisfactory result without considering positive and negative. Consider for example an impulse of which the time graphic representation is this:—

and for simplicity suppose it to be a condensational impulse and the ordinate of the curve to be excess of disturbed above undisturbed pressure; but the result would be equally applicable to distortional waves in an elastic solid.

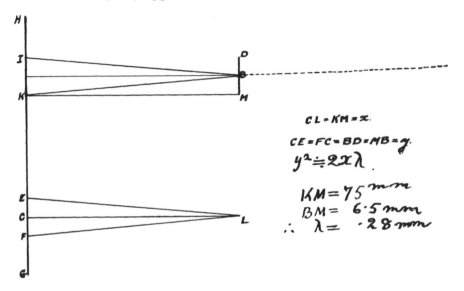

$$CL = KM = x.$$
$$CE = FC = BD = MB = y.$$
$$y^2 \doteqdot 2x\lambda.$$
$$KM = 75^{mm}$$
$$BM = 6.5\ mm$$
$$\therefore \quad \lambda = .28\ mm$$

Let HK be a screen, infinite if you please in the direction H, but having a straight edge-boundary perpendicular to the plane of the diagram through K. Let a plane impulsive wave (length λ) fall perpendicularly on it from a distant source on the left of the diagram. Make an isosceles triangle ELF such that $EL = CL + \lambda$: and let IBK be an equal and similar triangle. M will be the middle of the penumbra, B the dark border. There will be almost perfect darkness at D; and almost perfectly full light at L, as if there were no screen. The dotted line shows the continuation of the dark border of the penumbra to the right of B which is represented by the equation:$- y = \sqrt{2x\lambda}$

The principle is that the elements of the wave front which give the light to L are chiefly those between E and F. Whatever could come to L from more distant parts of the wave front than E or F, would necessarily be after the time that the complete length λ of the pulse has passed L. And we know that there is absolute quiescence at L after the pulse has passed it, if there is no solid such as the screen to leave echoes or resonances. It is not a very easy theory but I think all I have said is correct.

In the rigorous integration on the Huyghens' principle, when there is no disturbing screen, those of the effects at L due to portions of the wave front beyond E and F, which are not annulled by one another, $\langle$or$\rangle$ are annulled by belated parts of the effects from portions between E and F.

Yours
KELVIN

1 Kelvin has added a footnote here reading, 'Phil. Mag. a few years ago'. See the next letter, note 2.

2 See Kelvin's *Baltimore Lectures* (1904), pp. 98–9. Henry Augustus Rowland (1848–1901) was professor of physics at Johns Hopkins from 1875 to 1901.

595 KELVIN to STOKES, 24 July 1897
Stokes Collection, K333

Netherhall Largs Ayrshire
July 24. 1897.

DEAR STOKES,

I don't know if you have ever seen the paper of Rowland referred to in the enclosed letter from Tait which please return to me in no hurry. All the blue and red marks are Tait's except those which I have initialled.[1]

It seems to me quite clear that Rowland is wholly out of his depth in the affair. I formed this opinion last Monday when I glanced hurriedly through his paper in the R.S.E. rooms, and it is strongly confirmed by the extracts which Tait now gives me.

I saw, on the first or second page of R's paper your obviously correct rule for finding the line of vibration in light from a circular aperture due to a polarised source behind the aperture, condemned as wrong!

Rowland actually does not seem to know that in isotropic ether Maxwell's equations give absolutely the same as the elastic solid theory for the motions which constitute light; but perhaps I am doing him an injustice in this.

Various writers on refraction, reflection &c. have rejoiced in Maxwell's equations because they felt absolved by them from dynamical treatment of boundary conditions.

Yours,
KELVIN

P.S. Rayleigh's papers[2] of which I spoke to you are On Complete Radiation at a given Temperature. Phil. Mag. 1889 first half year pp 460–469 and On the Interference Bands of Approximately Homogeneous Light. Phil Mag 1892, 2; pp 407–410.

1 H. A. Rowland, 'On the propagation of an arbitrary electro-magnetic disturbance, on

spherical waves of light, and the dynamical theory of diffraction', *Phil. Mag.*, 17 (1884), 413–37. Tait's letter is in neither the Kelvin Collection nor the Kelvin Papers at Glasgow.

2 Rayleigh, 'On the character of the complete radiation at a given temperature', *Phil. Mag.*, 27 (1889), 460–9, and 'On the interference bands of approximately homogeneous light; in a letter to Prof. A. Michelson', *ibid.*, 34 (1892), 407–11. (Albert Abraham Michelson (1852–1931), the American physicist.)

596 STOKES to KELVIN, 26 July 1897
Kelvin Collection, S525

Lensfield Cottage, Cambridge, 26 July, 1897.[1]

MY DEAR KELVIN,

I pass over diffraction for the present in order to refer to a subject which is perhaps more immediately pressing.

I was struck with the (to me at least) novelty of the idea you threw out at the meeting of the Victoria Institute[2] that the free oxygen in our atmosphere may have owed its origin to the decomposition of carbonic acid by plants under the influence of light. It did not seem to me however necessary; I could not see why we might not suppose that there was free oxygen in the atmosphere before the origin of plants on earth.

I happened to meet Hooker on Thursday at a banquet in Salters' Hall. He told me that it had been found experimentally that plants will not live in an atmosphere containing as much as 25 per cent of carbonic acid.

I do not know why you rejected the idea of there being free oxygen in the atmosphere even independently of vegitation [*sic*]. Perhaps it was from the fact of most of the stars showing by their spectrum the presence of free hydrogen. Our own sun shows the same, and the earth may have been formed, and we might expect it to have been formed, out of similar materials.

But the presence of free hydrogen in the sun and stars by no means disproves the presence there of free oxygen, For [*sic*] under the conditions in which, in the laboratory, the spectrum of hydrogen is seen the vapour of water cannot exist; it is resolved into hydrogen and oxygen. Of course as the heavenly body cooled down to something like a full red heat the oxygen and hydrogen would unite to form water. But the chances would be adverse to those gases being just in the proportion to form water; in all probability there would be an overplus of one or the other. There seems no reason why the overplus should be of hydrogen rather than oxygen; and the fact of our having now no free hydrogen, whereas we have free oxygen, would seem to make it probable that the overplus was of oxygen rather than of hydrogen. Most of the free carbon we have on earth is in the shape of coal, for presumably the total weight of diamonds may be neglected in comparison of that of coal, and coal for the most part shows that it had its origin in vegetable life. It seems probable that at the time when the earth had cooled sufficiently to admit of vegetable life, the atmosphere consisted chiefly of nitrogen, carbonic acid, water in the condition of elastic vapour, and free oxygen. I suppose that oxygen is essential to the germination of seeds. The introduction of the flora (ferns, lepidodendron &c.) of which the remains are found in the coal measures would ultimately have the effect of adding to the oxygen and withdrawing most of the carbon in the atmosphere, thereby preparing the earth for the reception of animals.

I should think that oxygen must be, weight for weight, much the most abundant element in the earth. I have just opened Gmelin's handbook[3] translated, and find 'Oxygen is the most abundant of all known substances'. If then at the stage of the earth's progress when vegetable life became possible the atmosphere, besides nitrogen, which only with difficulty enters into combination, and compound gases, contained an uncombined overplus of some easily-combining element, it would seem a priori the most likely that that would be oxygen. And that supposition seems best to fit in with what seems the most probable history of the introduction of vegetable and animal life.

As you are probably engaged in looking over your Victoria address, I thought it best to bring this subject before you.

Yours sincerely,
G. G. STOKES

1 Kelvin has written on the envelope, 'Stokes. July 27. Origin of Atmospheric Oxygen'.
2 See Kelvin (363), his address to the Victoria Institute delivered 2 June 1897.
3 L. Gmelin, *Hand-Book of Chemistry*, trans. H. Watts, 19 vols. (London, 1848–72). Leopold Gmelin (1788–1853) was director of the Chemical Institute in Heidelberg. The first edition of his handbook appeared in three volumes from 1817 to 1819.

597 KELVIN to STOKES, 29 July 1897
Stokes Collection, K334

The University,
Glasgow.
July 29/97

DEAR STOKES

(Diffraction)

Would you not think it worth while to send to the Phil. Mag. a few lines, crushing Rowland in respect to his attack on you.[1] Your letter to me might suffice. I return it to you that you may see if you would wish to make any change (besides what I have done in red) and return it to me, that *I* may send it to the Phil. Mag. as communicated by me.

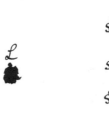

Is not the following a right way of putting the affair. I remember thinking of it when I was an undergraduate at Cambridge, and it still seems to me clear. Let L be a source of light S' an opaque screen S a surface across a hole in it. Let every point of S be held at rest, and every point at a surface infinitely near it on the right be caused (by application of force to it) to move just as it would under the influence of L, if S' were replaced by ether.

(Origin of the oxygen of our atmosphere)

I am exceedingly obliged to you for what you write. I talked to Moissan and Tilden on the subject and they both thought it unlikely oxygen could be emitted from liquid earth-material, on solidification. Tilden's analysis (recent Proc. R.S.)[2] shows carbonic acid, nitrogen, ethylene I think, or certainly some hydrocarbons in cavities in various igneous rocks, & *no oxygen*. I heard a great deal from Hooker and Thisleton Dyer[3] when we met on our way to Windsor, &c, last week, about oxygen as necessary for plant life. I shall treat the question *very* cautiously in my 'Address with additions written at different times from June to August /97'.[4]

Yours truly always
KELVIN

I have just returned from two days in London, and am on my way to Largs where I shall be till tomorrow week when we leave for America.[5]

1 So far as I know, Stokes published no reply to Rowland, certainly not in the *Philosophical Magazine* for 1897. For Rowland, see letter 595, note 1.
2 W. A. Tilden, 'On the gases enclosed in crystalline rocks and minerals', *Proc. Roy. Soc.*, 60 (1897), 453–7. William Augustus Tilden (1842–1926) became the first professor of chemistry at Mason College in 1880, leaving in 1894 to take the professorship of chemistry at the Royal College of Science.
3 William Turner Thiselton-Dyer (1843–1928) was director of the Royal Botanic Gardens at Kew from 1885 to 1905.
4 Kelvin (363).
5 Kelvin attended the meeting of the British Association for the Advancement of Science in Toronto. (See Thompson, II, 1001–4.)

Netherhall
Largs
Ayrshire
August 2. 1897.

DEAR STOKES,

I am very glad to hear (by yours, No. 2 of 30th July) that you are going to write a short article in reply to Laurenz [i.e., Lorenz], Gwyther, Rayleigh, Basset⟨t⟩ and Rowland;[1] and glad that I shall be able to tell this to Rowland, and others interested in the subject whom I may meet in America. I hope you will get your article ready for the Phil. Mag. of October. I shall write to Francis to be ready to accept it for October if it reaches him before the 10th September.

I do not quite agree with Rayleigh in calling the problem in any sense 'not determinate'. For the case of a grating ruled on metal or on glass, the boundary conditions for each scratch are exceedingly complex: witness the difference of brightness between corresponding spectrums on the two sides of the middle, when the diamond has cut unsymmetrically; and think how much dynamical knowledge of boundary conditions of etherial [*sic*] motion (ether–glass, or ether–metal) would be needed to include them in your theory.[2] Supposing the breadth of a scratch to be less than one, two, or three wave lengths, and supposing every scratch to be equal and similar to every other, each scratch (represented for the case of glass in Fig. 1) presents, for Fresnel's method, a source q which must be included in the integration along with ⟨one⟩ a contiguous P; P denoting the plane Fresnel source which you include in your integration. If the breadth of P were four or five wave lengths or more, and the breadth of each scratch less than a wave-length or half a wave-length I should think your results would be very close to the truth, and there would be very little of the inequalities of the corresponding ⟨parts of the⟩ spectra on the two sides of the middle, and very little of the disturbing 'ghosts' seen in the spectra of some gratings. But however narrow may be P, and however broad may be q, the synthetic principles are quite clear, and there is nothing indeterminate about them. When the vibrations of the incident light are parallel to AB (Fig. 1), Fig. 2 represents on a magnified scale the virtual source which q would be if the scratch is unequally steep on its two sides, and is of breadth less than half a wave-length. If the two sides of the scratch are equally steep EF is parallel to AB.

When the vibrations of the incident light are perpendicular to the plane of Fig. 1, and when the scratch is infinitely narrow, the source q is simply a bar of matter perpendicular to the plane of the diagram, vibrating in the direction of

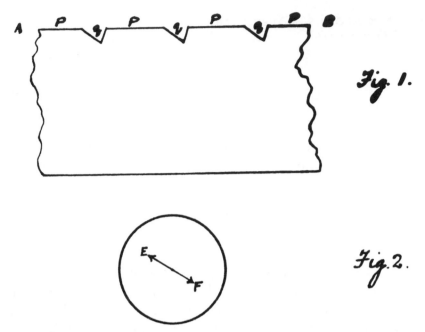

Fig. 1.

Fig. 2.

its own length. In this case there should be no differences of the brightness of corresponding spectrums on the two sides, and no 'ghostly' disturbances.

It seems to me that observations with polarised light incident first on one side, and again on the other side, of a fine grating ruled on glass, should suffice to clear away all the ambiguities which have been felt in respect to the interpretation of your theory.

I am almost absolutely ignorant of everything on the subject except your work,[3] and I only know *it* from recollections of many years back. I only know by hearsay that there have been ambiguities as to results of experimental work by others, with reference to your theory and your conclusion.

Yours,
KELVIN

P.S. My undergraduate method of which I wrote to you [two illegibly deleted words] two or three days ago is, I think identical with yours, though expressed somewhat differently.[4]

1 For Rowland's paper, see letter 595, note 1. See R. F. Gwyther, 'Note on Prof. Rowland's paper on spherical waves of light and the dynamical theory of diffraction', *Proc. Camb. Phil. Soc.*, 5 (1885), 296, title only, and 'The diffraction of a plane polarised wave of light', *Proceedings of the Manchester Literary and Philosophical Society*, 25 (1886), 78–95, which discusses both Rowland and Stokes. Reginald Felix Gwyther (1852–1930) was nineteenth wrangler in 1874 and was on the staff at Owens College, Manchester. There are twenty-five letters from him to Stokes in the Stokes Collection. See Lorenz, 'On the determination of the direction of vibrations of polarized light by means of diffraction', *Phil. Mag.*, 21 (1861),

321–31. Alfred Barnard Basset (1854–1930), who became a fellow of the Royal Society in 1889, was thirteenth wrangler in 1877 and was called to the bar in 1879, retiring in 1887. He wrote *A Treatise on Physical Optics* (Cambridge, 1892), in which he echoed (pp. 242–6) Rayleigh's comments on Stokes's theory of diffraction. See Rayleigh, 'Wave theory of light', *Encyclopaedia Britannica*, 9th edn, vol. **24** (Edinburgh, 1888), 452–4.

Although Stokes did not write an article responding to all these men, he did add a note to his (40) in *MPP*, II, 327–8, in which he commented on Lorenz's paper. See letter 649, note 3.

2 The letter is in Kelvin's secretary's hand, but Kelvin has inserted the passage *and think . . . your theory*.

3 Stokes (40).

4 In his own hand, Kelvin has added *though expressed somewhat differently*.

599 KELVIN to STOKES, 26 October 1897
Stokes Collection, K336

Oct 26/97
The University,
Glasgow.

DEAR STOKES

I am much obliged to you for your letter and Lady Kelvin has already written to Deck[1] for the remedy. ⟨Un⟩Fortunately I have been *perfectly* free from the trouble of my *No. 5* ever since our return home on Saturday, so unless this state of things ceases I shall not have a chance of testing its efficiency.

I was going to write to you just now on another affair – wave-heights. We had waves on our homeward voyage in the Campania which cannot have been less than 60 f^t high from hollow to crest. Standing on the upper bridge I many times, on Monday the 18th, saw dark unbroken waves (*not very distant*) with unbroken crests above the distant horizon. The eye of a person standing on the bridge was 60 f^t above the water, in still water. It is very improbable that ⟨the floor of⟩ any part of the bridge itself ⟨either⟩ ever went ⟨as low as⟩ down below its mean position as much as the lowest hollow of the surrounding waves went below mean level. The dip of the horizon for 60 f^t height of eye is 1/420, and this would make an object at 840 f^t distance, seen in line through the horizon in still water, just two feet below the level of the eye. But in a rough sea, the distant horizon is raised above the horizon of mean spherical surface, by the general height of crests above mean level. All things considered, I believe some of the unbroken crests were more than 60 f^t above mean level. We were on the banks of New Foundland, depth perhaps 40 fathoms at the time. But now!! I was told by several officers of the Campania that both in her and her sister-ship the Lucania, they had (standing on the bridge) seen unbroken wave-crests ⟨in line⟩ right ahead of them and quite near, in line with the 'crows nest' on the foremast. This is 90 feet above the sea, and a considerable distance, perhaps 60 or 100 feet, forward of the bridge. In the Lucania such crests had been seen just clear *under* the crows nest: in the Campania at one time just clear *over* the upper edge of the crow's [*sic*] nest. This would make the particular waves quite 90 feet above ⟨mean lev⟩ hollows. Did not Scoresby[2] make 30 feet above hollows (or was it 30 feet above mean level) as the highest crests that he observed? I am to be at Cambridge Friday morning till Sat afternoon when ⟨you⟩ I hope to see you and have an opportunity of talking over these and other subjects.

Yours
KELVIN

1 Arthur Deck was a pharmaceutical chemist in Cambridge.
2 See W. Scoresby, 'On Atlantic waves, their magnitude, velocity, and phenomena', *Brit. Assoc. Rep.* (1850), part 2, 26–31. William Scoresby (1789–1857) was the son of William Scoresby (1760–1829), the arctic explorer. He studied at Queens' College, Cambridge, and was vicar of Bradford from 1839 to 1847. His paper reports observations he made during trips across the Atlantic in October 1847 and March 1848.

600 KELVIN to STOKES, 28 October 1897[1]
Stokes Collection, K337

The University, Glasgow
October 28. 1897

See Proc. R.S. 1871 (vol. xix) p. 239 (C. F. Varley, communicated by Stokes).[2] Compare Wilde Lecture pp. 8, 9.[3]

I arrive Cambridge tomorrow morning at 10-25 and I am sorry to say must leave at noon on Saturday.

See print of Baltimore Lectures p. 111, compare with Wilde Lecture p. 22. See also formula at foot of page 106 showing formula for reciprocal of square of propagational velocity [one illegibly deleted word] to be unaffected by unembedded molecules when the period is infinitely small.

KELVIN

1 This is a post card addressed to Stokes.
2 C. F. Varley, 'Some experiments on the discharge of electricity through rarefied media and the atmosphere', *Proc. Roy. Soc.*, 19 (1871), 236–42.
3 Stokes (130).

601   STOKES to KELVIN, 22 May 1898
Kelvin Collection, S526

Lensfield Cottage, Cambridge, 22 May, 1898.

MY DEAR KELVIN,

Dr. Kerr was elected F.R.S. in 1890. His name is not among the medallists. I think it deserves to be.

As to the condition of an elastic isotropic solid in the space between the two waves, there is not the slightest shadow of doubt. The medium is NOT in its undisturbed state; of course I mean when the initial disturbance is arbitrary; for it *might* fulfil such conditions as to make the medium in the interval to be in its undisturbed condition. In the general case there will be displacement and velocity such as could exist in a perfect incompressible fluid which moves, or is displaced, irrotationally. At different distances from the origin of disturbance the displacement or velocity will vary inversely as the distance for either wave, but inversely as the cube of the distance for the irrotational displacement or velocity in the interval between the waves.

The reference to my little notice in the Comptes Rendus is Sur l'emploi du prisme dand [i.e., dans] la vérification de la loi de la double réfraction. C. R. LXXVII, (1873), pp. 1150–1152.[1]

Yours sincerely,
G. G. STOKES

1 Stokes (88).

602   KELVIN to STOKES, 2 July 1898[1]
Stokes Collection, K338

28, Chester Square,
S.W.
2nd July, 1898

DEAR STOKES,

I should be greatly obliged if you would instruct the University Press to send me copies of the sheets of your Vol. 3,[2] which are already printed off. This is not an unprecedented thing for them to do, as they have already sent you 112 pages of my Baltimore Lectures. I cannot however put my request on the ground that one good turn deserves another; because I don't think my proofs can do you any good, while I know that yours can do a great deal of good to me.

I do hope you are pushing on to finish the volume. Do put aside everything else of scientific work till you have done this. It is more important now than it has ever been, to have all your work about fluorescence readily available to every one.

Yours
KELVIN

1 A copy of this letter is in the Kelvin Papers at Glasgow, LB5/145.
2 Volume three of Stokes's *MPP* was not published until 1901. It did contain Stokes (42) on fluorescence, but, as it was the final paper in the volume, it was probably not in print in 1898.

603 STOKES to KELVIN, 6 July 1898
Kelvin Collection, S527

Lensfield Cottage, Cambridge, 6 July, 1898.[1]

MY DEAR KELVIN,

I went to London on Monday to go to an American Independence banquet on July 4, for which I had a long invitation. Next day there was a committee meeting in the late afternoon at the Royal Society, so I was not home till late. I called this afternoon at the Press, and they will send you sheets, as far as gone, of my vol. 3.[2]

Unfortunately I had not your assistance this time for the annual meeting of the Victoria Institute, and I undertook, rashly I fear, to give them something on the 18th.[3] I had thought of taking the subject of the perception of colour, on which indeed very little is known. Some curious results have recently been obtained by Blix and Goldschneider[4] [*sic*] on the perception of heat, cold, and pressure, which go to show that one set of nerve fibres on being excited give the sensation of heat, another of cold, a third set of pressure. This quite falls in with the Young–Helmholtz theory of perception of colour, according to which there are 3 sets of nerve fibres which on being respectively excited convey the three primary sensations of colour, whatever those may be.

Other physiologists however, as Foster tells me, do not accept this theory of colour-perception, though as far as I can judge they have nothing at all so good to put in its place.

Yours sincerely,
G. G. STOKES

1 Kelvin has written on the envelope, 'Stokes. July 7. promises advance sheets. Perception of Colour'.
2 Of Stokes's *MPP*.
3 See Stokes (135).
4 For Stokes's brief discussion of the work of the physiologists Magnus B. Blix (1849–1904) and (Johannes Carl August Eugen) Alfred Goldscheider, see his (135), pp. 262–4. He cited Blix, 'Experimentelle Beiträge zur Lösung der Frage über die specifische Energie der Hautnerven', *Zeitschrift für Biologie*, **20** (1884), 141–56; **21** (1885), 145–60, and Goldscheider, 'Neue Thatsachen über die Hautsinnesnerven', *Archiv für Anatomie und Physiologie Physiologische Abtheilung*. Supplement-Band. (1885), 1–110.

604 KELVIN to STOKES, 8 July 1898[1]
Stokes Collection, K339

> 28, Chester Square,
> S.W.
> 8th July 1898

DEAR STOKES,

I am very incredulous regarding three sets of nerves for heat, cold, and pressure; but I suppose you will look critically into Blix and Goldschneider [*sic*] before you give weight to their speculation.[2] As to colour it seems to me that the three sets of nerves for the Young–Maxwell–Helmholtz doctrine is not probably a reality. The doctrine seems to me a physiological approximation of a very admirable character, but only an approximation to the truth.

I hope to hear your address on the 18th,[3] and to leave next day, or the day but one after, for Aix-les-Bains.

Thanks for the sheets of your Vol. 3,[4] which, no doubt, will reach me tomorrow or in a day or two.

> Yours,
> KELVIN

1 A copy of this letter is in the Kelvin Papers at Glasgow, LB5/145.
2 See the previous letter, note 4.
3 Stokes (135).
4 Of Stokes's *MPP*.

---

605 KELVIN and RAYLEIGH to STOKES, 25 August 1898[1]
Stokes Collection, K340

> Netherhall.
> Largs.
> Ayrshire.
> 25th August. 1898.

DEAR STOKES,

Partly from a commission ⟨I hold⟩ which one of us holds from the Pitt Press, and partly from our own needs, we want you to tell us when Sheet 18 of Volume 3[2] will come from the Pitt Press. ⟨I am⟩ One of us is anxiously waiting for it to help ⟨me⟩ him on with ⟨my⟩ Baltimore Lectures, which are fourteen years in arrear, but are not to be so, ⟨I hope⟩ he hopes, for fourteen fortnights longer. We both join in urging you to our utmost that you push on with Vol. 3 at highest possible pressure till you get it finished.

> Yours truly and expectantly
> KELVIN
> RAYLEIGH

1 Except for Kelvin and Rayleigh's signatures, which are in their own hands, the letter, including the corrections, is in Kelvin's secretary's hand. A copy of this letter is in the Kelvin Papers at Glasgow, LB5/154.

2 Of Stokes's *MPP*.

606   KELVIN to STOKES, 5 September 1898[1]
Stokes Collection, K341

Netherhall.
Largs.
Ayrshire.
Sept. 5. 1898

DEAR STOKES,

In answer to your letter of 30th August, my experiments to which you refer were not on vowel sounds. They were on the beats on approximation to perfect harmonies of two simple harmonic sounds. They are described in Vol. 2. of my 'Pop. Lectures and Addresses' (On Beats of Imperfect Harmonies. p. 395).[2]

I am forwarding your letter to Lord Rayleigh and he will rejoice with me in learning that there is an early prospect of our having your Vol. 3.[3] complete. I am off tomorrow for the B[ritish] A[ssociation] at Bristol. I hope you and Lady Stokes are having a good time of it in Wales.

It was a great grief and shock to us to hear of the terrible disaster by which Hopkinson and his three children were lost.[4]

Yours v. truly,
KELVIN

1 A copy of this letter is in the Kelvin Papers at Glasgow, LB5/154.
2 Kelvin (224).
3 Of Stokes's *MPP*.
4 Hopkinson and his children died in a mountain climbing accident in Switzerland on 27 August 1898. (See letter 319, note 2.)

607   STOKES to KELVIN, 7 September 1898
Kelvin Collection, S528

5 Arvon Terrace[1]
7 Sept. 1898

MY DEAR KELVIN,

Thanks for the information, and referance[2] [*sic*]. I said 'vowel sounds' merely for shortness; for I had it in my mind that what you were experimenting about was beats of imperfect harmonies, such as a *nearly* perfect octave or fifth, and that you got sounds like oo-ah-oo-ah-oo-ah-. .[3] Hele Shaw has some beautiful photographs,[4] very interesting to you & me. By means of a thin stratum of viscous liquid between close glass walls, flowing past an interruption in the film, you can realise experimentally the theoretical stream lines in 2 dimensions in a perfect fluid flowing round a body represented in section by the obstacle.

I expect on Monday or so to be leaving for Ireland.

Yours sincerely
G. G. STOKES

1 Kelvin's secretary has written on the envelope, 'Sir George Stokes. Sept. 7/98'.
2 To Kelvin (224).
3 Kelvin has written, '? |oo-ah-ay-oo-ah-ay-oo| ? Nov 27, 1903'.
4 See H. S. Hele-Shaw, 'Experimental investigation of the motion of a thin film of viscous fluid', *Brit. Assoc. Rep.* (1898), 136–42, which was immediately followed by Stokes's comments in his (133). Hele-Shaw's photographs themselves are in his 'The flow of water', *Nature*, 58 (12 May 1898), 34–6.

608 STOKES to KELVIN, 22 and 23 November 1898
Kelvin Collection, S529

Lensfield Cottage, Cambridge, 22 Nov. 1898:[1]

MY DEAR KELVIN,

I several times thought of writing to you about a point on which I think we are not *quite* agreed, I mean about the question of the motion of a perfect incompressible fluid when the boundary presents a sharp salient angle. I am supposing the motion irrotational.

You say, We cannot regard the angle as absolutely sharp; we *must* regard an absolutely sharp angle merely as the limit of an angle with blunted edge as we make the amount of bluntness less and less indefinitely. I say, We *may* regard an infinitely sharp angle as the limit of a blunted angle as the bluntness decreases indefinitely; but we are not *obliged* so to regard it. A perfectly sharp edge presents a perfectly clear conception, and we may enquire what sort of motion would go on with a perfectly sharp edge; and we may *not* assume that no motion is possible with a perfectly sharp edge but that which is the limit of the motion which alone will take place with an edge of finite bluntness. It is a perfectly definite problem to ask what in such case the motion will be; and the fact that the unique continuous motion for finite bluntness presents velocities which increase indefinitely, near the edge, when the edge becomes sharper indefinitely, proves to my mind that *in the limit* a ⟨limit⟩ motion becomes possible other than that which is the uniquely possible motion *up* to the limit. There is no opposition between the two statements; it may be, and I feel convinced is, that the margin of stability of the unique continuous motion vanishes in the limit when the ⟨bl⟩ bluntness vanishes.[2]

To look at it otherwise: suppose a fixed disturbing cause, *as small as ever you please*, to exist, and then, starting with a blunt edge, make the bluntness less as [*sic*] less indefinitely. At first the motion will differ as little as ever you please from the continuous motion; but as you go on increasing increasing [*sic*] the sharpness, you will at last come to a sharpness for which the disturbing cause will be able to direct the motion into a new channel.

Suppose a point to move in a plane under the condition that a straight line drawn through it in the direction of the motion shall enclose with two axes a triangle of given area. The point may move along a straight line which encloses a triangle of the given area. Or it may move along the hyperbola which is the envelope of all such straight lines. Or it may move along one such straight line till it gets to the hyperbola, and may then continue its course along the hyperbola. Till it gets to the hyperbola its mode of motion is unique, in a straight line; but because the motion is thus unique until you reach the limit, it does not therefore follow that the same mode of motion is the only one then possible.[3]

this [*sic*] is meant merely for a rough illustration of the hydrodynamical question, or rather of the principle involved in it. Because the motion is unique (though with an indefinitely decreasing margin of stability) *up to* the limit of perfect sharpness, it does not therefore follow that the setting in of a different kind of motion *at* the limit is excluded. If such a motion be excluded, it must be on other grounds. What are those grounds?

If a surface of slip be formed, originating at the sharp edge and continued from thence to a greater or less distance according to the time elapsed since the motion began, not only must the normal component of the velocity be continuous across the slip, but the pressure must be continuous likewise. But there is nothing in this opposed to a discontinuity of velocity in passing across the slip, even though phi must be continuous from a point at one side to a point on the opposite side *provided* you travel *round* the slip and not across it. This allows ϕ and $\frac{d\phi}{dt}$ to change discontinuously if you travel *across* the slip. The expression for the pressure shows that the discontinuity of the square of the velocity is balanced by the discontinuity of $\frac{d\phi}{dt}$ in passing from a point on one side to a point on the opposite side of a surface of slip.

Suppose that motion has quite recently commenced past a sharp edge, and let the curved black line represent a (supposed) baby slip, and the red the slip surface grown to childhood.[4] Let the pencil lines denote the flow on what I will call the rush side of the slip surface. I will call the other side the quiet side: not that there is no motion at all there; there must be motion all over the fluid: but I think of the motion there as comparatively gentle. Let P be a point infinitely close to the slip surface on the rush side, Q a point infinitely near P but on the quiet side. Connect P with Q by a curve (dotted) going round the slip. Suppose, as we may, phi to be nil at P. (If we had taken it to be any arbitrary function of t that would have done just as well). Then phi at Q will equal the line-integral, from P to Q along the dotted curve, of the tangential velocity. This will be greater in childhood than babyhood, as the slip will have extended further. In front of the slip the lines $dx/u = dy/v = dz/w$ open out, and the line-integral for that part of the curve is therefore less than if the rush had reached it. Hence phi at Q is continually increasing, which is just what we require in order that in the expression for the pressure the discontinuity in the square of the velocity, in passing across a slip surface, may be balanced by the discontinuity in $\dfrac{d\phi}{dt}$. Hence there is nothing in the consideration of the pressure to condemn the supposition (which I believe to be true) that in a perfect fluid a perfectly sharp edge is the birthplace of a slip surface which continues to grow so long as there is motion, in one at least of the walls which meet at a sharp angle, in a direction *towards* the edge.

Is there any other argument against the supposition that a sharp edge is the birthplace of a slip surface? You said something once to me about some supposition involving the assumption of a creation of energy. I think it was about discontinuity that we were talking. The supposition I have just made does not involve that of a creation of energy. Setting aside (as we may) the consideration of forces (such as gravity) which act all over the mass, the only forces which do work are the pressures at the boundaries, or such of them as are moveable. But given the motion at the boundaries, it is not by any means true that the work done at the boundaries is given thereby. For the sake of shortness I will call the motion which takes place when there is a surface of discontinuity 'turmoil'. Suppose the motion at the boundaries given, then we may *not* suppose the pressure at the boundaries *also* given; the pressure at the bou[n]daries will be determined by the solution of the problem, and that pressure will be different according as there is or is not turmoil.

There are to be grand doings in Cambridge on Thursday, when Lord Kitchener is coming for a honorary degree, and I gave notice to my class that I would not lecture, so I have a respite till Saturday. If it had not been for my lectures I should probably have written to you before.

My present opinion is very much that which I expressed in my first paper[5] (See my vol. I, p. 11, middle) only I did not there consider how the motion there described is to be brought about in a perfect fluid.

Yours sincerely,

G. G. STOKES

Nov 23[d6]

1 Kelvin's secretary has written at the top of the letter, 'Answ[d] Nov. 25/98'.
2 Kelvin has drawn two lines down the right side of the final three lines of this paragraph, thus marking the passage, *may be, and I feel . . . bluntness vanishes.*
3 Kelvin has drawn a line down the left side of this entire paragraph and written in the margin, 'geometry'.
4 In the diagram, the longer curved line (on the left) is in red; the shorter in black. The two vertical lines on the right are in pencil.
5 Stokes (1) in *MPP*, I, 1–16.
6 Kelvin's secretary has written at the end of the letter, 'Sir G. Stokes. Nov. 22/98. Answ[d] Nov. 25/98'.

609   KELVIN to STOKES, 25 November 1898[1]
Stokes Collection, K342

The University,

Glasgow.

25th Nov. '98

DEAR STOKES,

What really happens in Nature and in hydraulics in respect to a sharp edge moving through a liquid is that it 'draws air'. You will see this proposition somewhat thoroughly hammered out (not beaten to tatters but found thoroughly coherent) in 'Nature', Vol. 50, 1894, p. 525.[2] If you look at this, correct Column 1, l.6, by substituting 'certain' for 'probable', and in same column, last line of text, for '32' substitute '1/32'.

To keep as closely as possible to the point (or edge!) of your letter of the 22nd, let E be an edge fixed to the interior of a cylinder, with two pistons clamped together by a connecting-rod as shewn in the diagram, and the space between them filled with incompressible inviscid liquid. Let the radius of curvature of the edge be 10^{-12} of a centimetre.

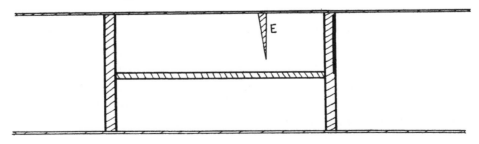

First, let all the material be perfectly strong and infinitely rigid and inextensible. Set the double piston in motion with velocity, say, 100 cms. per sec. We are all agreed as to the absolutely determinate character of the liquid motion produced. It will be that of minimum energy for the given velocity. There will be no slip of fluid on fluid. There will be enormous pressure tending to break the connecting-rod. Now let the connecting-rod be a bar of steel. It will be slightly stretched and the liquid will leave the solid before it comes to E. An infinitely strong rod between the pistons would be broken before there is slip, and *then* there would ⟨be⟩ not be slip. I would like to write a great deal more, but I shall not do so until I hear from you what you think of this.

Yours
KELVIN

P.S. If you look in the Vol. of 'Nature' referred to, you will find five little articles more or less relating to the finite slip question. For corrections on the first, (pp. 425–426) see p. 525. The 3rd is on p. 549. Delete from 'solid' in line 4 from commencement of article to 'ring' in line 9, and substitute a correct statement which I hope to write to you soon. I think all that follows is correct. Read particularly the footnote which is important and perhaps startling but certainly true. The 4th begins on p. 573 – no corrections on it at present; the 5th on p. 597 – no corrections on it at present.

I think I spoke to you of an article in the *Proc. Roy. Soc.* for Feb. 3, 1887 ('Coreless Vortices').[3] In p. 84 of it, line 8 from foot, for 'circles' substitute 'circuits'. The last paragraph but one needs amendment. It would, I believe, be quite true if the free surface with liquid on the one side and vacuum on the other possesses the property of surface-tension, which we know so well for ordinary liquids in the theory of capillary attraction. Indeed without this, or virtual cohesion, moving liquid would always fly into dust, unless it is kept within a vessel keeping the liquid within its own incompressible volume. Without such a property 'coreless vortices' would be unstable.

K[elvin]

1 A copy of this letter is in the Kelvin Papers at Glasgow, LB5/183.
2 Kelvin (339) and (340).
3 Kelvin (283).

610 STOKES to KELVIN, 2 December 1898
Kelvin Collection, S530

Lensfield Cottage, Cambridge, 2 Dec. 1898.[1]

MY DEAR KELVIN,

I am at present immersed in my lectures, besides certain other things, or I would have written to you before. I write at present to excuse me for a few days. There is an important general College Meeting on Thursday, for which I must give up my lecture, and the following Saturday is out of full term, so that I think I shall make my lecture on Tuesday my last.

I feel as convinced as ever that a perfectly sharp edge entails a surface of discontinuity, but I had difficulties about a surface which was not altogether sharp. But within the last day or two I see, I am pretty sure, daylight, and I think that even in that case we may have, in a perfect fluid, a surface of discontinuity formed. But I must postpone explanation for a few days days [*sic*].

Yours sincerely,
G. G. STOKES

1 Kelvin has written on the envelope, 'Stokes Dec 3/98'.

611 STOKES to KELVIN, 20, 21, and 26 December 1898[1]
Kelvin Collection, S531

Lensfield Cottage, Cambridge, 20 Dec. 1898.[2]

MY DEAR KELVIN,

A considerable time has elapsed since you wrote to me about discontinuity in the motion of a liquid. I have not forgotten the subject, but at the time I was engaged in my lectures; and though I did not agree with you there were some things I wanted to think out further, for which then I had not the leisure. My ideas have now on some points got clearer. I have not yet satisfied myself as to all the steps of certain transitions, but there is a good deal that I am ready to write about.

You will remember your cylindrical, water-tight vessel, with two frictionless pistons in it connected by a rod. The vessel pistons and rod are assumed to be perfectly rigid, the space between perfectly full of a liquid, and that liquid to be perfectly inviscid and incompressible. For brevity I will call the liquid water.

Allow me to imagine a figure differing from yours merely in having the axis of the cylinder turned into a vertical position, the fluid and pistons being exactly counterpoised (I suppose gravity acting) by a weight ⟨passing over a perfect⟩ the string of which passes over a perfectly frictionless pulley. The whole is in equilibrium. To fix ideas we may suppose the weight to be 10 tons, and the rod to be capable of sustaining a traction of 30 tons without breaking. All is perfectly still and quiet. Now let a house-fly perch on the upper piston. Its weight destroys the previously existing equilibrium, and the pistons begin to descend, though very slowly. But according to you, the edge being supposed to be perfectly sharp, the moment the fly has perch⟨as⟩ed the pistons begin to move, the water at the edge gets detached from the walls, and the strong rod breaks, all from the weight of the fly. What a wonderful house-fly!.

But the clock has struck XII, and it is time to go to bed.

Dec. 21. I resume. To narrow the field in which there appears to be a difference of opinion between us, I will restrict myself to motion in two dimensions. I postulate a perfect and perfectly incompressible fluid, and perfectly rigid boundaries in so far as the fluid is bounded. That we agree in. But I postulate, and maintain that I have a right to postulate, two more things to which you demur. I demand that the fluid shall not separate from nor penetrate into the walls (a), and (b) that I may consider an absolutely sharp edge.[3] I hold that with all these postulates the dynamical problem is not absurd, but is a perfectly definite one, even though we may be unable from the imperfection of our mathematics to find its actual solution. The question is, not what takes place in nature, but what would take place in the ideal dynamical problem which has been proposed. In nature we have no such thing as a perfect fluid; and the viscosity which actually exists would vitiate more or less, and in some cases completely alter, the character of the motion.

Dec. 26. I am writing this letter by snatches. I got yesterday yours of the 23rd., with the cannon ball which was to demolish me. It falls harmlessly from off me, like a drop of wather [sic] from a duck's back. As to the proposition you invoke, it is one with which I am familiar (See for instance my vol. I, p. 111, art. 14). (1845)[4] But your figure does not touch the argument, because the surface of discontinuity cuts the sphere. The application you make of the general principle begs the question of the absence of a finite slip. The continuity of the motion results from the continuity of the fluid and the continuity of the conditions to which it is subject; in particular, the continuity of the boundary conditions. The principle you rely on may rightfully be invoked to disprove the *occurrence*, anywhere *in the bosom* of the liquid of a finite slip, but does not disprove the possibility of a surface of finite slip originating at a discontinuity in the boundary, and being *paid out* from thence.[5]

Imagine the fluid and the boundary in the (your,) figure to be at rest, imagine the edge infinitely sharp, and imagine that at the edge you have an infinitely narrow, but inexhaustable, supply of a soluble, infinitely intense, colouring matter. Suppose now the fluid to be set in motion by a force, say a finite force, applied to a moveable boundary at a distance. An infinitely thin coloured ribbon[6] will be paid out from the sharp edge. You *assume* that the coloured ribbon *must follow* one of the sides of the wedge; or rather you endeavour to prove it by showing that the supposition that the ribbon enters the fluid mass leads to a violation of a known theorem. I deny that there is any violation, for I maintain that the application of the theorem to a spherical mass made up of parts lying on opposite sides of the ribbon is wholly illegitimate, as those parts were initially altogether separated. Your assumption leads to an infinite velocity at the edge. I hold (and in this you probably would agree) that the infinite velocity is an indication of an absurdity somewhere.[7] That would show one of two things:– either (1) the problem as posed is absurd, or (2) the solution is other than the limit of the solution for an edge which is rounded off. You seem disposed to regard the supposition of a perfectly ⟨straight edge⟩ sharp edge as absurd, and to say that we *must* suppose a certain amount of bluntness. I say I see no absurdity whatsoever in the supposition of perfect sharpness, and therefore I am led to adopt (2). And if it be objected that that would make the solution other than the limit of the solution for a rounded edge, I reply, Perfectly true, but that is no objection; as for example in the geometrical illustration of a point moving along a tangent to a hyperbola which I gave in a former letter, a motion of the point when it gets to the hyperbola is legitimate which is along a path which is altogether different from that it followed before it had reached the hyperbola. In connection with this, see my foot-note in Vol. I p. 311.[8]

The difference between us seems to me to involve a good deal that is merely metaphysical.[9] Nevertheless it is not all metaphysical. The idea of pressure in a fluid, temperature in a conducting solid &c. involves continuity. But it is perfectly easy to conceive motion in a liquid as discontinuous through finite slip;[10] and the only question is whether, and if so under what circumstances, motion with slip can be produced in a mass of fluid in which it did not previously exist. I hold that a liquid can be cut by an infinitely sharp knife so as to leave a scar in the ⟨shapt⟩ shape of a surface of discontinuity.[11] It is true that if left to itself the surface of the scar will increase indefinitely and the amount of slip decrease indefinitely, so that on passing to the limit as the time indefinitely increases you will have a motion which is ultimately continuous, though not in general irrotational.[12]

Yours sincerely

G. G. STOKES

1 Note that the next four letters were written while this letter was still being written.
2 Kelvin has written on the envelope, 'Stokes Dec 27/98'.
3 Kelvin has underlined the passages, *to which you demur* and *not separate from*, and written in the margin, 'no see p 3'. This comment is on the second page of Stokes's letter and refers to the comment in note 5 which is on the third page.

4 Stokes (11) in *MPP*, 1, 75–129.
5 Kelvin has written in the margin, 'See p 2'.
6 Kelvin has inserted 'separated from the solid' between the words *ribbon* and *will*.
7 Kelvin has underlined the passage, *velocity is . . . absurdity somewhere*, and written in the margin '*no*'.
8 Stokes (21) in *MPP*, 1, 237–313.
9 Kelvin has underlined the passage, *that is merely metaphysical*, and written in the margin, 'No'.
10 Kelvin has underlined the passage, *easy to . . . finite slip*, and written in the text after it, 'Yes'.
11 Kelvin has written in the text here, 'No it cannot'.
12 Kelvin has underlined the passage, *passing to . . . irrotational*, and written in the text after it, 'Not so'.

612 STOKES to KELVIN, 22 December 1898
Kelvin Collection, S532

Lensfield Cottage, Cambridge, 22 Dec. 1898.[1]

MY DEAR KELVIN,

When you wrote to me about discontinuity, I was engaged in my lectures, and was not disposed to go into the subject then. When my lectures were over other things stepped in, and I thought I would postpone discontinuity, which did not press. When I began to take it up, various ideas occurred to me which I had to think out. I began on Saturday to write to you what I expected would prove a longish letter, and resumed it late last night. I was delayed by having some things to think out; and even since writing last night my ideas have got clearer on one point. I write at once to mention one conclusion I have arrived at, which I don't think you at present believe in. I stick to what I wrote in my second paper (1843).[2] See the par. beginning near the bottom of p. 53 of my vol. I., only I did not see so clearly then as I do now how the instability came in.

Well. Take about the simplest possible case, that of uniform flow past a cylinder, as expressed by the well-known solution giving for stream-line function ψ

$$\psi = C\left(\frac{a^2}{r} - r\right)\sin\theta$$

I say the motion expressed by that equation is unstable in the rear. I am well aware that for a given motion at infinity, which takes the place of a given motion at an outer boundary, the above motion is that which has the smallest possible kinetic energy. But that does not prove that the motion is stable. If you think it does, you can probably tell me in three lines why you think so.

I am not responsible for what others may have written about 'dead water'. I never taught 'dead water'.

A happy Christmas to you and Lady Kelvin. I wish I had a better account to

713

give of Lady Stokes. Though not exactly suffering, she is able for only very little. Arthur and his wife are [to] be here for dinner tomorrow. Lady Stokes joins me in best Christmas wishes. She says she is very bad about writing now, she has so much rheumatic pain in her right arm, at least when she writes. One day she was suffering pain, and she tried Deck's neuralgic ointment with great success.

Yours sincerely,
G. G. STOKES

P.S. In my figure of a surface of discontinuity (Vol.I, p. 310)[3] I drew it short because I contemplated the motion as having not long gone on. In case you should be at Netherhall, and your books in Glasgow, I may as well mention that the passage referred to at p. 53 is that the motion deduced from the equations is unstable in the rear of the moving solid, and the resistance is represented by the kinetic energy in the tail of eddies.

1 Kelvin's secretary has written on the envelope, 'Sir G. Stokes. 23rd Dec/98. Answ^d 23rd' and 'another letter from Stokes (date 1880) enclosed. Found in Phil. Mag. 1874'.
2 Stokes (13) in *MPP*, I, 17–68.
3 Stokes (21) in *MPP*, I, 237–313.

613 STOKES to KELVIN, 22 December 1898
Kelvin Collection, S533

Lensfield Cottage, Cambridge, 22 Dec. 1898.[1]

MY DEAR KELVIN,

Don't mind what I said about the motion in the rear being unstable even in the complete absence of viscosity. As I was out walking I saw I had omitted one consideration. It is true thqt [*sic*] the fact of the kinetic energy being a minimum does not prove the motion to be stable; or at least instability does not involve a creation of energy, so as on that ground to pronounce it impossible.

It is hard to imagine that the instability which the commonest observation shows to exist is wholly due to viscosity: especially as an increase of viscosity seems to tend to increased stability, not the reverse.

Yours sincerely,
G. G. STOKES

1 Kelvin's secretary has written on the envelope, 'Stokes 2⟨7⟩6 Dec/98'.

614 STOKES to KELVIN, 23 December 1898
Kelvin Collection, S534

Lensfield Cottage, Cambridge, 23 Dec. 1898.[1]

MY DEAR KELVIN,

I interrupted my letter in which I had begun to write about the formation of a surface of discontinuity by a perfectly sharp edge when an idea occurred to me which seemed to show how such a surface could be formed in the rear of a moving solid even with the rear formed with continuous curvature; but further reflection made me doubt the possibility of the arrangement that I had imagined.

That in the case of an actual fluid such as water the motion in the rear *is* unstable, is shown by the commonest observation, and considering how slippery water is, it seems hard to imagine that the unsteadiness is only due to viscosity, especially as in general viscosity tends to prevent instability. Whether in the case of a perfect fluid the motion which satisfies the Laplacian equation and the boundary conditions is stable or unstable, seems to me a difficult matter to determine.

Yours sincerely,
G. G. STOKES

1 Kelvin's secretary has written on the envelope, 'Stokes 24 Dec/98'.

615 KELVIN to STOKES, 23 December 1898[1]
Stokes Collection, K343

The University,[2]
Glasgow.
23rd Dec. 1898

DEAR STOKES,

I am not going to walk into the snare which you set for me.

My paper on Vortex Motion (Trans. R.S.E. 1867–68)[3] contains (§10) the following statement:– 'The moment of momentum of every spherical portion of a liquid mass in motion, relatively to the centre of the sphere, is always zero, if it is so at any one instant for every spherical portion of the same mass'; which is rigorously demonstrated in §§11–15. Apply that to the spherical portion indicated in this drawing which is a magnified part of

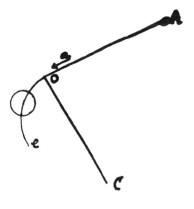

your drawing of Vol. I, p. 310,[4] with the circle added to it by myself. This absolutely disproves the finite slip.

Lady Kelvin sends her love to Lady Stokes. She is very sorry to hear of her ⟨being⟩ so suffering. She joins me in wishing you both a happy Christmas and a good New Year. We are going to Netherhall tomorrow and will be there till the 2nd or 3rd January.

Yours truly
KELVIN

1 A copy of this letter is in the Kelvin Papers at Glasgow, LB5/209.
2 Stokes has written at the top of the letter, 'rec^d 25 and ans^d 26 Decr 1898'.
3 Kelvin (167).
4 Stokes (21) in *MPP*, 1, 237–313.

616   STOKES to KELVIN, 27 December 1898
Kelvin Collection, S535

Lensfield Cottage, Cambridge, 27 Dec. 1898.[1]

MY DEAR KELVIN,

On thinking again this morning over the subject of discintinuity, [*sic*] my ideas got clearer on several points. I feel pretty well satisfied, I might say satisfied, that such a surface may arise; that the continuous motion which we contemplate as satisfying all the conditions of the problem is unstable. Furthermore, a sharp edge is not essential to the formation of such a surface. I can see in a general way how it is that it is towards the rear of a solid moving through a fluid that a surface of discontinuity is formed. I find that at the point of a solid which is the birthplace of such a surface, supposing for simplicity the solid to be at rest and the fluid to be flowing past, the flowing fluid must go off at a tangent, and the fluid at the other side of the surface of discontinuity must just at the birthplace be at rest; or rather this is what would happen if the birthplace were not at the moment moving along the surface of the solid; and if it were, then as regards the motion relatively to that of the birthplace.

Yours sincerely,
G. G. STOKES

1 Kelvin has written on the envelope, 'Stokes. 29th Dec'.

Netherhall.
Largs.
Ayrshire.
Dec. 27, 1898

DEAR STOKES,

The place of origin for the practical instability to which you refer in your letters of 22nd and 24th is, I believe, close to the surface of the moving solid. Its effect is greatest at sharp edges and places of intense curvature where there would be very great velocity relative to the solid, and great changes of velocity in small distances through the fluid, if the fluid were inviscid; but it exists everywhere over the surface of the solid. It depends essentially on viscidity and your own assumption, which I feel sure is true (though Helmholtz thought otherwise), that there is no finite slip between fluid and solid.

Imagine a real solid at rest in real water contained in a finite fixed ⟨containing⟩ closed vessel. Let the solid be set in motion with infinitely small acceleration. The water between it and the fixed containing vessel will move according to the solution of your viscous inertia-less problem.

Again let the solid be set in motion with exceedingly great acceleration but not great enough to call into play sensibly the compressibility of the water. The initial motion of the water will be exceedingly nearly that of an incompressible inviscid liquid (the motion of minimum kinetic energy). There will be an exceedingly thin stratum of fluid round the solid through which the velocity of the water varies continuously from the velocity of the solid to the velocity in the solution for inviscid fluid. It is in this layer that there is instability. The less the viscosity, the thinner is this layer for a given value of the initial acceleration; but the surer the liability to instability. Not very logical this. Certainly I think the truth is that there would be no instability at all if the viscosity exceeds a certain value depending on the initial acceleration and on shapes and dimensions of solids. (Several papers of mine in *Phil. Mag.* about 1887 touch inconclusively on this question. I am sorry I cannot give the precise reference).[2]

Let the fixed containing vessel be infinitely distant from the solid all round and let the solid be a globe. If the initial acceleration is exceedingly rapid, it is easy to determine analytically the initial motion in the transitional layer. In fact solving the problem for a given acceleration of a rigid plane set in motion in a viscous fluid in any direction in its own plane, taken in connection with the known solution for an inviscid fluid with a globe moving through it, suffices. Suppose now the acceleration to cease and the globe to be kept moving uniformly. If the velocity be sufficiently great, the motion of the fluid

717

at small distances from its surface all round will always be very nearly the same as if the fluid were inviscid, and the difference will be smaller near the front part than near the rear of the ⟨fluid⟩ globe. If now the whole fluid suddenly becomes inviscid and the globe be kept moving uniformly, the rotationally moving fluid will be washed off from it, and left moving turbulently in the wake, and mixing up irrotationally moving fluid among it. Thus the volume of space in the more and more distant wake which has momentum, will become larger and larger, and the component velocity parallel to the motion of the globe will become smaller and smaller. But there will be no loss of kinetic energy. All will be kept in the relative motions of different parts of the fluid, becoming frittered away in smaller and smaller quasi-thermal motions, ultimately diffusing out in all directions, I believe, according to the law of thermal conduction. I now believe that this is the fate of vortex rings, and of every kind of irrotational motion (with or without finite slip anywhere) in a limited portion of an infinite inviscid mass of fluid, which is at rest at great distances from the moving parts. This puts me in mind of a thirty-year-old letter of yours with a drawing in black and red ink suggesting instability of the motion of a columnar vortex, which I did not then believe. I must see if I can find the letter.

Yours,
KELVIN

1 A copy of this letter is in the Kelvin Papers at Glasgow, LB5/210.
2 Kelvin (272), (278), and (279).

618   STOKES to KELVIN, 30 December 1898
     Kelvin Collection, S536

Lensfield Cottage, Cambridge, 30 Dec. 1898.[1]

MY DEAR KELVIN,

Thanks for your long and clear letter. With most of it I thoroughly agree; on one point we distinctly differ.

But first for a minute matter, lest I should forget it, relative to your quotation from me in your article in Nature in 1894.[2] I said (with reference to a sector of more than 180 deg. ⟨'I think it⟩ 'It appears to me very probable there will be formed a surface of discontinuity extending some way into the fluid.' (Vol I. p. 53 bottom)[3] The words 'some way' were used because I thought of the motion of the vessel as having gone on for some little time from its commencement, not as having only just begun. But I had some suspicion that you supposed I meant the permanent state of things to be one in which a surface of discontinuity is continually formed and after lasting for a little way gets healed up. Yet I can hardly imagine that you supposed that I meant that.

I will ask a question lest I should forget it. I have not come across naval text books in which the 'dead water' theory is given. Could you kindly give me the name of one, and I could refer to it (through the author's name) in the University Library?

One difference between us was that I held that I had a right to suppose that we were dealing with a perfect and perfectly incompressible fluid; that the boundaries were absolutely rigid (though as in the case of a piston one or more might be moveable); and ⟨that we have a right to⟩ that we had a right to suppose a boundary as presenting a perfectly sharp edge; and to enquire what under those conditions would be the motion. You always shirked the perfectly sharp edge, or rather refused to accept one of my postulates (which I forgot to mention in the above enumeration) that the fluid shall not separate from or penetrate into the ⟨edge⟩ boundary.[4] I hold that the IDEAL problem I posed is perfectly rational, and that it has a solution.

However I will not dwell further on this now, for I am disposed to be more outrageous in my heresy, and to maintain that you may have a surface of discontinuity even without a sharp edge.

The question resolves itself into this:– Is the motion represented by the mike (i.e. minimum kinetic energy) solution stable or unstable? It seems to me that the demonstration of whichever ⟨be⟩ is the true answer would be very difficult. You seem to hold that the motion expressed by the mike solution is stable. My opinion would be that it is unstable, and that a surface of discontinuity would be paid out on both sides. I see now that if so, the fluid must leave the surface tangentially.[5] I still hold to what I wrote in 1843 (Vol. I, p. 53, bottom) I [sic] 'It appears to me very probable that the *spreading out* motion of the fluid, which is supposed to take place behind the middle of the sphere or cylinder, though dynamically possible, nay, the *only* motion dynamically possible when the conditions which have been supposed are accurately satisfied, is unstable; so that the slightest cause produces a disturbance in the fluid, which accumulates as the solid moves on, till th [sic] the motion is quite changed.' I did not when I wrote that speculate as to the way in which the instability would come about. The different outcome to which the two views would lead in the case you mention of a (suppose slightly) viscid fluid flowing past a sphere or cylinder, and then suddenly becoming inviscid, accentuates the difference of view. According to the one, the rotationally moving fluid near the body would be washed away, and the motion would rapidly tend to become that expressed by the mike solution. According to the other, the streams of right-handedly revolving and left-handedly revolving fluid at the two sides would have the rotationally moving fluid washed away, at least in the side trails, and the streams would give place to streams bounded by surfaces of finite slip, commencing at the solid, and then being paid out from thence. The subsequent motion would doubtless be of a very complicated character.

What you say of Helmholtz's finite slip of a fluid, in some cases, over the surface of a solid leads me to think that you have not noticed a paper read a few years ago to the Royal Society, and published in the Proceedings. I have not the reference at hand at the moment, but I could get it. I *think* the author was Whetham, a Fellow of Trinity.[6] He disproved Helmholtz's finite slip of water on chemically silvered glass by experiments on the transpiration of water through a glass capillary tube, at one time plain, at another chemically coated internally with a very thin film of silver, as in the interior of Helmholtz's glass bottle. No slip was found, though the experiment was I think many hundred times more sensitive for slip then [sic] Helmholtz's. Of course I don't for a moment suppose that there is any finite slip in actual water; a perfect fluid is an ideal abstraction.

I am sorry you are suffering from your old enemy the tic. have [sic] you Deck's ointment by you to try? It contains a powerful drug, and should be used with some care, so that none should get into the eye, nor, I believe, on an abrasion of the skin, and the hands ought to be washed after rubbing it in.

I saw in the Standard of today the death of Bartholomew Price.[7] I was not aware that he had been ill. I have known him a long time, and have received great kindness from him.

Lady Stokes joins me in wishing you and Lady Kelvin a happy new year. She hopes to write soon to Lady Kelvin.

Yours sincerely,
G. G. STOKES

1 Kelvin has written on the envelope, 'Stokes. Jan 1/99 (1)'.
2 Kelvin (340).
3 Stokes (13) in *MPP*, I, 17–68. The quotation is actually in Stokes (21) in *MPP*, I, 310, which is the reference given in Kelvin (340) in *Nature*, 50 (1896), 549.
4 Kelvin has underlined the passage, *not separate . . . boundary*, with two lines under *not separate*.
5 Kelvin has underlined the passage, *leave the surface tangentially*, with two lines under *leave*.
6 W. C. D. Whetham, 'On the alleged slipping at the boundary of a liquid in motion', *Phil. Trans.*, series A (1890), 559–82. William Cecil Dampier Whetham (1867–1952) took his B.A. at Cambridge in 1889, placing in the first class in part II of the natural sciences tripos, and was elected a fellow of the Royal Society in 1901.
7 Bartholomew Price (1818–98) received his B.A. from Oxford in 1840, was Sedleian professor of natural philosophy there from 1853 to 1898, and was master of Pembroke College, Oxford, from 1892 to 1898. There are some fifty letters from Price in the Stokes Collection, dating from 1847 to 1895.

619 STOKES to KELVIN, 31 December 1898
Kelvin Collection, S537

Lensfield Cottage, Cambridge, 31 Dec. 1898.[1]

MY DEAR KELVIN,

The difference between us lies in a nutshell, but the shell is too strong for my crackers. The question is, Is the motion expressed by the ⟨mkle solutioh⟩ mike solution stable or unstable? I cannot demonstrate the answer, but I strongly incline to the opinion that it is unstable. We need not speculate as to how a deviation might be imagined to arise; the question is, Is the mike solution proof against being entirely altered by a⟨n⟩ minute but otherwise arbitrary departure from its exact fulfilment?

In considering the nature of an alteration which, so far as I can perceive, may be permanent, I was driven to abandon one or two modes of motion which at first I thought might be possible, and to perceive that the fluid leaving the solid must go off at a tangent, the fluid on the other side of the ribbon being at rest at the point of issue, and practically, I should think, moving but little (at least in most cases) in the rear of the solid inside the ribbon. I see no reason why the fluid moving past must squeeze out the fluid between itself and the boundary.

My opinion is that the mike motion is unstable, like the motion of a sphere rolling down the highest generati⟨on⟩ng line of an inclined circular cylinder.

A happy new year,

Yours sincerely,
G. G. STOKES

1 Kelvin has written on the envelope, 'Stokes (2). Jan 1/99'.

620 KELVIN to STOKES, 2 January 1899
Stokes Collection, K345

Netherhall ⟨De⟩ Jan 2/99

DEAR STOKES

I believe the radius of the 'nutshell' containing the difference that will remain between us will prove to be as small as the radius of curvature of any edge however sharp that we may agree to think of.[1] *I* don't object to its being infinitely small, and the fluid being infinitely fine in molecular structure, and perfectly homogeneous and incompressible; and the containing vessel infinitely strong (otherwise a 'housefly' might burst it by lighting on the top of a frictionless Brahmah-press-plunger[2] of 10^{-20} of a centimetre diameter fitted on to it.

Supposing the radius of the 'nutshell' not yet reduced to zero (is it not so?)

you will at least agree with me that if the movable body in the diagram,[3] (given at rest in the liquid ⟨at⟩ all at rest) is moved to any other position, or moved and brought back to the primitive position, the liquid will all be brought to rest at the instant when the movable solid is brought to rest.

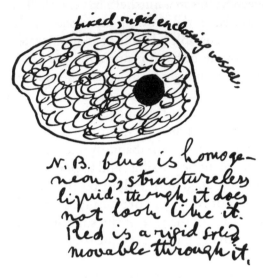

I note that you, in more than one of your letters, assume that no liquid ever passes from or to contact with the solid. I am content.

We leave tomorrow for

Broome Hall
Holmwood
Surrey

where we shall be till this day week when we start, not on a geodetic line, for return to Glasgow.

Yours
KELVIN

P.S. I knew of Whetham's paper;[4] proving for polished silver what Poiseui[l]le's experiments[5] interpreted by your theory, had proved for glass.

P.S. I forgot to say that the dead-water-behind-finite-slip-theory does not appear in books on Naval Dynamics and would not be believed by their authors or users. It was started by Helmholtz; & adopted by Rayleigh (Glasgow 1876 British Assoc[n],[6] but now that he has a sailor-son I believe he will abandon it). It is taught in German professors' special courses, & in Besant[7] & Lamb's[8] books in England.

K[ELVIN]

1 Kelvin has added a footnote here reading, 'And I don't care if the shell is then uncrackable!!'
2 Joseph Bramah (1748–1814) patented his hydraulic press in 1795.
3 In the diagram, the dark circle is in red and is surrounded by blue.
4 See letter 618, note 6.
5 Poiseuille, 'Recherches expérimentales sur le mouvement des liquides dans les tubes de très petits diamètres', *Comptes Rendus*, 11 (1840), 961–7, 1041–8; 12 (1841), 112–15.
6 Rayleigh, 'On the forces experienced by a lamina immersed obliquely in a fluid stream', *Brit. Assoc. Rep.* (1876), part 2, p. 31, title only, but published as 'On the resistance of fluids', *Phil. Mag.*, 2 (1876), 430–41.
7 W. H. Besant, *A Treatise on Hydrostatics and Hydrodynamics* (Cambridge, 1859). William Henry Besant (1828–1917) was senior wrangler in 1850 and was lecturer in mathematics at St John's College, Cambridge.
8 H. Lamb, *A Treatise on the Mathematical Theory of the Motion of Fluids* (Cambridge, 1879). Horace Lamb (1849–1934) was second wrangler in 1872 and held professorships at the University of Adelaide and at Owens College, Manchester.

621 STOKES to KELVIN, 5 January 1899
Kelvin Collection, S538

Lensfield Cottage, Cambridge, 5 Jan. 1899:[1]

MY DEAR ⟨LE⟩ KELVIN,

The nutshell is the question, Is the mike motion stable or unstable?, and the kernel is the answer. I do not profess to have cracked the shell, and I have my doubts whether you can do so either. In that case the nature of the kernel is a matter of opinion. My opinion is that the motion is unstable; yours appears to be that it is stable.

To make my meaning clear, I will take a dynamical illustration. Imagine a perfectly smooth hollow anchor ring with its axis horizontal, and consequently its equatorial plane of symmetry vertical.

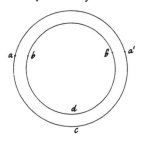

For fig. see p. 4[2]

Let the equatorial plane of symmetry cut the inner surface in a pair of circles, of which the larger one is *aca'*, and the outer surface in a pair of circles of which the smaller is *bdb'*. Let *a,b,b',a'* be in the same horizontal plane. ⟨Suppose an infinitely small particle was were placed at *a* and left to itself.⟩ In the figure ⟨*aba*⟩ *a, b, b', a'*, have accidentally been drawn above the centre, and therefore we have to imagine the particle constrained to move along the surface, as the weight alone would not suffice when the particle is above the centre. Suppose now a particle placed at a and left to itself. It will descend towards c, go up to a', descend towards c, go up to a, and so on. (I ought to have drawn the four points all below the centre instead of above,[3] and in what I am about to say suppose they had been so drawn; excuse the sacrifice of what I have drawn and written.) The same would be the case of [sic] the particle had been placed at b and left to itself: it would go on to b', go back to b, and so on. At any future time, the place of momentary rest would in the one case be a or a', in the other b or b'.

But there is this important difference between the two cases. suppose [sic] the motion to have been infinitesimally disturbed. In the former case when at any future time the particle is momentarily at rest, or infinitesimally nearly at rest, its place must be infinitesimally near a or a', whereas in the second case we can only say it must be in or infinitesimally near to some point in a section of the inner in the one case, outer in the other, skin of the ring by a horizontal plane passing through the 4 points. The motion in fact in the one case is stable, in the other unstable.

Now this is analogous to what we respectively conceive of the motion of a perfect fluid within a rigid interior, the enclosure containing together with the fluid a solid, suppose a sphere. Let the whole be at first at rest, and then let the sphere be moved about anyhow, and then brought to rest. The mike solution is a theoretically possible solution; and if that expresses the motion the fluid will be at rest when the sphere is at rest.

But if that motion be, as I believe it is, ⟨altog stab⟩ unstable, the actual motion may be altogether different. In that case the moving sphere may go on *chruning* [sic] the fluid; and if the motion go on long enough the fluid will be left with a highly complex structure.

I still retain the opinion I expressed in 1843,[4] that the mike motion is unstable. I had not then considered how the altered motion came in; and indeed it is only within the last few days that my ideas on this head have cleared up.

I all along thought that a *sharp* edge would or might give rise to a surface of discontinuity, but partly from your strongly-expressed opinion, and partly from the difficulty of seeing how discontinuity would originate with finite curvature, I followed you in the idea of continuity belonging to finite curvature. But then how are we to pass from a nearly sharp to a perfectly sharp edge? I got over the difficulty by the conjecture that when a rounded edge became sharper and sharper, the margin of stability became less and less, until, on reaching the limit of perfect sharpness, the discontinuous motion is that which takes place.

But further consideration leads me to the conclusion that you don't even want an approach to sharpness, but that even without that the motion is unstable in the rear, and that a surface of discontinuity will be formed, but in a manner which involves continuity in the setting in of discontinuity. Further (taking the general case of motion in 3 dimensions) I have been led to the conclusion that the slip surface intersects the surface of the solid in a closed curve, which was born as an infinitely narrow ring with infinitely small slip, which widens out, the amount of slip at the same time becoming finite. When the discontinuous motion is fairly established, I believe that the motion near the solid is pretty nearly steady, or at least may be so, but further on the motion is essential[l]y unsteady.

Yours sincerely,
G. G. STOKES

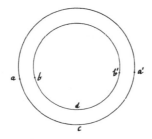

1 Kelvin has written on the envelope, 'Stokes Jan 8/99. Instability of particle on ⟨out⟩ inner circle of outer surface of hollow anchor ring'.
2 This refers to the figure at the end of the letter, which is page four of Stokes's letter.
3 Stokes has written above the line, 'See right fig. on p. 4'.
4 Stokes (13).

622   STOKES to KELVIN, 7 January 1899
Kelvin Collection, S539

Lensfield Cottage, Cambridge, 7 Jan. 1899.[1]

MY DEAR KELVIN,

A line to say that I retract what I said about discontinuity *coming on* in the absence of a sharp edge, as I am not clear about it. Supposing however it already exists (say in the case of a sphere) does a surface of discontinuity continue, being continually paid out, or is it washed away? I know what your answer would be, but query? are you right?

It is an exceedingly difficult matter (at least so it seems to me) to prove that the mike[2] motion is stable or unstable, whichever be the truth.

Yours sincerely,
G G STOKES

1 Kelvin's secretary has written on the envelope, 'Stokes Jan 8/99'.
2 Kelvin has underlined *mike* and written 'minimum kinetic energy, K Nov 27, 1903'.

Lensfield Cottage, Cambridge, 14 Feb. 1899.[2]

MY DEAR KELVIN,

I had some thoughts of writing to 'Nature' about the time that your discontinuity papers[3] came out, and possibly I may do so still. I wish however to put on record, even though only in a private letter to you, that I do not agree with you. We diverge at the very outset. You say that it is now generally known that when a perfect and incompressible fluid is set in motion by a given motion of the boundary the fluid can only take that unique kind of motion for which the kinetic energy is a minimum. What you speak of as 'now generally known' I hold to be (in its unqualified statement) untrue. It is true that the function ϕ satisfies (when such function exists) the same partial differential equation as the permanent temperature in an isotropic conducting solid, or the potential of electrical or gravitational attraction. But the motion of a fluid lends itself, which ⟨that of⟩ permanent temperature does not, to the idea of discontinuity. The idea of a perfect fluid lends itself quite easily to the conception of a perfect slip as existing. I say 'as existing', to put out of consideration for the present the question of how such a motion could be produced.

In the thermal problem the permanent temperature is, from the nature of the case, continuous; it represents what I may call a local entity. So in the hydrodynamical problem the pressure represents a local entity, and must be continuous. But ϕ does not represent a local entity, but only *the integral* of a local entity taken along some line,[4] namely, $\int (udx+vdy+wdz)$. And if we suppose the initial point, or origin, of the integral given, the integral at the final point, though not representing a local entity, has a definite value, depending on the locality, *only* on the condition that the different paths by which we imagine the initial and final points joined may pass continuously into one another without going out of the fluid, or passing through a plqce [*sic*] where the motion is rotational, or crossing a surface of finite slip. The treatment of the hydrodynamical problem by means of the function ϕ on the same lines as the thermal problem is treated by the function which represents the permanent temperature is ⟨letimate⟩ legitimate *only* on condition that we assure ourselves of the continuity of the motion. This leads us to the question, When may we assume the continuity of the motion?

Now I think we may take it as an axiom that discontinuity cannot arise, that a surface of finite slip cannot be born, right[5] in the bosom of the fluid. But the case is different at the boundary of a mass of fluid, where a discontinuity in the boundary, such for example as a perfectly sharp edge, a thing perfectly conceivable, *may* give rise to a surface of discontinuity. The *onus probandi* is thrown on anyone who maintains that it cannot. The facts that there is one unique solution for which the kinetic energy is less than for any other motion, and that that is the only solution of the problem *if* the motion is continuous, do not suffice to prove that the motion *is* continuous. Seeing that a perfectly sharp edge is perfectly conceivable, seeing that there is no reason *a priori* why this discontinuity of boundary should not beget a surface of discontinuity, seeing that the solution of the problem on the *assumption* of continuity leads to a (negatively) infinite pressure when the fluid flows over the edge (there may in a special case be a flow of parting or reunion at a sharp edge which does not involve diwcontinuity), [*sic*] it is clear to my mind that in general there *will* be a generation of a surface of discontinuity at such an edge.

Suppose the fluid initially at rest, and to be then set in motion by finite forces applied to the boundaries or some of them. Let t be the time from the commencement of the motion, r the distance of any point of the fluid from the sharp edge, and suppose t and r both very small. Let the state of things at the time and point in question (in a sense which will be readily understood) be denoted by $f(t, r)$. Then the limit to which $\langle t \rangle f(t, r)$ tends when t and r vanish may be, and as I would contend is, wholly different according to the manner in which we suppose[6] the independent quantities t and r to tend to their limiting values. We may consider

(a) The limit to which $f(t, r)$ tends when t vanishes, which will be a function of r, $\langle ((F(R)\ F_9r)\ F_9r) \rangle\ F(r)$, and we may then consider what that becomes when r vanishes; or

(b) the limit to which $f(t, r)$ tends when r vanishes, which will be a function of t, $\langle F\frac{1}{2}(t)\ F.9 \rangle\ F.(t)$, and we may then consider what becomes of $F.(t)$ when t vanishes.

(a) represents the conception of the motion as produced by impulsive forces applied to the boundaries, and the motion corresponding to that is the solution for which the kinetic energy is the least possible. For this the velocity at the distance r from the edge increases indefinitely as r vanishes.

(b) represents a different conception altogether. In this the motion is thought of as having started, and you look to see of what sort it is in the neighbourhood of the edge. I hold that at one face of the wedge the fluid shoots past, leaving at the other face a small space near the corner where there is little motion, then further from the corner the flow is inwards, that is, from the corner.

$\langle$If t and r are both small,$\rangle$ If t be small and r not small, then the motion is sensibly the same whether we adopt conception $\langle$a$\rangle$ (a) or conception (b). But

727

it does not follow from that, nor, as I contend, is it true, that the motion is the same in the two cases near the edge.

The distinction between (a) and (b) constitutes, as I hold, the true explanation of the paradox of the wonderful house-fly.

Yours sincerely
G. G. STOKES

1 S541 in the Kelvin Collection is Stokes's typed copy of S540. The three changes in wording between the copy and the original are pointed out in notes 4, 5, and 6.
2 Kelvin has written on the envelope, 'Stokes Feb 16/99. copy of answer enclosed same date'.
3 Kelvin (340).
4 S541 omits *taken along some line*.
5 S541 omits *right*.
6 S541 omits *we suppose*.

624 KELVIN to STOKES, 16 February 1899
Stokes Collection, K346[1]

The University,
Glasgow.
Feb. 16, 1899.

DEAR STOKES,

From your letter of yesterday and our previous correspondence I think we are quite agreed on the following statements, with reference to a fixed body A in a cylinder containing a perfect liquid between two pistons which are kept with absolutely constant distance between them; all given at rest to begin with; A being a body with no sharp edge, but with radius of curvature at a and b very small, say for example 10^{-50} of any diameter of A. Cause the pistons gradually or suddenly to commence moving as in the diagram; the motion of the liquid will be irrotational throughout, and must remain so for ever, supposing the pistons to be moved backwards and forwards arbitrarily. As you agree with me in this, I am content to leave the ideal infinitely sharp edge in your hands.

Yours
KELVIN

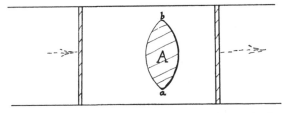

1 LB5.51 in the Kelvin Collection is a draft of this letter, and K347 in the Stokes Collection is a carbon copy of it. The letter is typed.

625 STOKES to KELVIN, 18 February 1899
Kelvin Collection, S542

Lensfield Cottage, Cambridge, 18 Feb. 1899.[1]

MY DEAR KELVIN,

The difference between us (if there be a difference, which I rather think there is) appears to me to be this:– that you hold that the mike motion is stable, and I that it is unstable. I doubt if either of us could give a mathematical demonstration of the correctness of the opinion which he holds.

Yours sincerely,
G. G. STOKES[2]

1 Kelvin has written on the envelope, 'Stokes Feb 20. copy of answ Feb 21'.
2 Below Stokes's signature, Lady Kelvin has copied Kelvin's reply (i.e., the next letter). There are no important differences between Kelvin's original and Lady Kelvin's copy.

626 KELVIN to STOKES, 21 February 1899[1]
Stokes Collection, K348

12 Grosvenor Gardens[2]
London S.W.
Feb 21/99

DEAR STOKES

Enclosures speak for themselves.[3]

I was very glad to receive your short letter yesterday in London.

I think if you consider such case as this you will see that there cannot be instability.

Fixed containing cylinder, finite length: fixed column from floor to roof: surfaces not necessarily circular cylinders. E, E', e projecting edges, of finite curvature everywhere (*I* don't care how sharp!)

Let a perfect liquid quite filling the vessel be given in a state of irrotational revolution as indicated by the dotted arrow.

By your own early equations of motion you see that rotationality cannot supervene. This you fully admit. Now the irrotational motion within the given boundary is determinate and unique. Therefore there can be no 'instability' in the *given* motion.

Yours
KELVIN

1 See the previous letter, note 2.
2 Kelvin has written at the top of the letter, 'I am here till Saturday next Feb 25'.
3 Whatever the enclosures were, they are no longer with the letter.

627   STOKES to KELVIN, 22 February 1899
Kelvin Collection, S543

Lensfield Cottage, Cambridge, 22 Feb. 1899.[1]

MY DEAR KELVIN,

Perhaps we may meet tomorrow, for I am engaged to dine with Preece,[2] and I intend to be at the R.S. meeting.

I got your letter, but I do not see that it alters the case. I will not explain at present, for as I said perhaps we may meet tomorrow.

Yours sincerely,
G. G. STOKES

1 Kelvin has written on the envelope, 'Stokes Feb 23'.
2 William Henry Preece (1834–1913), who became a fellow of the Royal Society in 1881, was an electrical engineer employed by the Post Office from 1870 to 1904. There are twenty-two letters between Kelvin and Preece in the Kelvin Collection (including two from Kelvin in January and February of 1899) and four in the Kelvin Papers at Glasgow.

628   KELVIN to STOKES, [10 April 1899][1]
Kelvin Collection, LB5.105

⟨DEAR STOKES

Consider a globe somehow or other kept moving with constant vel^y thro' real water. We all know that there is a region of eddies wh. is comparatively thin in front, & wh in the rear extends to a considerable distance behind the globe. At greater & greater dist^{ce} outside this region the motion of the water is more & more nearly irrot^l.⟩

1 The date of the letter is determined by its position in the letter-book. The whole letter has been deleted, so presumably was not sent.

629 KELVIN to STOKES, 10 April 1899[1]
Stokes Collection, K349

> The University,
> Glasgow.
> April 10, 1899

DEAR STOKES,

It was very kind of you to think of my N° 5 nerve. I did try Deck's remedy some time after you first told me of it, but not very thoroughly. I have given it a very careful trial on being reminded of it again by you; but I am afraid it is not to do much good.[2] However I may probably try again.[3] I have had cocaine, menthol, and various other anodynes prescribed at different times, but have not got any real benefit, and little, if any, temporary relief from any of them. It is sometimes rather troublesome, but on the whole I think *waning*.[4]

We are leaving tomorrow for Paris and Rome to be away a month, and after that settled in London.

> Yours,
> KELVIN

1 LB5.106 in the Kelvin Collection is a draft of this letter. Changes from the draft to the letter are pointed out in the following notes.
2 LB5.106 reads: '⟨and⟩ but I am afraid it ⟨can scarcely⟩ is not to do much good'.
3 LB5.106 reads: 'However, I ⟨shall⟩ may probably try again'.
4 LB5.106 reads: 'It is sometimes rather ⟨bad⟩ troublesome; ⟨but really if it is never any worse, I am content to go on as I am. I am thankful that it is no worse⟩'.

630 STOKES to KELVIN, 4 June 1899
Kelvin Collection, S544

> Lensfield Cottage, Cambridge, 4 June, 1899.

MY DEAR KELVIN,

Lady Stokes told me your address was Curzon Street, giving no number. I asked the Master of Peterhouse,[1] and he knew of none except your old address 28 Chester Square. So I am sending my Wilde Lecture[2] there, with a note by way of a flying shot addressed without a number to Curzon Street.

> Yours sincerely,
> G. G. STOKES

1 James Porter.
2 Stokes (130).

631 KELVIN to STOKES, 5 June 1899[1]
Stokes Collection, K350

28 Chester Square
London, S.W.
June 5, 1899.

DEAR STOKES,

Many thanks for the Wilde Lecture,[2] which I received this morning, and your note to Curzon Street, grieving me very much, this evening. I am *awfully* sorry you had the trouble and uncertainty as to my address. I intended to give it to Lady Stokes, and am exceedingly sorry that I forgot to do so and gave you all this trouble.

I have read the Lecture through, and am greatly pleased with the 'Additional Note', giving, as it does, the complete solution for diffraction in the shortest way possible.[3]

Yours
KELVIN

1 LB5.130 in the Kelvin Collection is a draft of this letter.
2 Stokes (130).
3 LB5.130 reads: 'I have read the Lecture through, and am greatly pleased with the ⟨short and simple way in wh you determine the diffraction⟩ "additional note". ⟨It⟩ giving, as it does, the complete solution in the shortest way possible'.

632 STOKES to KELVIN, 9 and 10 June 1899
Kelvin Collection, S545

Lensfield Cottage, Cambridge, 9 June, 1899.[1]

MY DEAR KELVIN,

I have thought a little of the general nature of the problem you spoke to me about – that of diffraction in a Green elastic medium. It would doubtless be complicated, but I am not sure but that it might be feasible.
(Resumed June 10). The three partial differential equations which the dependent variables (which in Green's notation are u, v, w) have to satisfy lead by elimination to what Cauchy called the 'characteristic equation', which any one of the independent variables and others, such as $\dfrac{du}{dx}+\dfrac{dv}{dy}+\dfrac{dw}{dz}$ derived from them, have to satisfy. In the present case the operative symbol of the characteristic equation may ⟨v⟩ be written in a conventional sense as

$$\left(\frac{d^2}{dt^2}-\frac{d^2\,\phi}{du^2}\right)\left(\frac{d^2}{dt^2}-\frac{d^2\,\phi}{dv^2}\right)\left(\frac{d^2}{dt^2}-\frac{d^2\,\phi}{dw^2}\right)-\left(\frac{d^2}{dt^2}-\frac{d^2\,\phi}{du^2}\right)\left(\frac{d^2\,\phi}{d\langle y\rangle\,v\,d\langle z\rangle\,w}\right)^2$$

$$-\left(\frac{d^2}{dt^2}-\frac{d^2\phi}{dv^2}\right)\left(\frac{d^2\phi}{dw\,du}\right)^2-\left(\frac{d^2}{dt^2}-\frac{d^2\phi}{dw^2}\right)\left(\frac{d^2\phi}{du\,dv}\right)^2-2\,\frac{d^2\phi}{dv\,dw}\,\frac{d^2\phi}{dw\,du}\,\frac{d^2\phi}{du\,dv} \qquad (1.)$$

The convention is this:– ϕ is a quadratic function of first differential coefficients of u, v, or w with respect to x, y, or z, and we are supposed to treat such a term as $\left(\frac{d^{\langle2\rangle}u}{dx^{\langle2\rangle}}\right)^2$ or $\left(\frac{d^2u}{dy\,dz}\right)\frac{du}{dy}\frac{dv}{dz}$ as if it were simply a product $\frac{d^2}{d\langle t\rangle x^2}\cdot u^2$ or $\frac{d}{dy}\frac{d}{dz}\cdot uv$ and take the second differential coefficient of ϕ with respect to u, v, or w accordingly, so that after the differentiation nothing is left but symbols of operation. If Ω be taken for the dependent variable in the characteristic equation, that equation will be of the form

$$\frac{d^6\Omega}{dt^6}-P_2\frac{d^4\Omega}{dt^4}+P_4\frac{d^2\Omega}{dt^2}-P_6\Omega=0 \qquad (2)$$

where P_2, P_4, P_6 are homogeneous integral functions of $\frac{d}{dx}$, $\frac{d}{dy}$, $\frac{d}{dz}$ of the orders 2, 4, 6 respectively, involving only even powers of those symbols.

In the general case, the surface of wave-slowness, the equation of which can readily be written down, is a central surface with three sheets. If the medium be isotropic, the characteristic equation takes the form

$$\left(\frac{d^2}{dt^2}-A\nabla\right)\left(\frac{d^2}{dt^2}-B\nabla\right)^2\Omega=0 \qquad (3)$$

and the surface of wave-slowness (and of course in this case the wave surface also) consists of 3 concentric spheres, two of which (answering to transverse vibrations) are coincident.

There can be no reasonable doubt that in the general case the disturbance arising from an initial disturbance confined to a portion of the medium within the closed surface S will be analogous to what it is in the particular case of isotropy. Let P be a point, say outside S, where the disturbance is sought. Make P the ⟨centre of a wave surface which beginning as a poi⟩ centre of a wave surface (not that of Fresnel) which beginning as a point at P swells outwards with the appropriate velocity of propagation. There will be no disturbance at P till the surface reaches S, and when all the sheets have passed outside S the disturbance at P will cease. Between those two times there will be disturbance at P. The disturbance will be expressed, partly by a triple integral extending over such portion of S as lies between the outer and inner shells, partly by a double integral extending over such portion of the respective shells as may lie within S. If the distance of P from S be large compared with the

733

dimensions of S, the disturbance at P expressed by the triple integrals will be very small compared with the part depending on the double integrals.

We may form any ⟨syp⟩ symmetrical function of the roots of an algebraic equation even though we may be unable to solve the equation itself, so as to get the individual roots. It is conceivable by analogy that we might be able to solve the proposed dynamical problem, or rather to get some result of a nature not to involve a specification of the individual sheets of the wave surface, even though the characteristic equation (2) might not split up into three, so as to be of the form

$$\left(\frac{d^2}{dt^2} - P\right)\left(\frac{d^2}{dt^2} - Q\right)\left(\frac{d^2}{dt^2} - R\right)\Omega = 0$$

where P, Q, R are integral quadratic functions of $\frac{d}{dx}$, $\frac{d}{dy}$, $\frac{d}{dz}$.

Yours sincerely,
G. G. STOKES

1 Kelvin's secretary has written on the envelope, 'Stokes June 12/99. wave-surface in a "Green" medium'.

633 KELVIN to STOKES, 2 August 1899
Stokes Collection, K351

Aix-Les-Bains
Grand Hôtel Britannique
Aug 2, 1899

DEAR STOKES

I send you, along with this but by parcel post, the promised Address giving in permanent form, the congratulations and good wishes which I expressed to you *short* in the Senate-house on the 2nd of June on the part of the Royal Society of Edinburgh.[1]

We came here a few days ago for the sake of the baths for Lady Kelvin who has got much benefit from them several times before, but I am taking them also as advised that they may help to stop my neuralgia which has been very troublesome for some time back. It is however, baths or no baths outward bound just now I believe, and I hope very soon to be practically free from it, at least for a time.

I am trying to push on my volume of Baltimore Lectures, but just at present with little success. I hope your Vol III.[2] is going on swimmingly if it is not already launched (a sad ⟨confusion⟩ derangement of epitaphs this!)

We hope Lady Stokes is keeping well. Lady Kelvin joins in kindest regards.

Ever yours
KELVIN

1 In June 1899 Cambridge celebrated Stokes's jubilee as Lucasian professor. The order of the proceedings is published in *Trans. Camb. Phil. Soc.*, 18 (1899), vii–xv, and the congratulatory addresses from various institutions are in Stokes's *Memoir*, 1, 433–70, that from the Royal Society of Edinburgh being on page 449.
2 Of Stokes's *MPP*.

634 KELVIN to STOKES, 19 September 1899
Stokes Collection, K352

Sep 19, 1899
The University,
Glasgow.

DEAR STOKES

I am not one of the electors of my successor here,[1] but the testimonials of all the candidates have been sent to me (officially) and it is probable I may be asked to advise.

Can you tell me anything regarding the relative merits of Townsend[2] and McClelland?[3]

Townsend's paper (Phil. Trans. 1896)[4] on the Magnetization of Liquids seems to me much the strongest thing that has come from either. They are both I believe very good men. I see in McClelland's Testimonials a short statement that you gave him last ⟨Jan⟩ February when he was candidate for the chair of Physics in the University of Sydney.[5]

I am very anxious, as you may imagine, that the best possible man may now be got for Glasgow, so I hope you will excuse my asking if you can help me to advise. Anything you can tell me would be a great help.

Did you ever publish an account of some very interesting experiments which you told me a good many years ago you had made on phosphorescence. I cannot remember, exactly what they were, but I well remember thinking them of great importance in respect to dynamical theory.

I hope you have been enjoying your visit to Dover, where I see by the Times you have been. Lady Kelvin joins in kind regards to yourself and Lady Stokes and we hope she has been keeping fairly well through the summer.

Yours always
KELVIN

1 Kelvin retired from his Glasgow professorship in 1899 and was replaced by Andrew Gray.
2 John Sealy Edward Townsend (1868–1957) took his B.A. at Cambridge in 1897 and was Wykeham professor of physics at Oxford from 1901 to 1941.
3 John Alexander McClelland (1870–1920) took his B.A. at Cambridge in 1898 and was professor of physics at University College, Dublin, from 1900 to 1920.
4 Townsend, 'Magnetization of liquids', *Phil. Trans.*, series A (1896), 533–49.
5 M53a in the Stokes Collection is a testimonial for McClelland by Stokes, dated 11 February 1899, and M53, dated 11 September 1899, is a letter from McClelland to Stokes, asking Stokes's permission to use the February testimonial for the Glasgow position.

635   STOKES to KELVIN, 22 September 1899
       Kelvin Collection, S546

Lensfield Cottage, Cambridge, 22 Sept. 1899.[1]

MY DEAR KELVIN,

I have just returned from the meeting of the british [sic] Association at Dover. My wife forwarded to me your letter to Dover, but I could not well answer it during the bustle of the meeting. It bears the Dover postmark of Sept. 20. Yesterday was devoted to the excursion to Boulogne and back.

Two candidates, Townsend and Wilson,[2] asked me for testimonials. I seemed to have it on my mind that there was a third, but on looking over the letters I only found those from Townsend and Wilson. I thought to look into what they had done respectively; but I found that I did not know enough about their merits to venture to say anything, and so I wrote a letter to the Board of Electors, which you probably have seen. It was later, and after the time had passed, that I found a letter from Mc. Clelland [sic] asking for a testimonial.[3] This accounts for my not having said anything about him in my letter to the electors.

Townsend lent me a proof copy of a paper of his that is going into the Phil. Trans. It is entitled 'The diffusion of ions into gases'.[4] I suppose you have before you the abstract, but the Phil. Trans. paper is not yet published.

The paper is one with which I should probably – almost certainly – not feel myself competent to deal even if I had time to study it. I have glanced into parts of it, and as far as I can judge by such a very cursory examination, if I can even call it so much, it seems to me a strong paper.

I have no time to look into McClelland's work, as I want you to get this by tomorrow's morning post.

Mary has been by no meams [sic] well during my absence.

Yours most sincerely,
G. G. STOKES[5]

1 Kelvin's secretary has written on the envelope, 'Stokes – Sepr 23/99. with Copy of Answer. re. Townsend's Paper on Diffusion of ions. Glasgow election (to abstract)'.

2 Charles Thomson Rees Wilson (1869–1959) took his B.A. at Cambridge in 1892, placing in the first class for part II of the natural sciences tripos. He held various positions at Cambridge until 1934 and won a Nobel Prize in 1927. See the letters from him to Stokes, 4 and 14 September 1899, Stokes Collection, W794 and W795.

3 See the previous letter, note 5.

4 J. S. E. Townsend, 'The diffusion of ions into gases', *Phil. Trans.*, series A (1900), 129–58.

5 Below Stokes's signature, Kelvin's secretary has copied Kelvin's reply (i.e., the next letter). There are no important differences between Kelvin's letter and his secretary's copy.

636 KELVIN to STOKES, 23 September 1899[1]
Stokes Collection, K353

> The University,
> Glasgow.
> Sept. 23/99

DEAR STOKES,

I thank you for your letter of yesterday. I wish I had been with you at Dover and on your visit to France on Thursday.

A copy of your letter to the Board of Electors came to me next morning after I wrote to you. When I wrote to you, I had seen the proof copy of Townsend's last 'Transactions' paper.[2] It is certainly, as you say, very strong. One little awkward matter of notation in it may give trouble to a mathematician looking through it. I suggested to Townsend to put θ everywhere instead of θ^2: but he told me it was too late, as he had received final copies. He is going to have an amendment inserted '$d(\theta^2)$' for '$d\theta^2$'. The work on p. 135 shows great capacity and originality. The theorem (6b) is beautiful, and is much wider than the required application; but it is more easy to prove the general theorem than to prove it for the particular case (7b) of p. 136. P. 136 is virtually Sturm[3] and Liouville of which applications to Bessel's functions are[4] well known, although their general theorems are not, I believe, very generally known to mathematical people at the end of the 19th century.

Townsend's problem, is, if applied to thermal conduction, a curious, hitherto untouched, problem:– a liquid or gas continually enters one end of a long cylindrical tube at a uniform temperature all over the cross-section. The fluid moves[5] rigorously according to the viscous law for[6] 'steady' motion. The boundary of the tube is kept at zero temperature. It is required to find the quantity of heat carried per unit of time across any section. *N.B.* Where the fluid enters and throughout the tube, the velocity is assumed to be Const. $\times(a^2 - r^2)$.

> Yours very truly
> KELVIN

1 See the previous letter, note 5. LB6.35 in the Kelvin Collection is a draft of this letter in Kelvin's secretary's hand.
2 See the previous letter, note 4. LB6.35 has a different version of the first two sentences of this paragraph, which is deleted.
3 Charles François Sturm (1803–55) was both professor of mechanics in the Faculty of Sciences and professor of analysis and mechanics in the École Polytechnique from 1840 to 1855.
4 In LB6.35, '⟨quite⟩' is written after *are* and deleted.
5 In LB6.35, '⟨with⟩' is written after *moves* and deleted.
6 In LB6.35, '⟨non-turbulent⟩' is written after *for* and deleted.

637   KELVIN to STOKES, 1 January 1900
Stokes Collection, K354

> Jan 1, 1900
> Netherhall.
> Largs.
> Ayrshire.

DEAR STOKES

I sympathise with you deeply in the great grief which has come.[1] For ourselves we both feel the loss very keenly of one who has so long been our friend.

It will be very hard for you to bear up, but you have a consolation that cannot fail.

Lady Kelvin joins in love and I remain

> Yours always
> KELVIN

1 This refers to the death of Stokes's wife.

638   KELVIN to STOKES, 14 July 1900[1]
Kelvin Collection, LB7.62

> Jy 14 '00

DEAR STOKES,

I am very sorry I cannot go to the V[ictoria] I[nstitute] meeting [with] you on Monday as I am going to Edinburgh that day for the R.S. to return here on Tuesday.

1 This is a draft in Kelvin's secretary's hand of the letter which does not survive.

639 STOKES to KELVIN, 23 November 1900
Kelvin Collection, S547

Cambridge 23^{d} Nov. 1900[1]

MY DEAR KELVIN,

I have much pleasure in accepting your kind invitation. I am sorry I cannot ask you here, as just about that time we shall be in the confusion of moving. Indeed I do not know in which of two houses I shall then be. My son-in-law[2] has purchased this house and the adjacent one on the west, and I am going to live with them in the latter, and this house has already been let from Christmas.

I am afraid I am still a heretic as to the possibility (instability of motion apart) of discontinuous motion in[3] a perfect fluid. Kindest regards to Lady Kelvin.

Yours sincerely
G. G. STOKES

1 Kelvin has written on the envelope, 'Stokes Nov 24. "Heretic". enclosed Copy of answ. Dec 13 to this & a second letter (Dec 7 or 8) ⟨enclosed⟩'.
 He has written at the top of the letter, 'See p 2. K Dec 13'. This refers to the marginal line mentioned in note 3.
2 Laurence Humphry (1856–1920) took his B.A. at Cambridge in 1877, was lecturer in medicine at Cambridge from 1901 to 1911, and was physician to Addenbrooke's Hospital.
3 Kelvin has drawn a line down the left side of part of this paragraph, marking the passage, *I am afraid . . . motion in.*

640 STOKES to KELVIN, 8 December 1900
Kelvin Collection, S548

Lensfield Cottage, Cambridge, 8 Dec. 1900.

MY DEAR KELVIN,

Our intended interview on the 2nd. did not come off in consequence of our playing hide and go seek. We cannot have a talk for some time, for I am going to Shrewsbury next week, and you to Scotland. I suppose you will not be back for some considerable time.

I have not the least conception how you imagine discontinuity in (otherwise) irrotational motion disproved by your little sphere. You spoke of it in a letter as rolling; but it would not roll. You referred me to a paper of yours in the Edinburgh transactions.[1] When you get access to your books, would you kindly give me the volume and page? Meanwhile I must confess that I am a sceptic.

As regards the question of the possibility or otherwise of discontinuity in a perfect fluid, we must of course keep two different questions distinct, namely,

(1) does the motion satisfy all the conditions of the problem?, (2) if it does, is the motion stable or unstable?

Yours sincerely,
G. G. STOKES

1 Kelvin (167).

641 KELVIN to STOKES, 13 December 1900[1]
Stokes Collection, K355

Netherhall.
Largs, Ayrshire.
Dec. 13th. 1900.

DEAR STOKES,

The paper[2] to which I referred you is in the Transactions of the Royal Society od [sic] Edinburgh for 1869.[3] Its title is 'On Vortex Motion'. The following is §10 of it:– 'The moment of momentum of every spherical portion of a liquid mass in motion, relatively to the centre od [sic] the sphere, is always zero, if it is so at any one instant for every spherical portion of the liquid.' This[4] makes it certain that a surface of finite slip cannot come into existence in a pehfect [sic] liquid set at motion from rest by giving any motion to its boundary (for example, by setting a solid in motion through ito [sic].

I think if you find time to look at the paper you will see that[5] §§11, 15, and 16, establish the truth of §10 without the possibility of doubt: and shew that no sharpness of edge or points of solids in contact with the moving liquid can introduce any exception.

Yours ⟨truly⟩,
Signed (KELVIN)

I am sorry that by our 'hide and seek' after St. Mary's we had so short and meagre a discussion of finite slip.

1 This is a carbon copy of the typed original. LB8.34 in the Kelvin Collection is a draft of the letter in Kelvin's secretary's hand.
2 Kelvin (167).
3 Kelvin has added a footnote here reading, 'Trans. R.S.E. 1869, vol. XXV p. 217'.
4 In LB8.34, '⟨I think you will see that it absolutely disproves the idea of⟩' is written before *This* and deleted.
5 In LB8.34, '⟨the demonstration of §10 give a⟩' is written after *that* and deleted.

Ivy House Kingsland[1]
Shrewsbury 18 Dec. 1900

MY DEAR KELVIN,

Thanks for the reference,[2] which I will look up after my return to Cambridge, which will be probably on the 27th. Like you I am going to a wedding. A great nephew of mine,[3] who is an assistant master in Rugby School, is to be married in Rugby on the 27th.

As far as I can guess, the article to which you refer me comes to much the same thing as the proposition with which you and I are familiar, that in any continuous mass of fluid if the motion is once irrotational it will remain irrotational. In one of my early papers[4] I pointed out the connection of this with molecular angular velocity and moment of inertia. The demonstrations given by Lagrange and Poisson are essentially faulty, but Cauchy's is unexceptionable. You may possibly put the proposition in some new light, but I don't think you can make the demonstration more complete than Cauchy's, on the ground that you cannot have more perfect than perfect.

Some 3 or 4 years ago I was led to look more closely into the matter of discontinuity from some conversations with you, and was led to go into some questions connected with discontinuity that I had not before attended to, and my notions were cleared up.

I must frankly say I still think you are wrong in denying the intellectual possibility of discontinuity of motion in an intellectually conceivable perfect fluid.

There are 2 distinct questions for consideration (1) can discontinuity of motion begin as the result of pressures applied at the boundaries (2) if begun can it be continued?

(2) is the simpler in some respects, and I feel satisfied that the answer is, yes. It would however take too long to go into this on paper.

As to (1) I am not prepared at present to explain the how?, but I think that your objections involve an assumption of the nature of $\text{limit}_{x=a}$ of $\text{limit}_{y=b}$ of $f(x, y)$ is equal to $\text{limit}_{y=b}$ of $\text{limit}_{x=a}$ of $f(x, y)$ a proposition generally true but which fails at certain singular points, and I think a sharp edge ⟨However it would take⟩ is just such a point.

However it would take too long to discuss these matters on paper.

A happy Christmas to you and Lady Kelvin.

Yours sincerely
G. G. STOKES

P.S. The possibility of such and such a motion should be kept distinct from that of the stability of the motion if possible. The stability or instability is a question for ulterior consideration. The motion of a rough sphere rolling down the highest generating line of an inclined circular cylinder is possible but unstable. So as regards a fluid the possibility is not disproved by saying that the motion if it existed would be unstable.

1 Kelvin's secretary has written on the envelope, 'Stokes of Nov 24, Dec ⟨9⟩ 9, [Dec] 18. With copy of answer'. Kelvin has written '1900' at the side, placed *x*'s after *Nov 24* and *answer*, and written, 'not found Nov 27 1903'.
2 Kelvin (167).
3 William Fenwick Stokes (1859–1945) was eighth wrangler in 1881 and was at Rugby from 1889 to 1920.
4 Stokes (11).

643 STOKES to KELVIN, 19 and 20 December 1900
Kelvin Collection, S550

Ivy House, Kingsland, Shrewsbury[1]
19 Dec. 1900

MY DEAR KELVIN,

I recollect that in one of your letters to me you drew a figure something like

where *ab* represents a surface of slip, and *s* a very small sphere of the fluid, cut by the surface of slip. You said, Imagine the sphere to roll down the surface *ab*.

But surely the supposition of a rolling sphere utterly violates the fundamental idea of a surface of slip. The two portions of *s* would pass relatively to the surface *ab* into positions such as s_1, s_2. I say '*relatively* to the surface *ab*' in order to provide for the case of *ab*'s changing its position in space as the time goes on.

A surface of discontinuity, supposed to be paid out like the paper in a Morse telegraph receiving instrument would of course become very complicated in form. The surface would stretch out as it became older, and at the same time the amount of slip would get less and less.

Suppose a stream flowed into an expanse, as represented in the figure. The spiral lines on the right (I have drawn them only on the right) represent a surface of discontinuity at the same moment, the direction of the arrows

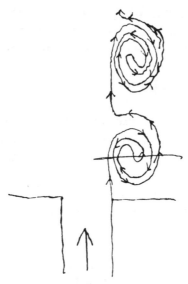

indicating increasing age (from birth at the corner). Imagine that you travel along the surface in the direction of the arrows. Then you always have the swifter fluid on your left. Draw a line (pencil) through the ammonite. This line is cut in a great number of points where there are slips in opposite directions alternately. But they don't neutralise one another on account of the difference of age. The younger prevail over the older, so that if we regard the spires as very close and numerous and treat the motion in an ammonite as if it were continuous we get a vortex or eddy though working with a perfect fluid.

As to the reason why the fluid of the stream pushes the surface of junction in the manner drawn, the inflowing fluid, though it tends to keep to a stream of its own, is not kept to this by any rigid boundary, and does widen a bit. This checks the velocity and increases the pressure and the fluid of the stream pushes outwards the fluid in the expanse as in the figure. It might have been well to have coloured one of the two portions of fluid forming an ammonite. I will do the thing roughly with a pencil.[2]
Of course this is only the rudest figure, but it will show what I mean.

Yours sincerely
G. G. STOKES

P. S. I feel little doubt that this is the way in which eddies are actually produced. It seems evident that the mere viscosity of water would be utterly insufficient to account for them when they are formed on a large scale, as in a mill pool or whirlpool.

If I cared to spend time over it I would have drawn a better ammonite on the opposite page.[3]

Of course eddies are *modified* by viscosity, but except on quite a small scale I hold that viscosity is subordinate. Of course it prevents a finite slip, which it converts into a rapid shear, but viscosity tends to stability not instability. Reynolds pointed out that the dimensional relations which contain the conditions of dynamical as well as geometrical similarity are applicable *to the setting in* of turbulance, and to the mean effects when the motion is eddying.

Dec. 20, 1900.

1 Kelvin has written on the envelope, 'Stokes. two letters ⟨Dec. 20⟩ of Dec 19th, 1900'.
2 Beside the figure Stokes has written, 'I did not mean to have drawn the shaded and unshaded parts so unequal in thickness'.
3 'The opposite page' in Stokes's letter includes the previous figure.

644 STOKES to KELVIN, 20 December 1900
Kelvin Collection, S551

Ivy House, Kingsland, Shrewsbury[1]
20 Decr 1900

MY DEAR KELVIN,

After posting my letter I thought I would write a line to point out how the difference between us depends *entirely* on the question of stability. We agree as to the unique solution, the same as for the conduction of heat. Does the solution represent a stable or unstable state of things? I say, from heat stable, from fluid motion unstable. You say stable from both. Never mind for the present *how* an infinitesimal slip may have originated: the question is, Will it be continued or mended, the abnormality being carried away? You say the latter, I say the former if the rift be suitably originated. It must not be in the bosom of the fluid, but abutting against a boundary. It may be at a sharp corner, in which case it must be a prolongation of one of the sides. I will go deeper in heresy and say it may be at a boundary of continuous curvature, in which case it must be tangential to the boundary.

Yours sincerely
G. G. STOKES

1 Kelvin has written on the envelope, 'Stokes. Dec 20, 1900'.

Lensfield, Cambridge, 4 Jan. 1901.[1]

MY DEAR KELVIN,

I have looked into your terrible Sect. 10,[2] which was to have demolished me. I can only say 'there is life in the old dog yet'. Instead of some fearful apparition, I found only an old familiar friend, in fact, the fundamental theorem about irrotational motion first proved in an unexceptionable manner by Cauchy. In one of your letters you took a sphere which you supposed to be cut in two by a surface of slip. Of course the moment of momentum in that s[p]here is not nil, nor is there any reason why it should [be]. The fundamental proposition applies only where there is absence of discontinuity. That is to say it applies to either portion of the fluid interrupted by a surface of discontinuity, but it does not apply to a mongrel sphere made up partly of the one portion and partly of the other. The very demonstration of the pr[o]position warns us against such a misapplication. Cauchy's equations are three which with the omega notation are of the type

$$\omega = \frac{dx}{da}\,\omega_\circ + \frac{dx}{db}\,\omega'_\circ + \frac{dx}{dc}\,\omega''_\circ$$

where x, y, z are the actual, and a, b, c the imitial [*sic*] coordinates. If we like to consider a slip as the limit of a continuous change of velocity of course we may, though I do not see that that helps us, as the conception of a slip is perfectly simple. But if we do like to consider it in that way we may; only we must remember that in that case the diff. cos. of x, y, z ⟨bec⟩ with respect to a, b, c become infinite.

I feel almost absolutely certain that we may have a slip surface. Never mind at present how it was started; the question is, will it be sustained? I say, Yes; not in the bosom of the liquid, but, under suitable conditions, where the liquid is interrupted by a boundary. I mentioned ⟨toy ou⟩ to you I think some time ago the conclusions at which I had arrived relative to the direction which a surface of slip, if there be one, must take in leaving a boundary. Perhaps we may have a talk about this some day, but at present I suppose that you are at Netherhall, and are likely to remain there for some time. A happy new year and century to you and Lady Kelvin.

Yours sincerely,
G. G. STOKES[3]

1 Kelvin has written on the envelope, 'Stokes, of ⟨Dec 31⟩ Jan 4, 1901 and copy of answer of Jan 7 enclosed. Keep, with correspondence on same subject of two or three years ago, about Xmas time'.
2 Of Kelvin (167).

3 Kelvin has written beneath Stokes's signature, 'See copy of answer attached. K Jan 7, 1901'.

646 KELVIN to STOKES, 7 January 1901[1]
Stokes Collection, K356

Jan 7th '01. Netherhall.

DEAR STOKES,

I always thought Cauchy's proof of the fundamental theorem of irrotationality in the motion of a frictionless incompressible fluid unexceptionably valid. Neither in the neighbourhood of a boundary nor in the 'bosom of the liquid' can irrotationality come into existence unless there is irrotationality some where in the liquid to begin with.

Certainly there can be 'slip-surfaces' and if once started a slip surface will last for ever. Consider a rigid body (a globe if you like) set into motion through a perfect liquid initially at rest. Then, with no longer any force acting on the rigid body or the liquid, let the former suddenly lose rigidity. We have now a slip surface *'in the bosom of the liquid'* with no boundary anywhere. The motion is now horribly unstable.

Lady Kelvin joins me in thanking you for your good wishes and in wishing you in return a Happy New Year and happy ninety nine remaining years of the twentieth century.[2]

Yours always.
Signed (KELVIN)

1 This is a copy in Kelvin's secretary's hand.
2 Kelvin's footnote here reads, 'See Calendar instructions in the Prayer Book!'

647 STOKES to KELVIN, 9 and 10 January 1901
Kelvin Collection, S553

Lensfield, Cambridge, 9 Jan. 1901.[1]

MY DEAR KELVIN,

Your letter of the 7th. leads me to think that perhaps after all there is not much, if any, difference between us in the matter of finite slip. I do not hold that discontinuity can arise *in the bosom* of the perfect liquid. I was not always clear about this point, or rather, perhaps, I had not taken it into serious consideration, but after one of our conversations I felt satisfied that it could not. It does not however follow from this that it cannot originate at a boundary, where the continuity of the fluid all round, that is, in all directions from a particle at the boundary, ceases. Cauchy's equation does not disprove this, for the application of differentiation postulates continuity. The possible existence of a singular point where discontinuity may begin remains open to examination. I think that in all probability discontinuity *may* commence at some point of a boundary. However as I said before supposing such a discontinuity to have just begun, will it be continued or will it be healed? By healing I merely mean, Will it behave like a small rift supposed to exist in the bosom of a perfect liquid? In that case the surface of slip, as time goes on, will become infinitely extensive and the amount of slip infinitely small. In other words, Will the *normal* motion be stable or unstable? By 'normal' I don't mean the motion resolved perpendicular to the surface; I use the word normal merely for shortness, to designate the kind of motion, with continuous phi, with which we are both familiar.

However as I said in a former letter let us for the present not consider how a discontinuity at the boundary may be conceived to have originated; suppose it already there, at a suitable part of the boundary, and pose the question, Will the surface of slip continue to be formed at the boundary, being paid out like the paper in a telegraph receiver, or will it be washed away, leaving the motion Normal? Observe I said, 'at a suitable part of the boundary'; the question is, Will it be found somewhere or nowhere? The case I am considering is that of a solid immersed in a flowing stream, which it will be convenient to suppose as flowing in an infinitely long tunnel closed on all sides. The question is, Will the 'normal' notion [sic] be stable or unstable? You say, Certainly stable. I say, Certainly unstable. Of course I allow that the normal motion is ideally possible, just as the motion of a sphere rolling down along the highest generating line of a circular inclined cylinder is ideally possible. But I hold that the former motion is not any more realisable than the latter, on account of the instability of that motion in the former case just as in the latter. In the corresponding solution for the uniform propagation of heat in an isotropic conducting solied, [sic] we have only the 'normal' solution, because while the fluid has two strings to its bow the heat has not.

Now what reason can you give for supposing that the 'normal' motion would be stable? You said to me one day that for a perfect fluid moving with given motion of the boundaries, the normal $\langle n \rangle$ motion was that of minimum kinetic energy. Perfectly true; but what has that got to do with stability of the motion? Take our tunnel with fluid flowing through it, and let the stream at one place be interrupted by a solid which the fluid has to flow round. Regard as moving boundaries the surface of particles in two sections at very great distances, one in front and one in rear. Supposing for simplicity the tunnel to be uniform, the velocity over the front section will ultimately be uniform, and that over the rear section will ultimately be uniform, and the two must be the same on account of incompressibility. Moreover the pressure over the front section will ultimately (i.e. at a sufficiently great distance from the interrupting solid) be uniform and the pressure over the rear section will ultimately be uniform. The velocity at the sections may be supposed given and likewise the pressure at one (*but not both*) of them may be supposed given. The difference of pressures at great distances front and rear depends upon the kind of motion about the interrupting solid. If the motion be 'normal' the pressures at great distances front are [*sic*] rear are equal, but for motion of any other character the pressure at a distance in front is necessarily greater than the pressure at a great distance in the rear.

Just the same is true if the fluid be unlimited instead of being confined by the walls of a tunnel, only of course in this ⟨cas⟩ case the pressure would not be constant over the whole of a section taken at a distance in a direction perpendicular to the flow.

So the upshot is that the stability of the 'normal' motion is 'not proven', nor do I expect it to be proven, for I hold it to be not true.

I don't think you can convict the prayerbook of setting us wrong about the end of the 19th century. A century I take to mean 100 consecutive years. Thus from 1746 to 1845, both inclusive, is a century. Just so if you have a table which holds good up to 1899 inclusive, the next century will be from 1900 to 1999, both inclusive. It is only when you affix an ordinal number to a century, which the prayerbook does not do, that you are concerned with the origin of the time.

A happy new century to you and Lady Kelvin.

Yours sincerely,
G. G. STOKES

10 Jan. 1901.

1 Kelvin has written on the envelope, 'Stokes. Jan 12 1901. Fluid motion (finite slip). Keep with predecessors. K Jan 12 1901'.

648 KELVIN to STOKES, 20 April 1901[1]
Stokes Collection, K357

15, Eaton Place,
S.W.
April 20ᵗʰ 1901.

DEAR STOKES,

My investigation (Pres. Address, 1892; Pop. Lect. and Addresses vol ii p. 521)[2] to which you refer in your letter of yesterday took into account the question of long waves or short waves in ether. A sudden disturbance[3] comprised within a time of a few seconds would[4] diminish much less with distance from the sun than according to the static law for gradually changing magnetism. But if the duration of the disturbance is two or three times the 8 minutes that light takes to come from the sun, the diminution of intensity with distance would[5] be fairly close to the static law. I took all this into account however.

I have had rather a bad time with the demon of number 5, but the warmer weather I think is going to send him away to wait for worse times, when I suppose he will attack me again. Otherwise we are both well. Lady Kelvin thanks you for your kind message.

Yours
KELVIN

1 LB9.129 in the Kelvin Collection is a draft of this letter in Kelvin's secretary's hand.
2 Kelvin (331).
3 In LB9.129, '⟨of period to⟩' is written after *disturbance* and deleted.
4 In LB9.129, '⟨not⟩' is written after *would* and deleted.
5 In LB9.129, '⟨follow⟩' is written after *would* and deleted.

649 KELVIN to STOKES, 2 July 1901[1]
Kelvin Collection, LB10.89

July 2

DEAR STOKES,

Thanks for your note of 29[th]. If you look in the second vol. of my PL&A p 538 or Pres. Add to Roy Soc Nov 30 1893[2] you will find a reference wh I made to Bentl[e]y letter & to Daniel Bernoulli's counter view.

Can you tell me whether ⟨it was⟩ the Lorentz [i.e., Lorenz] of Copenhagen or Lorentz of Leiden.[3]

I hope you are not forgetting your promise to bring out vol iii[4] by August.

Yours

1 This is a draft of the letter in Kelvin's secretary's hand.
2 Kelvin (338).
3 On the facing page in the letter-book, Kelvin's secretary has written:

the Lorentz you refer to in vol II p 328 of your M & P papers was ⟨the one of⟩
    Do you know if any one has made your polarizational diffraction exp with a Rowland grating?

See Stokes (40) in *MPP*, II, 243–328, in which on page 328 he cites Lorenz, not Lorentz. See letter 598, note 1. Hendrik Antoon Lorentz (1853–1928) was professor of theoretical physics at Leiden from 1877 to 1912.
4 Of Stokes's *MPP*.

Kelvin Collection, S554

4 Windsor Terrace[1]
Malahide C° Dublin 16 Sept. 1901

MY DEAR KELVIN,

I don't know where you are now, but I write a few lines to let you know that last Saturday (Sept. 14) I returned to press the title page and contents of my vol. III.[2] I heard at the press before I left Cambridge that they had got something from you. I don't know whether you or I have won our tortoise race.[3] My vol. runs to 415 pages, but only takes me to 1852. I hope to get on when I return to Cambridge. I mean to add but little; but how long a man who has entered on his 83^d year can carry on such work we cannot tell.

It so happens that the very day I returned my title page for press was my sister's birthday, when she attained the age of 91.[4] She is wonderfully well, bright and able to go about. She is able to go to church, walking some hundreds of yards up hill, and goes out now and then, walking to afternoon teas.

I hope you are not suffering from your 5th nerve, and that Lady Kelvin is well.

Yours sincerely
G. G. STOKES

1 Kelvin has written on the envelope, 'Stokes. Announcing Vol III. complete. Keep. Answ^d Sep 22 Sunday'.
2 Of his *MPP*.
3 Volume III of Kelvin's *MPP* had been published in 1890, but volume IV was not published until 1910.
4 Elizabeth Mary Stokes.

Kelvin Collection, S555

4 Windsor Terrace Malahide[1]
C° Dublin 24 Sept. 1901

MY DEAR KELVIN,

As you have got my finished sheets, I would be glad if you would kindly look at 2½ pages of letter press, pp. 410–412, an addition I put to my paper on the change of refrangibility of light.[2] I did not take a memorandum of the observation on the fluorescence (or phosphorescence, whichever you like to call it) of certain glasses which led me to the view as to the nature of fluorescence there mentioned, but it must have been some time (in the summer probably) before Kalley Miller[3] took his degree, for I recollect I was keen about the problem when I was making questions for the Smith's Prize for his year, and I feel almost certain, I may say certain, I was thinking of setting it, but changed my mind and merely set a problem about a finite instead of an infinite loaded string. I think both you and Routh[4] arrived at analogous conclusions as to a change from exponential to circular-function form in analogous dynamical problems. However it is the physical question I have chiefly in view, and I should be glad to know what you think of my sign-post, pointing out the road that would lead to an explanation of fluorescence.

Yours sincerely

G. G. STOKES

1 Kelvin has written on the envelope, 'Stokes. Sep 25 1901. Fluoresence [*sic*] or Phosphorescence. Answ^d few days later'.
2 Stokes (42) in *MPP*, III, 267–413.
3 Robert Kalley Miller (1842–89) was first Smith's prizeman in 1867 and became a fellow of Peterhouse the same year. He had taken an M.A. at Glasgow before coming to Cambridge.
4 Edward John Routh (1831–1907) was senior wrangler in 1854 and became the leading coach for the mathematical tripos.

652   KELVIN to STOKES, 4 October 1901[1]
Stokes Collection, K358

Netherhall,
Largs,
Ayrshire.
Oct. 4, 1901.

DEAR STOKES,

I have been prevented from sooner answering your last letter[2] by a promise I had given to Professor Kamerlingh Onnes[3] of Leiden to send an article[4] [']Aepinus Atomized'[5] for a volume commemorating the jubilee of[6] Professor Bosscha[7] before Oct. 10. I got it dispatched last nigrt [*sic*] but it has taken all my time for the last fortnight.[8]

When you get back to Cambridge if you look into vol. 1 of my Popular Lectures and Addresses (p. 211[9] in the second edition and probably the same in the first)[10] you will see that at some time which in 1883 I called long ago you had told me of an explanation of fluorescence or phosphorescence or stored up or latent light which had occurred to you. I am greatly interested now in seeing it in your volume 3,[11] and seeing that the long ago was some time bedore [*sic*] 1867. I am very glad that you have at last given it to the world. The change of colour with lapse of time of which you tell in pp. 410, 411 and your explanation of it seem to me most important. I think there must certainly be truth in the dynamics which you describe in pp. 411–413. I feel difficult[12] about the total quantity of luminous energy to be explained, but full consideration of the diffusion of vibratory mitions [*sic*] inwards throughout large superficial layers or the whole intereor [*sic*] of the phospherescent [*sic*] body may make the whole thing clear.[13]

I hope you have been having a good holiday and enjoying it with your sister and friends in Ireland, and when you get bacx [*sic*] to Cambridge will feel thoroughly invigorated and ready to start immediately on volume 4.

Will[14] you dine with me[15] at Peterhouse on the 29th. of this month, our anniversary day? Lady Kelvin and I hope to be at Cambridge for a few days at that time, probably to stay with the George Darwins.

1 This is a carbon copy of the typewritten original. LB11.32 in the Kelvin Collection is a draft in Kelvin's secretary's hand. Differences between LB11.32 and K358 are pointed out in several of the following notes.
2 In LB11.32, *letter* is followed by 'till today'.
3 Heike Kamerlingh Onnes (1853–1926) was an assistant to Johannes Bosscha at Delft from 1878 to 1882 and from 1882 to 1924 was professor of physics at Leiden. There are ten letters between him and Kelvin in the Kelvin Collection.
4 In LB11.32, '⟨short⟩' has been written and deleted before *article*.
5 Kelvin (375H).
6 In LB11.32, '⟨his colleague⟩' has been written and deleted after *of*.
7 Johannes Bosscha (1831–1911) received his Ph.D. at Leiden in 1854 and was professor and director at the Delft Polytechnic.
8 In LB11.32, a new sentence has been begun and deleted after *fortnight*: '⟨I remember you telling me a long time ago⟩'.
9 In LB11.32, '⟨if you have⟩' has been written and deleted after *211*.
10 Kelvin (262).
11 Stokes (42), to the reprint of which Stokes included an 'Addition'. (*MPP*, III, 410–13.)
12 In LB11.32, the word is *difficulty*.
13 In LB11.32, the following paragraph after *clear* has been deleted. There were many modifications and deletions within the paragraph before the whole thing was deleted.

Another thing which occurred to me is that metallic reflexion of the brightest silver, corresponding to $\mu^2 = \langle R\sqrt{-1}$ where R is real$\rangle$ a real negative number is to be explained ⟨by the shortest period of the free oscillations in the solid being longer than the ⟨longest⟩ shortest of the totally reflected⟩ incident light. This gives acceleration of phase in light passing thro an exceedingly thin ⟨metallic film wh is a result[?] of obst[?]⟩ totally reflected incident light being all of shorter period than the shortest ⟨of the natural[?] periods⟩ molecular periods of the ⟨solid⟩ metal ⟨and⟩

14 In LB11.32, '⟨We shall be⟩' has been written and deleted before *Will*.
15 In LB11.32, '⟨us⟩' has been deleted and replaced by 'me'.

653 STOKES to KELVIN, 8 October 1901
Kelvin Collection, S556

Lensfield Cambridge[1]
8 Oct. 1901

MY DEAR KELVIN,

I have made a note in my pocket book of your kind invitation for the 29th, which I have much pleasure in accepting.

I think the familiar phenomenon of the change of character (increase of wavelength and diminution of height) in the annular rings which spread out from the place of disturbance when you throw a stone into still water is analogous to fluorescence, depending on a similar dynamical principle. The wave problem may be subjected to mathematical calculation, though rather complicated; but if you had a complex system of molecules bathed in ether what do you think of the mathematics of such a system.

Yours sincerely
G. G. STOKES

1 Kelvin's secretary has written on the envelope, 'Answ[d] Oct. 17. 'o1'.

654 KELVIN to STOKES, 17 October 1901[1]
Stokes Collection, K359

Netherhall.
Largs.
Ayrshire.
October 17 1901.

DEAR STOKES,

I am not coming up to Cambridge on the 29th. as I have been suffering rather badly for several weeks from my no. 5 nerve, and the Master tells me that there is not important business at the college meeting, on account of which I should come to Cambridge. I am sorry to lose the pleasure this time of having you as my guest at dinner in Peterhouse Hall, to which I had been looking forward; but I hope we shall be able to make a short[2] visit to Cambridge some time a little later, when I can enjoy more meeting you and other friends.

The mathematics of waves traversing a complex system of molecules in ether would certainly have some analogy to surface water waves spreading out from a centre but would be far more difficult. I[3] hope we shall have a good talk over the whole subject when we meet.

Yours
KELVIN

1 LB11.51 in the Kelvin Collection is a draft of this letter in Kelvin's secretary's hand.
2 LB11.51 omits *short*.
3 After *I* in LB11.51, Kelvin's secretary has written and deleted '⟨w[d] like to have a good talk with⟩'.

655 KELVIN to STOKES, 28 October 1901[1]
Kelvin Collection, LB11.72

28. Oct. '01

DEAR STOKES,

⟨I had already⟩ A year or two ago you kindly allowed me to have ⟨advance proofs⟩ copies of all that was in print of your vol iii[2] which have been most useful to me. A few weeks ago I received copies of the remainder of ⟨vol iii⟩ the completed vol wh I have sent to be bound altogether. ⟨I am more the happy poss⟩ This morning the one you sent me has reached me. Shall I send it back to you? or might I ⟨send⟩ give it to my nephew Dͬ J. T. Bottoml[e]y who wd value it highly. But don't hesitate to say if there is any ⟨other⟩ better way of disposing of it. My nephew can always see my copy whenever he pleases.

As to the ⟨rec⟩ suggested 'reciprocal theorem' I ⟨follow⟩ ⟨adopt⟩ very often do as Paley[3]⟨'s statement⟩ says ⟨almost always in such cases⟩ mathematicians do when a new theorem is put before them. Try it in a particular case. Let the liquid be contained within an endless tube ⟨such as this⟩ as in the sketch ⟨and let the motion⟩. Two motions are geometrically possible. ⟨One⟩ (1) irrotational circulation[?] (2) rotation round a curved axis with angular vel. prop[ortional] to the linear velocity in (1).

(1) is a steady motion wh. if started will go on for ever of itself with no force except the pressure of the containing vessel acting on the liquid. In (2) there will be ⟨mo⟩ several times more revolutions per sec[ond] at A than at B. Hence this ⟨motio⟩ rotational motion cannot be steady: ⟨⟨unless force was applied⟩ because a line of particle[s] wh. at any time lies along axes of molecular rotation always continues to be a line of axes according to one of Helmholtz's theorems.[4]

⟨A very curious result would follow if on⟩ ⟨Having some relatio⟩ In connection with this question I think you might be interested in looking at a short paper of mine in the Phil Mag 1889 [*sic*] 1ˢᵗ half year p. 459. 'On the Stability of Steady & of Periodic Fluid Motion'.[5]

⟨Yours⟩

I am going today to Lords where I shall be at 15 Eaton Place S.W. for about ten days.

Yours
[KELVIN]

---

1 This is a draft of the letter in Kelvin's secretary's hand.
2 Of Stokes's *MPP*.
3 Presumably William Paley (1743–1805), Archdeacon of Carlisle, best known for his *Natural Theology; or, Evidences of the Existence and Attributes of the Deity. Collected from the Appearances of Nature* (London, 1802).

4 See Helmholtz, 'Ueber Integrale der hydrodynamischen Gleichungen, welche den Wirbel-bewegungen entsprechen', Crelle's *Journal für die reine und angewandte Mathematik*, 55 (1858), 25–55.

5 Kelvin (278), published in 1887.

656 STOKES to KELVIN, 29 October 1901
Kelvin Collection, S557

Lensfield, Cambridge, 29 Oct. 1901.[1]

MY DEAR KELVIN,

The reciprocal theorem I mentioned applies to the general case of rotational motion. The conditions for possible steady motion are the three

$$\left(\xi\frac{d}{dx}+\eta\frac{d}{dy}+\zeta\frac{d}{dz}\right)\begin{matrix}u\\v\\w\end{matrix}=\left(u\frac{d}{dx}+v\frac{d}{dy}+w\frac{d}{dz}\right)\begin{matrix}\xi\\\eta\\\zeta\end{matrix}$$

where ξ, η, ζ are the components of the angular velocity. The theorem follows at once from the equations. In the particular case of irrotational motion, each of the equations is satisfied identically, and the theorem does not hold *unless* the particular case of irrotational steady motion contemplated is the limit of a possible rotational steady motion, which doubtless is not in general true. I do not know that there is any case in which it is true. I cannot help thinking that the exceptional character in this respect of irrotational motion is connected with the instability of the theoretical motion of a perfect fluid in the rear of a body moving through it; an instability in which I believe though you don't.

In a perfect fluid between two similar and coaxal elliptic cylinders (motion in 2 dimensions) there is a possible steady motion for which the angular velocity is constant, and in which the particles in a radius vector remain in a radius vector. There is also a possible irrotational steady motion of circulation. But if you superpose the two for an init[i]al motion, the subsequent motion will not be steady.

Pray give my volume[2] to Bottomley. I hope the 'tic' is not troubling you badly.

Yours sincerely,
G. G. STOKES

1 Kelvin has written on the envelope, 'Stokes. Oct 30 1901'.
2 Volume III of Stokes's *MPP*.

NOTE TO THE INDEXES

In the indexes, Roman numerals refer to *page* numbers in the first volume's introductory material. Arabic numerals refer to *letter* numbers in the correspondence. An *h* and *n* following the number of a letter refer, respectively, to the heading of the letter and to a footnote to it. An italicized Arabic numeral signifies that the letter carries a footnote identifying the person referred to.

The numbering of Kelvin's and Stokes's articles in the Index of publications by Kelvin and Stokes is based on that in the *Catalogue of Scientific Papers*, compiled by the Royal Society of London, 19 vols., vols. I–XII (London, 1867–1902), vols. XIII–XIX (Cambridge, 1914–1925). Decimal notation (e.g., 29.1 and 29.2 under Kelvin) indicates articles listed separately which the Royal Society's *Catalogue* lists together. A number followed by a capital letter (e.g., 50A under Kelvin) indicates an article not listed in the Royal Society's *Catalogue*. For a more complete list of Kelvin's articles than that in the Royal Society's *Catalogue*, see Thompson, II, 1223–74. For example, 375H, 375L, 375P, and 375JJ are, respectively, 631, 635, 639, and 659 in Thompson. Abbreviations used for titles of books and journals are those listed on pages xiii–xiv of the first volume (pages viii–ix in volume 2).

INDEX OF PUBLICATIONS BY
KELVIN AND STOKES

KELVIN

Baltimore Lectures (1884) xvii, xxxi, xxxvi–xxxix, xlii, xliv–xlvi, 460n, 467

Baltimore Lectures (1904) xvii, xl, xlv–xlvi, 516n, 522n, 548, 550, 564n, 566, 576, 594, 600, 602, 605, 633

MPP 249, 413, 416, 426, 449, 473, 548, 650

PEM 379, 400, 421, 548

PLA 606, 648–9, 652

TNP xvi–xvii, xxxiii, 214, 218, 226–7, 244, 250, 269, 283, 334, 345, 428, 435, 443, 445, 451–2, 528

(1) 'On Fourier's expansions of functions in trigonometrical series', *Camb. Math. J.*, 2 (1841), 258–62. xlii

(2) 'On the uniform motion of heat in homogeneous solid bodies, and its connection with the mathematical theory of electricity', *Camb. Math. J.*, 3 (1843), 71–84. 48, 115

(6) 'Notes on orthogonal isothermal surfaces', *Camb. Math. J.*, 3 (1843), 286–8. 12–13

(8) 'On the equations of the motions of heat referred to curvilinear co-ordinates', *Camb. Math. J.*, 4 (1845), 33–42. 12

(9) 'Elementary demonstration of Dupin's theorem', *Camb. Math. J.*, 4 (1845), 62–4. 12–13

(10) 'Note on some points in the theory of heat', *Camb. Math. J.*, 4 (1845), 67–72. 53

(17) 'Extrait d'une lettre sur l'application du principe des images à la solution de quelques problèmes relatifs à la distribution d'électricité', *Journal de mathématiques pures et appliquées*, 10 (1845), 364–7. 22

(19) 'On the mathematical theory of electricity in equilibrium', *Camb. Dub. Math. J.*, 1 (1846), 75–95. 115

(25) 'On a mechanical representation of electric, magnetic, and galvanic forces', *Camb. Dub. Math. J.*, 2 (1847), 61–4. xlv, 5–6, 34, 548

(27) 'On the forces experienced by small spheres under magnetic influence; and on some of the phenomena presented by diamagnetic substances', *Camb. Dub. Math. J.*, 2 (1847), 230–5. 123n–4

(28) 'On a system of magnetic curves', *Camb. Dub. Math. J.*, 2 (1847), 240. 369

(29.1) 'On the equation of continuity', *Camb. Dub. Math. J.*, 2 (1847), 282–6. xliii, 17, 401, 405

(29.2) 'On the equation of the bounding surface', *Camb. Dub. Math. J.*, 3 (1848), 89–93. xliii, 17, 19, 21, 25, 401, 405

(30) 'Système nouveau de coordonnées orthogonales', *Journal de mathématique pures et appliquées*, 12 (1847), 256–64. 22

(32) 'On the equilibrium of magnetic or diamagnetic bodies of any form under the influence of the terrestrial magnetic force', *Brit. Assoc. Rep.* (1848), part 2, 8–9. 28–9, 31

(33) 'On the theory of electro-magnetic induction', *Brit. Assoc. Rep.* (1848), part 2, 9–10. 28–9, 31

(35) 'Note on the integration of the equations of equilibrium of an elastic solid', *Camb. Dub. Math. J.*, 3 (1848), 87–9. 25

(40) 'On the *vis-viva* of a liquid in motion', *Camb. Dub. Math. J.*, 4 (1849), 90–4. xliii, 23, 32, 401, 405

(42) 'An account of Carnot's theory of the motive power of heat, with numerical results deduced from Regnault's experiments on steam', *Trans. Roy. Soc. Edinb.*, 16 (1849), 541–74. xlii, 34, 57

(43) 'On the theory of magnetic induction in crystalline substances', *Brit. Assoc. Rep.* (1850), part 2, 23. 65, 75

(47) 'The effect of pressure in lowering the freezing point of water, experimentally demonstrated', *Phil. Mag.*, 37 (1850), 123–7. xlii, 59

(48) 'On the forces experienced by inductively-magnetized ferromagnetic or diamagnetic non-crystalline substances', *Phil. Mag.*, 37 (1850), 241–53. 67, 123n–4

(50) 'On the theory of magnetic induction in crystalline and non-crystalline substances', *Phil. Mag.*, 1 (1851), 177–86. 65, 67, 75, 77, 79

(50A) 'Note on the effect of fluid friction in drying steam which issues from a high-pressure boiler through a small orifice into the open air', *Phil. Mag.*, 1 (1851), 474; 2 (1851), 273–4. 81

(52) 'Applications of the principle of mechanical effect to the measurement of electromotive forces and of galvanic resistances in absolute units', *Phil. Mag.*, 2 (1851), 551–62. 115

(53) 'A mathematical theory of magnetism', *Phil. Trans.* (1851), 243–86. 54, 59, 65

(54) 'On the sources of heat generated by the galvanic battery', *Brit. Assoc. Rep.* (1852), part 2, 16–17. 421

(55) 'On certain magnetic curves; with applications to problems in the theories of heat, electricity, and fluid motion', *Brit. Assoc. Rep.* (1852), part 2, 18. 124

(56) 'On the equilibrium of elongated masses of ferromagnetic substance in uniform and varied fields of force', *Brit. Assoc. Rep.* (1852), part 2, 18–20. 124

(58) 'On the mechanical action of radiant heat or light', *Phil. Mag.*, 4 (1852), 256–60. 89

(59) 'On a universal tendency in nature to the dissipation of mechanical energy', *Phil. Mag.*, 4 (1852), 304–6. xlii

(62) 'On the dynamical theory of heat; with numerical results deduced from Mr. Joule's "equivalent of a thermal unit", and M. Regnault's "observations on steam"', *Trans. Roy. Soc. Edinb.*, 20 (1853), 261–88. xlii, 106n

(63) 'On a method of discovering experimentally the relation between the mechanical work spent and the heat produced by the compression of a gaseous fluid', *Trans. Roy. Soc. Edinb.*, 20 (1853), 289–98. xlii

(64) 'On the dynamical theory of heat:– on the quantities of mechanical energy contained in a fluid in different states as to temperature and density', *Trans. Roy. Soc. Edinb.*, 20 (1853), 475–82. xlii

(66) 'On the mutual attraction and repulsion between two electrified spherical conductors', *Phil. Mag.*, 5 (1853), 287–97; 6 (1853), 114–15. 379

(67) 'On transient electric currents', *Phil. Mag.*, 5 (1853), 393–405. 115

(70) 'Remarques sur les oscillations d'aiguilles non cristallisées de faible pouvour inductif paramagnétique ou diamagnétique', *Comptes Rendus*, 38 (1854), 632–40. 124, 173

(72) 'Note sur la densité possible du milieu lumineux et sur la puissance mécanique d'un mille cube de lumière solaire', *Comptes Rendus*, 39 (1854), 529–32. xlv, 111

(73) 'Mémoire sur l'énergie mécanique du système

solaire', *Comptes Rendus*, 39 (1854), 682–7. 100, 105, 107, 111, 178

(78) 'On the theory of the electric telegraph', *Proc. Roy. Soc.*, 7 (1854–5), 382–99. 115–16, 118–19, 122, 125–30

(86) 'Elementary demonstrations of propositions in the theory of magnetic force', *Phil. Mag.*, 9 (1855), 241–8. 123–4n

(87) 'On the magnetic medium, and on the effects of compression', *Phil. Mag.*, 9 (1855), 290–3. 123n

(88) 'On the electro-statical capacity of a Leyden phial', *Phil. Mag.*, 9 (1855), 531–5. 115

(91) 'Elements of a mathematical theory of elasticity', *Phil. Trans.* (1856), 481–98. xxviii, xliv, 145, 150, 152–5, 249

(92) 'On the electro-dynamic qualities of metals', *Phil. Trans.* (1856), 649–752. xxvii, xliv, 133, 135, 137, 141–2, 144, 148–9, 151, 153–6, 158–62, 258, 327, 365

(93) 'On peristaltic induction of electric currents', *Proc. Roy. Soc.*, 8 (1856–7), 121–32. 151

(94) 'Dynamical illustrations of the magnetic and the helicoidal rotatory effects of transparent bodies on polarized light', *Proc. Roy. Soc.*, 8 (1856–7), 150–8. xlv, 151, 162, 165

(95) 'On practical methods for rapid signalling by the electric telegraph', *Proc. Roy. Soc.*, 8 (1856–7), 299–307. 154

(95A) 'On the electrodynamic qualities of metals: effects of magnetization on the electric conductivity of nickel and iron', *Proc. Roy. Soc.*, 8 (1856–7), 546–50. 162

(96) 'On the electric conductivity of commercial copper of various kinds', *Proc. Roy. Soc.*, 8 (1856–7), 550–5. 162, 185

(100A) 'Thermomagnetism' and 'Telegraph', in J. P. Nichol, ed., *A Cyclopaedia of the Physical Sciences* (London, 1857). 175n

(101) 'On the dynamical theory of heat – thermo-electric currents', *Trans. Roy. Soc. Edinb.*, 21 (1857), 123–72. 121

(102) 'On thermo-elastic and thermo-magnetic properties of matter', *Quarterly Journal of Mathematics*, 1 (1857), 57–77. 123

(103) 'On the calculation of transcendents of the form $\int_0^x e^{-x^2} fx \, dx$' *Quarterly Journal of Mathematics*, 1 (1857), 316–20. 125

(104) 'Remarks on the interior melting of ice', *Proc. Roy. Soc.*, 9 (1857–9), 141–3. 173n

(105) 'On the stratification of vesicular ice by pressure', *Proc. Roy. Soc.*, 9 (1857–9), 209–13. 166, 173n

(108) 'On atmospheric electricity', *Proc. Roy. Inst.*, 3 (1858–62), 277–90. xlvi, 187, 400

759

(111) 'On the necessity for incessant recording, and for simultaneous observations in different localities, to investigate atmospheric electricity', *Brit. Assoc. Rep.* (1859), part 2, 27–8. 175, 178, 421

(113) 'Analytical and synthetical attempts to ascertain the cause of the differences of electric conductivity discovered in wires of nearly pure copper', *Proc. Roy. Soc.*, 10 (1859–60), 300–9. 179–80, 185, 195n

(114) 'Measurement of the electrostatic force produced by a Daniell's battery', *Proc. Roy. Soc.*, 10 (1859–60), 319–26. 180, 182

(115) 'Measurement of the electromotive force required to produce a spark in air between parallel metal plates at different distances', *Proc. Roy. Soc.*, 10 (1859–60), 326–7. 180, 182, 185

(117) 'Notes on atmospheric electricity', *Brit. Assoc. Rep.* (1860), part 2, 53–4. 400

(118) 'Recent investigations of Le Verrier on the motion of Mercury', *Proceedings of the Royal Philosophical Society of Glasgow*, 4 (1860), 263–6. 178n

(119) 'On photographed images of electric sparks', *Proceedings of the Royal Philosophical Society of Glasgow*, 4 (1860), 266–7. 368n

(121A) 'Velocity of electricity', in J. P. Nichol, ed., *A Cyclopaedia of the Physical Sciences*, 2nd edn (London, 1860). 175n

(121B) 'Telegraph', in Nichol, ed., *Cyclopaedia* (1860). 175n

(121C) 'Atmospheric electricity', in Nichol, ed., *Cyclopaedia* (1860). 175n, 421

(122A) 'New proof of contact electricity', *Proceedings of the Manchester Literary and Philosophical Society*, 2 (1862), 176–8. 215n

(125) 'On the measurement of electric resistance', *Proc. Roy. Soc.*, 11 (1860–2), 313–29. 201–3

(128) 'On the secular cooling of the earth', *Trans. Roy. Soc. Edinb.*, 23 (1861), 157–70. 221

(129A) 'Note on the electromotive force induced in the earth's crust by variations of terrestrial magnetism', *Phil. Trans.* (1862), 637–8. 217

(130) 'On the rigidity of the earth', *Phil. Trans.* (1863), 573–82. xxviii, xliv, 204–6, 207n–8, 213–16, 218, 220, 223

(131A) 'On sound emitted by air when suddenly subjected to electric force', *Proceedings of the Manchester Literary and Philosophical Society*, 3 (1863), 159–60. 548

(132A) 'Note on two paragraphs of Mr. C. Chamber's paper on "The nature of the sun's magnetic action on the earth"', *Phil. Trans.* (1863), 515–16. 232

(133) 'Dynamical problems regarding elastic spheroidal shells and spheroids of incompressible liquid', *Phil. Trans.* (1863), 583–616. xxviii, xliv, 207, 213, 218–24, 226, 232–41, 244

(141) 'On the secular cooling of the earth', *Trans. Roy. Soc. Edinb.*, 23 (1864), 157–70. 451–3n

(151) 'The "doctrine of uniformity" in geology briefly refuted', *Proc. Roy. Soc. Edinb.*, 5 (1866), 512–13. 452n–3n

(161) 'On vortex atoms', *Phil. Mag.*, 34 (1867), 15–24. xlv, 250, 296

(162) 'On a self-acting apparatus for multiplying and maintaining electric charges, with applications to illustrate the Voltaic theory', *Phil. Mag.*, 34 (1867), 391–6. 254–5

(167) 'On vortex motion', *Trans. Roy. Soc. Edinb.*, 25 (1869), 217–60. 615, 640–2, 645

(170) 'On the fracture of brittle and viscous solids by "shearing"', *Proc. Roy. Soc.*, 17 (1869), 312–13. 262

(171A) 'On the effect of changes of temperature on the specific inductive capacity of dielectrics', *Proc. Roy. Soc.*, 17 (1869), 470. 258–9, 263

(172) 'On the size of atoms', *Nature*, 1 (1870), 551–3. xxxv, xlv

(173) 'Presidential address', *Brit. Assoc. Rep.* (1871), pp. lxxxiv–cv. xxxiv–xxxv, xxxvii, xlv–xlvi, 275n–6, 279–80n, 315

(177A) 'Ripples and waves', *Nature*, 5 (1871), 1–3. 281n

(178) 'Hydrokinetic solutions and observations', *Phil. Mag.*, 42 (1871), 362–7. 281n

(179) 'The influence of wind on waves in water supposed frictionless', *Phil. Mag.*, 42 (1871), 368–74. 281n

(180) 'Waves under motive power of gravity and cohesion jointly, without wind', *Phil. Mag.*, 42 (1871), 374–7. 281n

(182) 'Modification of Wheatstone's bridge to find the resistance of a galvanometer-coil from a single deflection of its own needle', *Proc. Roy. Soc.*, 19 (1871), 253. 271

(184) 'On the determination of a ship's place from observations of altitude', *Proc. Roy. Soc.*, 19 (1871), 259–66. 274

(190) 'On the motion of rigid solids in a liquid circulating irrotationally through perforations in them or in any fixed solid', *Proc. Roy. Soc. Edinb.*, 7 (1872), 668–82. 488

(196A) 'On vortex motion', *Proc. Roy. Soc. Edinb.*, 8 (1873), 80. 294

(198A) 'Obituary notice of Archibald Smith', *Proc. Roy. Soc.*, **22** (1874), pp. i–xxiv. 176n, 296–7, 302

(201) 'On deep-sea sounding by pianoforte wire', *Journal of the Society of Telegraph Engineers*, **3** (1874), 206–19. 307, 325n

(204A) 'Exhibited and described his tide calculating machine, also his improved tide-gauge; he also described certain capillary phenomena, with experiments'. *Proc. Roy. Soc. Edinb.*, **8** (1875), 445. 301

(206A) 'Instructions for the observation of atmospheric electricity for the use of the Arctic Expedition of 1875', in *Manual of the Natural History, Geology, and Physics of Greenland* (London, 1875), 20–4. 310

(207.1) 'Effects of stress of magnetization', *Phil. Trans.* (1876), 693–713. xxviii, xliv, 306, 311, 332, 334, 365

(207.2) 'Effects of stress on the magnetization of iron, nickel, and cobalt', *Phil. Trans.* (1879), 55–85. xxviii, xliv, 311, 339, 341, 343–4, 365

(209) 'Effects of stress on inductive magnetism in soft iron', *Proc. Roy. Soc.*, **23** (1875), 473–6. xxix, xliv, 306, 311

(210) 'On an alleged error in Laplace's theory of the tides', *Phil. Mag.*, **50** (1875), 227–42. 314

(211) 'Note on the "oscillations of the first species" in Laplace's theory of the tides', *Phil. Mag.*, **50** (1875), 279–84. 314

(212) 'General integration of Laplace's differential equation of the tides', *Phil. Mag.*, **50** (1875), 388–402. 314

(213) 'On an instrument for calculating $(\int \phi (x) \psi (x)\, dx)$, the integral of the product of two given functions', *Proc. Roy. Soc.*, **24** (1876), 266–8. 316–17, 321n

(214) 'Mechanical integration of the linear differential equations of the second order with variable coefficients', *Proc. Roy. Soc.*, **24** (1876), 269–71. 316–17, 321n

(215) 'Mechanical integration of the general linear differential equation of any order with variable coefficients', *Proc. Roy. Soc.*, **24** (1876), 271–5. 316–17, 321n

(215A) 'An application of Prof. James Thomson's integrator to harmonic analyses of meteorological, tidal, and other phenomena, and to the integration of differential equations', *Proc. Roy. Soc. Edinb.*, **9** (1876), 138. 321n

(217) 'Presidential address to section A', *Brit. Assoc. Rep.* (1876), part 2, 1–12. 322, 451–2

(222A) 'Elasticity', in *Encyclopaedia Britannica*, 9th edn (Edinburgh, 1875–89), VII, 796–825. 337

(223) 'On compass adjustments in iron ships', *Nature*, **17** (1878), 331–4, 352–4, 387–8. 325n

(224) 'On beats of imperfect harmonies', *Proc. Roy. Soc.*, **9** (1878), 602–12. 606–7

(227) 'Harmonic analyzer', *Proc. Roy. Soc.*, **27** (1878), 371–3. 331n, 336n, 341

(231) 'The effects of stress on the magnetization of iron, cobalt, and nickel', *Proc. Roy. Inst.*, **8** (1879), 591–3. 339

(231A) 'On the effect of stress on the magnetization of iron, nickel, and cobalt', *Nature*, **18** (1878), 215. 339

(232) 'On a machine for the solution of simultaneous linear equations', *Proc. Roy. Soc.*, **28** (1879), 111–13. 347n

(237) 'Vibrations of a columnar vortex', *Proc. Roy. Soc. Edinb.*, **10** (1880), 443–56. 429

(242) 'On maximum and minimum energy in vortex motion', *Brit. Assoc. Rep.* (1880), 473–6. 400n, 413

(243A) 'Heat', in *Encyclopaedia Britannica*, 9th edn (Edinburgh, 1875–89), XI, 554–89. 125, 379, 394

(244) 'On an experimental illustration of minimum energy in vortex motion', *Brit. Assoc. Rep.* (1880), 491–2. 400n, 413

(249) 'The tide gauge, tidal harmonic analyzer, and tide predicter', *Proceedings of the Institution of Civil Engineers*, **65** (1881), 2–25. 339, 363n

(249A) 'The tide predicter', *Nature*, **23** (1881), 482, 578. 363n

(257) 'Elasticity viewed as possibly a mode of motion', *Proc. Roy. Inst.*, **9** (1882), 520–1. xlv

(259) 'On the figures of equilibrium of a rotating mass of fluid', *Proc. Roy. Soc. Edinb.*, **11** (1882), 610–13. 428

(261) 'Electrical units of measurement', *Nature*, **28** (1883), 91–2. 434n

(262) 'The size of atoms', *Proc. Roy. Inst.*, **10** (1884), 185–213. 350n, 395n, 436, 439–41, 443, 451, 652

(262A) 'On the dynamical theory of dispersion', *Proc. Roy. Soc. Edinb.*, **12** (1883), 128. 436n

(263) 'Steps towards a kinetic theory of matter', *Brit. Assoc. Rep.* (1884), 613–22. 443n

(265) 'The wave theory of light', *Journal of the Franklin Institute*, **118** (1884), 321–41. 461n

(267B) 'On the dynamics of reflection and refraction in the wave theory of light', *Proc. Roy. Soc. Edinb.*, **13** (1884), 2. 468

(267C) 'On the distribution of energy between

colliding groups of molecules', *Proc. Roy. Soc. Edinb.*, **13** (1884), 2. 468

(267D) 'On Kerr's discovery regarding the reflection of light from a magnetic pole', *Proc. Roy. Soc. Edinb.*, **13** (1884), 2. 468

(267E) 'The Bangor laboratories', *Nature*, **31** (1885), 409–13. xliii

(272) 'On stationary waves in flowing water', *Phil. Mag.*, **22** (1886), 353–7, 445–52, 517–30; **23** (1887), 52–8. 617

(274) 'On the vortex theory of the luminiferous aether. (On the propagation of laminar motion through a turbulently moving inviscid liquid)', *Brit. Assoc. Rep.* (1887), 486–95. xlv

(278) 'On the stability of steady and of periodic fluid motion', *Phil. Mag.*, **23** (1887), 459–64, 529–39. 617, 655

(279) 'Stability of motion. Broad river flowing down an inclined plane bed', *Phil. Mag.*, **24** (1887), 272–8. 617

(282) 'On the waves produced by a single impulse in water of any depth, or in a dispersive medium', *Proc. Roy. Soc.*, **42** (1887), 80–3. 487

(283) 'On the formation of coreless vortices by the motion of a solid through an inviscid incompressible fluid', *Proc. Roy. Soc.*, **42** (1887), 83–5. 487, 530, 609

(283A) 'On models of the minimal tetrakaidekahedron', *Proc. Roy. Soc. Edinb.*, **15** (1887), 33. 492

(294) 'On Cauchy's and Green's doctrine of extraneous force to explain dynamically Fresnel's kinematics of double refraction', *Proc. Roy. Soc. Edinb.*, **15** (1889), 21–33. 493

(302) 'Sur une constitution gyrostatique adynamique pour l'éther', *Comptes Rendus*, **109** (1889), 453–5. 461n

(307) 'Ether, electricity, and ponderable matter', *Journal of the Institution of Electrical Engineers*, **18** (1890), 4–37, 128. xlii, 117n

(315) 'On a mechanism for the constitution of ether', *Proc. Roy. Soc. Edinb.*, **17** (1891), 127–32. 461n

(331) 'Presidential address', *Proc. Roy. Soc.*, **52** (1893), 300–10. 648

(337) 'On the elasticity of a crystal according to Boscovich', *Proc. Roy. Soc.*, **54** (1894), 59–75. 516n–17

(338) 'Presidential address', *Proc. Roy. Soc.*, **54** (1894), 377–89. xlvi, 522, 546, 649

(339) 'Towards the efficiency of sails, windmills, screw-propellers in water and air, and aeroplanes', *Nature*, **50** (1894), 425–6. 609

(340) 'On the doctrine of discontinuity of fluid motion, in connection with the resistance against a solid moving through a fluid', *Nature*, **50** (1894), 524–5, 549, 573–5, 597–8. 525–8, 609, 618, 623

(344) 'On the electrification of air', *Proceedings of the Royal Philosophical Society of Glasgow*, **26** (1895), 233–43. 538

(347) 'Presidential address', *Proc. Roy. Soc.*, **59** (1896), 107–24. 542

(349) 'Velocity of propagation of electrostatic force', *Nature*, **53** (1895–6), 316, 364–5. 543

(350) 'On Lippmann's colour photography with obliquely incident light', *Nature*, **54** (1896), 12–13. 553n, 574, 576–7

(352) 'On the generation of longitudinal waves in ether', *Proc. Roy. Soc.*, **59** (1896), 270–3. xlii, 545, 547–8

(353) 'Note on Lord Blythswood's paper', *Proc. Roy. Soc.*, **59** (1896), 332–3. 553n, 555, 563–4, 566–7

(354) 'On the motion of a heterogeneous liquid, commencing from rest with a given motion of its boundary', *Proc. Roy. Soc. Edinb.*, **21** (1897), 119–22. 592

(363) 'The age of the earth as an abode fitted for life', *Phil. Mag.*, **47** (1899), 66–90. 533n, 575n, 590–1, 593, 596–7

(364) 'Contact electricity of metals', *Proc. Roy. Inst.*, **15** (1899), 521–54. 590

(373) 'On the duties of ether for electricity and magnetism', *Phil. Mag.*, **50** (1900), 305–7. xlii

(375H) 'Aepinus atomized', *Phil. Mag.*, **3** (1902), 257–83. 652

(375L) 'The scientific work of Sir George Stokes', *Nature*, **67** (1903), 337–8. xlii

(375P) 'Recollections of Professor J. P. Nichol', *Nature*, **68** (1903), 623–4. xliii, 175n

(375JJ) 'On the motions of ether produced by collisions of atoms or molecules, containing or not containing electrions', *Phil. Mag.*, **14** (1907), 317–24. xlv

Kelvin, Beattie, and Smolan

(3) 'Electric equilibrium between uranium and an insulated metal in its neighbourhood', *Nature*, **55** (1897), 447–8. 591

Kelvin, Bottomley, and Maclean

(1) 'Measurement of electric currents through air at different densities down to one five-millionth of the density of the density of ordinary air', *Brit. Assoc. Rep.* (1896), 710–11. 591

Kelvin and Evans

(1) 'On the tides of Port Louis, Mauritius, and Freemantle, Australia', *Brit. Assoc. Rep.* (1877), part 2, 40. 330n
(2) 'On the tides of the Southern Hemisphere and of the Mediterranean', *Brit. Assoc. Rep.* (1878), 477–81. 330n

Kelvin and Joule

(3) 'On the thermal effects of fluids in motion', *Phil. Trans.* (1853), 357–66. 129
(4) 'On the thermal effects of fluids in motion', *Phil. Trans.* (1854), 321–64. 121, 129
(6) 'On the thermal effects of fluids in motion. Temperature of a body moving slowly through air', *Proc. Roy. Soc.*, 8 (1856–7), 41–2, 556–64. 148
(7) 'On the thermal effects of fluids in motion', *Proc. Roy. Soc.*, 10 (1859–60), 502. 189
(8) 'On the thermal effects of fluids in motion. On changes of temperature experienced by bodies moving through air', *Phil. Trans.* (1860), 325–36. 190
(10) 'On the thermal effects of fluids in motion', *Phil. Trans.* (1862), 579–89. 217, 225

Kelvin and Tait

(1) 'Energy', *Good Words* (1862), 601–7. 91n

STOKES

Burnett Lectures xxxviii–xxxix, xlvi, 449–50, 469, 592
MPP ix, 10n, 299, 343–4, 348, 352, 355, 366, 369–71, 373, 375, 378, 381n, 394, 401, 403, 405–6, 409n, 411, 415–16, 426, 433, 449, 473, 480, 484n, 527, 531, 536, 548, 552, 598n, 602n–6, 608, 611–12, 615, 618, 633, 649–52, 655–6
(1) 'On the steady motion of incompressible fluids', *Trans. Camb. Phil. Soc.*, 7 (1842), 439–54, 465. xliii, 11, 167, 242, 386, 608
(5) 'On the aberration of light', *Phil. Mag.*, 27 (1845), 9–15; 29 (1846), 62–3. 31
(6) 'Report on recent researches in hydrodynamics', *Brit. Assoc. Rep.* (1846), 1–20. 369, 381, 401
(11) 'On the theories of the internal friction of fluids in motion, and of the equilibrium and motion of elastic solids', *Trans. Camb. Phil. Soc.*, 8 (1845), 287–319. xliii, xlv, 3–6, 17–18, 24, 26, 63–4, 66–9, 72, 176, 495, 611, 642
(12) 'On the resistance of a fluid to two oscillating spheres', *Brit. Assoc. Rep.* (1847), part 2, 6. 369–71, 373, 378
(13) 'On some cases of fluid motion', *Trans. Camb. Phil. Soc.*, 8 (1843), 105–37; 8 (1846), 409–14. 9–10, 13, 15, 164, 166, 378, 527, 612, 618, 621
(16) 'On the Dynamical Equations', *Camb. Dub. Math. J.*, 3 (1848), 121–7. xliii, 21–3, 25, 348, 352, 355, 401, 403, 405–6
(19) 'Demonstration of a fundamental theorem', *Camb. Dub. Math. J.*, 3 (1848), 209–19. xliii, 23, 26–7, 266, 348, 352, 355, 401, 403, 405, 415
(20) 'On the constitution of the luminiferous ether', *Phil. Mag.*, 32 (1848), 343–9. xlv–xlvi
(21) 'On the critical values of the sums of periodic series', *Trans. Camb. Phil. Soc.*, 8 (1847), 533–83. 10, 11, 13, 19, 118n, 221–3, 366, 401, 403, 531, 611–12, 615, 618n
(22) 'On a difficulty in the theory of sound', *Phil. Mag.*, 33 (1848), 349–56. 174, 409–11, 415–16, 435
(23) 'On the theory of certain bands seen in the spectrum', *Phil. Trans.* (1848), 227–42. 18, 42
(26) 'On the perfect blackness of the central spot in Newton's rings, and on the verification of Fresnel's formulae for the intensities of reflected and refracted rays', *Camb. Dub. Math. J.*, 4 (1849), 1–14. 18, 23, 26, 147
(27) 'On attractions, and on Clairaut's theorem', *Camb. Dub. Math. J.*, 4 (1849), 194–219. xliii, 45–50, 253, 425
(28) 'On waves', *Camb. Dub. Math. J.*, 4 (1849), 219–40. xliii, 23, 32, 35, 42–5, 348, 352, 355, 401, 403, 405
(29) 'On the theory of oscillatory waves', *Trans. Camb. Phil. Soc.*, 8 (1847), 441–55. 227–8, 273, 369–70, 373, 375, 382, 401
(30) 'On the formation of the central spot of Newton's rings beyond the critical angle', *Trans. Camb. Phil. Soc.*, 8 (1848), 642–58. 18, 32
(31) 'On the variation of gravity at the surface of the earth', *Trans. Camb. Phil. Soc.*, 8 (1849), 672–95. xliii, 45, 253, 425
(32) 'Discussion of a differential equation relating to the breaking of railway bridges', *Trans. Camb. Phil. Soc.*, 8 (1849), 707–35. 57, 411
(33) 'On some points in the received theory of sound', *Phil. Mag.*, 34 (1849), 52–60. 59–60, 435
(34) 'On the theory of sound, in reply to Prof.

Challis', *Phil. Mag.*, **34** (1849), 203–4, 348–50, 501–2. 59–60, 435

(35) 'Supplement to a paper "On the theory of certain bands seen in the spectrum"', *Phil. Mag.*, **34** (1849), 309–11. 18

(39) 'On Haidinger's brushes', *Brit. Assoc. Rep.* (1850), part 2, 20–1. 147n

(40) 'On the dynamical theory of diffraction', *Trans. Camb. Phil. Soc.*, **9** (1849), 1–62. 62–3, 435, 466, 598n, 649n

(41) 'On the numerical calculation of a class of definite integrals and infinite series', *Trans. Camb. Phil. Soc.*, **9** (1850), 166–87. 256

(42) 'On the change of refrangibility of light', *Phil. Trans.* (1852), 463–562; (1853), 385–96. 68, 83–4n, 87–90, 97, 104, 146–7, 278n, 435n, 438, 602n, 651–2

(44) 'On the conduction of heat in crystals', *Camb. Dub. Math. J.*, **6** (1851), 215–38. 74, 75, 77, 106, 113

(45) 'On the alleged necessity for a new general equation in hydrodynamics', *Phil. Mag.*, **1** (1851), 157–60, 393–4; **2** (1851), 60. 53

(46) 'An examination of the possible effect of the radiation of heat on the propagation of sound', *Phil. Mag.*, **1** (1851), 305–17. 435, 552

(47) 'On the effect of the internal friction of fluids on the motion of pendulums', *Trans. Camb. Phil. Soc.*, **9** (1850), [8]–[106]. 18, 176, 209, 256, 473, 552, 583–4n

(48) 'On the colours of thick plates', *Trans. Camb. Phil. Soc.*, **9** (1851), [147]–[176]. 552

(49) 'On the change of refrangibility of light, and the exhibition thereby of the chemical rays', *Proc. Roy. Inst.*, **1** (1853), 259–64. 98, 146–7

(52) 'On the total intensity of interfering light', *Trans. Roy. Soc. Edinb.*, **20** (1853), 317–20. 89

(54) 'On the metallic reflexion exhibited by certain non-metallic substances', *Phil. Mag.*, **6** (1853), 393–403. 147

(62) 'On the effect of wind on the intensity of sound', *Brit. Assoc. Rep.* (1857), part 2, 22–3. 435

(63) 'On the polarization of diffracted light', *Phil. Mag.*, **13** (1857), 159–61. 435

(65) 'On the existence of a second crystallizable flourescent substance (paviin) in the bark of the horse-chestnut', *Journal of the Chemical Society*, **11** (1859), 17–21. 164, 166

(66) 'On the bearing of the phenomena of diffraction on the direction of the vibrations of polarized light, with remarks on the paper of Prof. F. Eisenlohr', *Phil. Mag.*, **18** (1859), 426–7. 435

(67) 'Note on paviin', *Journal of the Chemical Society*, **12** (1860), 126–8. 186

(69) 'Note on the simultaneous emission and absorption of rays of the same definite refrangibility discovered by M. Foucault, and rediscovered and extended by M. Kirchhoff', *Phil. Mag.*, **19** (1860), 196–7. 140, 142, 277

(71) 'On the intensity of the light reflected from or transmitted through a pile of plates', *Proc. Roy. Soc.*, **11** (1860–2), 545–57. 463

(72) 'Report on double refraction', *Brit. Assoc. Rep.* (1862), 253–82. xlv, 456n, 467, 492–3n

(79) 'On the internal distribution of matter which shall produce a given potential at the surface of a gravitating mass', *Proc. Roy. Soc.*, **15** (1867), 482–6. 253–4, 425

(86) 'Explanation of a dynamical paradox', *Messenger of Mathematics*, **1** (1872), 1–3. 290n

(87) 'On the law of extraordinary refraction in Iceland spar', *Proc. Roy. Soc.*, **20** (1872), 443–4. 247n, 290, 303, 493

(87A) 'On the principles of the chemical composition of object glasses', *MPP*, **IV**, 344–54. 290n

(88) 'Sur l'emploi du prisme dans la vérification de la loi de la double réfraction', *Comptes Rendus*, **77** (1873), 1150–2. 290n, 301, 303, 601

(91) 'The early history of spectrum analysis', *Nature*, **13** (1876), 188–9. 315n

(96) 'On certain movements of radiometers', *Proc. Roy. Soc.*, **26** (1878), 546–55. 337

(99A) 'Supplement to a paper on the theory of oscillatory waves', *MPP*, **1**, 314–26. 382, 401, 480

(100A) Addition to Reynolds, 'Note on thermal transpiration', *Proc. Roy. Soc.*, **30** (1880), 301–2. 393–4

(101) 'Note on the reduction of Mr. Crookes's experiments on the decrement of the arc of vibration of a mica plate oscillating within a bulb containing more or less rarefied gas', *Phil. Trans.* (1882), 435–46. 419n

(104) 'Solar physics', *Nature*, **24** (1881), 593–8, 613–18. 420n

(105) 'On the cause of the light border frequently noticed in photographs just outside the outline of a dark body seen against the sky; with some introductory remarks on phosphorescence', *Proc. Roy. Soc.*, **34** (1883), 63–8. 395n

(106) 'On the highest wave of uniform propagation. Preliminary notice', *Proc. Camb. Phil. Soc.*, **4** (1883), 361–5. 433n, 446n

(130) 'On the nature of the Röntgen rays', *Memoirs and Proceedings of the Manchester Literary and Philosophical Society*, **41** (1897), no. 15, 28 pp.; **44** (1900), no. 3, 1 p. 553n, 600, 630–1

(131) 'Sur l'explication d'un résultat expérimental attribué à une déviation magnétique des rayons X', *Comptes Rendus*, **125** (1897), 216–18. 553n

(132) 'An annual address (chiefly on the subject of the Röntgen rays)', *Journal of the Transactions of the Victoria Institute*, **30** (1898), 13–25. 553n

(133) 'Mathematical proof of the identity of the stream lines obtained by means of a viscous film with those of a perfect fluid moving in two dimensions', *Brit. Assoc. Rep.* (1898), 143–4. 607n

(134) 'On the nature of the Röntgen rays', *Proc. Camb. Phil. Soc.*, **9** (1898), 215–16. 553n, 590

(135) 'On the perception of colour', *Journal of the Transactions of the Victoria Institute*, **31** (1899), 254–68. 603–4

(137) 'On the maximum wave of uniform propagation', *MPP*, v, 146–59. 401n

Stokes and Hopkinson

(1) 'On the optical properties of a titano-silicic glass', *Brit. Assoc. Rep.* (1875), 26–7. 319n

INDEX OF NAMES AND SUBJECTS

771

Fraunhofer, Joseph 84n, 277
  A line 99
  B line 99, 450
  C, F, G, and H lines 450
  D line 98–104, 140–2, 247, 275, 277, 279, 315, 450
  E line 100, 450
  group a 99
Freeman, Alexander *259n*
Fresnel, Augustin xxii, xxiv
  diffraction 598, 632
  dispersion 438
  double refraction 166, 492–3
  extraordinary refraction 247
  Fresnel's rhomb 68
  Newton's rings 18
  optic axes 450
  reflection 462, 573
friction 335
Froude, William 271n, *288*, 361–2, 455n

Galileo 553n
Galitzine, B. *see* Golitsyn, Boris Borisovich
Galle, Johann Gottfried *48n*
galvanic resistance 154
galvanism 12, 61
  terrestrial 256, 420
gases
  absorption and radiation of heat by 199–200
  diffusion of ions into 635
  dynamical theory of 209, 249
  effusion of 367
  elasticity of 165
  electric conductivity of 591
  electric discharge in 592
  equipartition of energy in 468, 532
  Joule and Kelvin's research on 191
  kinetic theory of xxxiv–xxxv, xxxviii, 312
  thermal diffusion of 368
  thermodynamic properties of 189
  transpiration of 209–10, 367–8
  viscosity of 209–10, 245–6, 473, 495
  see also air
Gauss, Carl Friedrich xxii, 12–13, 48n, 54, 58, 61
Gay-Lussac, Joseph Louis 111, 281n
Geikie, Archibald *522*
Geological Society xxv
geology 26, 109
  Cambridge school of xxii
German Admiralty 333
Gerstner, Franz Joseph von *369*, 381
Gilbert, L. W. 277
  Gilbert's *Annalen der Physik* 277
Girard, Pierre Simon *209*

glaciers 17, 172–3
Glaisher, James Whitbread Lee *294*
Glasgow Herald 553
Glasgow University x, xvi, xix
  curriculum xxiii–xxv, xxx
  deputy professorship of natural philosophy 485
  Elder professorship of naval architecture 460
  Kelvin's chancellorship xliii
  Kelvin's Jubilee xxxix, 579–80
  Library ix
  natural philosophy laboratory xxv, 181, 225–6n, 289, 485
  professorship of astronomy xv, 176–7
  professorship of mathematics xv–xvi, xxv, 34n–43, 48
  professorship of natural philosophy xvi, xxii, xxv, 634–6
glass
  and fluorescence 651
  compressibility of 24
  crown 450, 462
  electric conductivity of 448
  electric resistance of 426
  flint 462
  heavy 161–2
  Poisson's ratio for 249
  specific inductive capacity of 258–9
Glazebrook, Richard Tetley 450, 460, 470, 486, 493
Gmelin, Leopold *596*
God xxxvii–xxxviii
Goldhammer, Dmitrij Aleksandrovič *577*
Goldscheider (Johannes Carl August Eugen) Alfred *603*–4
Goldstein, Eugen, *546*
Golitsyn, Boris Borisovich *568*, 571n–2, *574*
Goode, Henry *64*, 68, 72
Gordon, James Edward Henry *326*
Gordon, Lewis Dunbar Brodie xliv, *305*
Government School of Mines, professorship of physics in xv
Graham, Thomas 209–11, 348n, 357n, 367
  Graham lecture (Glasgow Philosophical Society) 553
  Graham's laws 209–10
Grant, Robert *244*
Gray, Andrew xlii, 203n, *327*, 331, 334, 338n, 345n, 448, 634n
Gray, David, *42*
Gray, John *592n*
Gray, Thomas *426*, 448
Great Eastern 248–9
Great Exhibition of 1851 86
Great Western Telegraph Company 289

Lightning Source UK Ltd.
Milton Keynes UK
UKHW031123120919
349629UK00003B/25/P